TEACHER GUIDE

10th–12th Grade

Includes Student Worksheet

Math

Weekly Lesson Schedule

M000252125

Principles of Algebra 2: Applied Algebra from a Biblical Worldview

MASTERBOOKS® CURRICULUM

Authors:
Katherine [Loop] Hannon and
Dr. Adam Hannon

Master Books Creative Team:

Editor: Craig Froman

Design: Jennifer Bauer

Cover Design:
Diana Bogardus

Copy Editors:
Judy Lewis
Willow Meek

Curriculum Review:
Kristen Pratt
Laura Welch
Diana Bogardus

First printing: March 2021

For information write:

Master Books®, P.O. Box 726, Green Forest, AR 72638

Master Books® is a division of the New Leaf Publishing Group, Inc.

ISBN: 978-1-68344-232-5
ISBN: 978-1-61458-762-0 (digital)

Unless otherwise noted, Scripture quotations are from the King James Version of the Bible.

Where marked ESV, Scripture quotations are from the ESV® Bible (The Holy Bible, English Standard Version®), copyright © 2001 by Crossway, a publishing ministry of Good News Publishers. Used by permission. All rights reserved.

Printed in the United States of America

Please visit our website for other great titles:
www.masterbooks.com

Table of Contents

Based on and designed to go with *Principles of Algebra 2: Applied Algebra from a Biblical Worldview Student Textbook*. Please see the *Student Textbook* for further information and sources.

We've adapted and included math problems from late 1800 or early 1900 math books. We've attempted to mark each of these problems with different symbols for easy identification. The sources are listed here for your reference. Feel free to look up the books and have fun with additional problems. These sources, especially *Franklin Elementary Algebra*, inspired other problems as well.

Problems marked with a 📖 were adapted from Eugene Henry Barker, *Applied Mathematics for Junior High Schools and High Schools* (Boston: Allyn and Bacon, 1920). Available on Google Books, http://books.google.com/books?id=-t5EAAAAIAAJ

Problems marked with a 📚 were adapted from Edwin Seaver and George Walton, *The Franklin Elementary Algebra* (Boston: William War & Co., 1882), https://books.google.com/books?id=RA8AAAAAYAAJ&dq=franklin's%20elementary%20algebra

Problems marked with a 📖 were adapted from Jos. V. Collins, *Practical Algebra: First Year Course* (New York: American Book Co., 1910), https://books.google.com/books?id=hNdHAAAAIAAJ

Problems marked with a 📚 were adapted from Henry Lewis Rietz, Arthur Robert Oratoren, and Edson Homer Taylor. *School Algebra* (New York: Henry Holt and Co., 1915), https://books.google.com/books?id=FawXAAAAIAAJ

Note: In putting this material together, many different resources were consulted, many of which are footnoted where appropriate. We do not necessarily recommend these materials; while they were consulted for facts, some do not claim to be from a biblical worldview and should be approached with discernment.

Using This Teacher Guide

Features: The suggested weekly schedule enclosed has easy-to-manage lessons that guide the reading, worksheets, and all assessments. The pages of this guide are perforated and three-hole punched so materials are easy to tear out, hand out, grade, and store. Parents/teachers are encouraged to adjust the schedule and materials as needed in order to best work within their unique educational program.

Lesson Scheduling: Students are instructed to read the pages in the *Student Textbook* (or watch the lesson video if using the optional ecourse and then consult the textbook as needed) and then complete the corresponding section provided by the teacher. There is a quiz after each chapter, and a test after each quarter, plus a final exam. Space is provided on the weekly schedule for assignment dates, and flexibility in scheduling is encouraged. Parents/teachers may adapt the scheduled days per each unique student situation. As the student completes each assignment, this can be marked with an "X" in the box.

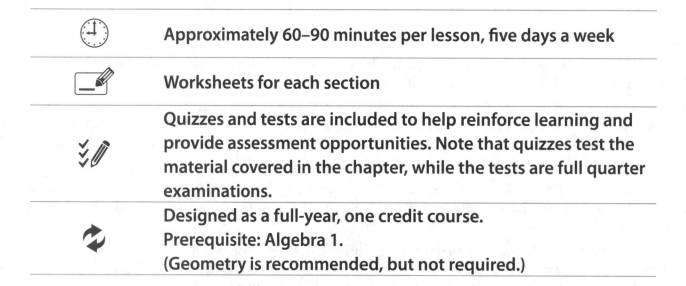

	Approximately 60–90 minutes per lesson, five days a week
	Worksheets for each section
	Quizzes and tests are included to help reinforce learning and provide assessment opportunities. Note that quizzes test the material covered in the chapter, while the tests are full quarter examinations.
	Designed as a full-year, one credit course. Prerequisite: Algebra 1. (Geometry is recommended, but not required.)

Course Objectives: Students completing this course will

- See to an even deeper level how algebra's very existence points us to a faithful Creator we can trust.

- See algebra in connection with God's creation, understanding how it applies outside of a textbook and brings a deeper understanding of God's world.

- Have a solid foundation for precalculus, understanding and knowing how to work with advanced equations and functions.

- Further develop problem-solving skills that will help in future math and science courses, as well as in real-life settings.

Course Description

This complete Algebra 2 program not only teaches algebra, but also shows students why they're learning concepts and how algebra's very existence points us to God. Students will see algebra in action . . . and find their biblical worldview built along the way.

Preparing to Use the Curriculum

The *Student Textbook* contains all the explanation of the material. Important terms are **bolded** in the textbook so you can easily spot them. Examples you can work through with the student if needed (or use to teach a classroom) are all included there. Here is one suggestion for how to prep the information in this *Teacher Guide*:

- ✔ Tear out the schedule, quizzes, and tests.
- ✔ Put them in a binder to use as needed.
- ✔ Hand the student the rest of the guide to work from when instructed.

Note that the pages in the *Teacher Guide* are hole punched for you and ready to go.

The schedule on page 9 explains what to assign each day. This schedule can be adapted to fit your needs. For example, if you only want to do math 3 days a week, then simply spread the work assigned for the week over 3 days instead of 5.

Teachers using the program in a classroom or co-op will find that there are about 2–3 presentations of concepts per week. Those 2–3 lessons could be taught in the classroom using the student text as a guide (with students able to read the textbook later for more clarity/reminders if needed), with the worksheets assigned as homework.

Additional Resources and Corrections

The *Solutions Manual* includes notes, step-by-step explanations on problems, and other features to make grading easier.

Please see the Book Extras page on ChristianPerspective.net for links to helpful online resources, along with additional notes and information related to this course.

Supplies Needed

- [ ] *Principles of Algebra 2: Applied Algebra from a Biblical Worldview* — This textbook contains the presentation of the concepts. Teachers can use it as a basis for presentations. Students should either read through it if learning the material on their own or use it as a reference/read as instructed if they are using the Academy eCourse or have a teacher explaining the concepts.

- [ ] *Principles of Algebra 2 Solutions Manual* — Contains solutions to all the worksheets, quizzes, and test problems.

- [ ] **Principles of Algebra 2 eCourse** (optional) — These videos offer presentations of lessons produced by the author. They're great for students that are more visual/auditory in learning or need more walking through the concepts. Students using the videos should watch the video for that lesson then look over the text, studying it as needed. The eCourse is available through the Master Books Academy at MasterBooksAcademy.com. *Note:* The *Student Book*, *Teacher Guide*, and *Solutions Manual* are required when using the eCourse.

- [ ] **Binder with Lined Paper or Other Note-Taking Method** — Whether a binder or something else (like a computer program), students should have a way to take/store/organize their notes.

- [ ] **Calculator (or Online Calculator)** — For most problems, students only need a scientific calculator (one that can handle exponents, roots, and scientific notation). However, there are a good number of problems that also require the ability to graph equations, as well as a few that require the ability to solve matrices. Students can use free online calculators for these functions; however, if students are planning on heading to college, owning their own graphing calculator and becoming familiar with it is recommended. Examples in this course are explained using the TI-83 Plus or TI-84 Plus. Other calculators can be used; students should consult their user manuals to see how to perform certain operations on them. *Important:* Students should *not* use a calculator to simplify algebraic expressions — simplifying algebraic expressions is an important skill for them to learn to do off a calculator, and it will also save them time in the long run. (*Example:* When asked to simplify $\frac{8a}{a}$, this should be done by hand, not with the help of a calculator.) It's suggested that students only use a scientific calculator (one without the graphing feature) on quizzes and tests except where specified; if a graphing calculator is used, that feature should not be used.

- [ ] **A College Notebook** — Students should have a notebook in which they can work out their problems and write their answers, as problems at this level require significant space to solve. They should number all problems and make it easy to see what their final answer is (perhaps by circling it). If students get a problem wrong, looking back at how they solved the problem can be helpful in finding the error (and in awarding partial credit if appropriate).

- [ ] **A Second Notebook or Additional Lined Paper** — Students should have a separate notebook or paper to use for quizzes and tests.

- [ ] **Index Cards (optional)** — Making flashcards of definitions or formulas can be a helpful way to learn and review the material. Students are encouraged to use index cards to make flashcards as needed or to use a computer program to do so.

- [ ] **Graph Paper** — Students will need graph paper for some of the graphing problems.

- [ ] **Computer Programs** (optional) — Excel, Google Sheets, or Libre Office.

General Instructions for Students

Don't panic when you hit hard problems. Some problems on the worksheets are designed to challenge you. Worksheets should be viewed as learning aids to help build problem-solving skills and exercise the mathematical tools being taught rather than as something to panic over getting wrong. If you get a problem wrong, you have a second chance to go back and figure it out with whatever hints your parent/educator deem appropriate before your grade for the worksheet is determined. (Don't abuse this—if you start making careless errors, your parent/educator may count those problems wrong the first time.) Just like when you learned to walk, you probably fell quite a bit, it's okay if you struggle on problems too, so long as you then get up and learn from it. Note that by the quizzes and tests you should have learned the material, so you won't have the same second chance on them.

Some problems are labeled as "Challenge Problems" and marked with a ◎. Ask your parent/educator if they want you to complete them. Note that they are designed to stretch your thinking in an extra way . . . but many will give you amazing glimpses into how algebra applies.

Here are a few notes to keep in mind when solving problems in this course.

- ✔ **Review** — If at any point you hit a concept that does not make sense, back up and review. Be sure to take advantage of any notes you've taken.

- ✔ **Calculator** — You will need a graphing calculator for some problems in this course and are allowed to use a calculator except where instructed not to. However, while some calculators can perform calculations with variables for you, it's important for you to learn how to do them yourself. If you master the skill, you should be able to perform many more problems much more quickly than you could with a calculator — and you'll have a better understanding of the concepts. So if your calculator can simplify algebraic expressions, don't use that feature.

- ✔ **Simplify Your Answers** — Unless otherwise indicated, **simplify your answers** as much as possible. Simplified answers are easier to read and work with. Plus, that way your teacher will not have to work so hard to grade your problems, as your answer will be in the same form as the *Solutions Manual. Note:* When you simplify fractions in algebra, **do not convert improper fractions to mixed numbers.** However, simplify the fraction as much as possible. For example, simplify $\frac{10}{4x}$ to $\frac{5}{2x}$ (the improper fraction is simplified but left as an improper fraction).

- ✔ **Units of Measure** — Unless told otherwise, always include units of measure in your answer when they were part of the problem. *Example:* 8 in + 2 in. *Answer:* 10 in. An answer of 10 to this problem would only get partial credit. Note that in this course, units of measure are not italicized, while letters standing for unknowns are.

- ✔ **Showing Steps** — As problems increase in complexity, writing down each step used to solve them in an orderly fashion becomes more and more important. On word problems or problems with a lot of steps especially, try to show how you obtained your answers. Writing down enough steps that someone can see the process followed is a helpful habit to develop, as it makes it easier to find any errors. You could potentially get partial credit if you set the problem up correctly. It is also required in many college courses.

- ✔ **Indicate Your Answer Clearly** — For grading purposes, make sure you circle or clearly indicate your answer to each problem.

- ✔ **Pi (π)** — In solving problems, you can use whatever rounded value of π you've memorized (such as 3.14) or simply use the π button on your calculator.

- ✓ **Fractions Versus Decimals** — To keep things simple to grade, if a problem is given to you in fractional form and there's a fractional part in the answer, give your answer as a fraction. If there's a decimal in the problem and there's a fractional part in the answer, then give the answer using a decimal. If a problem has both fractions and decimals, you can give your answer in either form.

  Example: Find $\frac{1}{2a} + \frac{1}{3a}$.   *Answer:* $\frac{5}{6a}$.

  Example: Find $0.5a + 0.333a$.   *Answer:* $0.833a$

  Example: Find $\frac{1}{2}a + 0.25a$ *Answer:* $\frac{3}{4}a$ or $0.75a$

- ✓ **Rounding** — Unless otherwise indicated, when giving a decimal answer, **round your final answer** in this course to the third decimal (the thousandths' place). (Note that you shouldn't round until the very end.) And when you rounded when solving a problem, try to use the approximately sign ($\approx$) rather than an equal's sign to let others know it's a rounded value. (If needed, see the footnote for a reminder on how to round.[1])

  Example: Round an answer of 6.7888 to $\approx$ 6.789.

  Exception: In Chapter 12, you'll be instructed to round population growth down to the nearest whole value, as a part of a person, animal, etc., doesn't make sense. You'll also be instructed in problems to round dollars to the nearest cent.

- ✓ **Case Matters** — If an answer is listed in the *Solutions Manual* as $8v$, $8V$ is not an acceptable answer. Whether you use uppercase or lowercase matters! It's important to form the habit of using the correct case, as you might encounter problems that have both an uppercase and lowercase letter in the same problem, each representing a different unknown. Always use the case given in the problem; if v is used, use v, not V.

- ✓ **Specific Instructions** — You'll be given specific instructions on how to show graphs you graphed on a calculator on Worksheet 7.3B, how to list answers containing complex numbers on Worksheet 9.5, how to list answers when factoring and finding roots on Worksheet 9.6, and how to list answers to simplifying transformed functions on Worksheet 14.2A. Make notes of these instructions as you come to them, as following them will make grading easier since your answer will then be in the same format as the *Solutions Manual*.

Studying for Quizzes/Tests

Here are a few suggestions to help you study for quizzes/tests:

- ✓ Start by looking at the chapter synopsis (or synopses) for the chapter(s) you're studying. Review any concepts listed there you may have forgotten. Look over the worksheets for the chapter(s), especially the final review worksheet at the end of each chapter or quarter. Except where it says otherwise, the end-of-chapter worksheets and the test review worksheets give you a type of "pretest" to help you figure out what concepts to study. When studying for a test, also go back over the quizzes for the chapters covered on the test. And it's always a good idea in general to look at any concepts or problems you know were hard for you to make sure you understand them.

- ✓ Review any concepts you know were more challenging for you.

- ✓ Look at any notes you've taken. Review any flashcards you've made (or make some if you've not made any yet).

---

1   When rounding, look at the value to the right of the place to which you want to round. If it is 5 or greater, round up; if it is less than 5, you just round down, or in the case of decimals, leave the place you're rounding to as it is. For example, if rounding 9.578542 to the 3rd decimal, we would look at the 4th decimal place, which is a 5. Since 5 is 5 or greater, we'd round the 3rd decimal place up to the next number, giving us a rounded value of 9.579. But if we had 9.578342 instead, we'd round to 9.578 instead.

First Semester Suggested Daily Schedule

While the schedule shows how to complete the course in one school year, different students may require different amounts of time. Feel free to let students go faster if they are able, especially through the first quarter, which includes a lot of review from Algebra 1. In fact, it's suggested that students who already have a firm grasp of Algebra 1 get ahead in the first quarter if possible to allow for extra time on some of the more advanced concepts in the latter parts of the book (or to start their next course of study earlier).

Those using the eCourse on the Master Books Academy (MasterBooksAcademy.com) should complete the corresponding lesson there first, using the *Student Textbook* as a reference. For example, on Day 1, students would watch video 1.1 and then work the worksheet, consulting their textbook as needed.

Date	Day	Assignment	Due Date	✓	Grade
		First Semester-First Quarter			
Week 1	Day 1	Lesson 1.1 (*Student Textbook*, pages 11–16) Worksheet 1.1 (*Teacher Guide*, page 19)			
	Day 2	Lesson 1.2 (*Student Textbook*, pages 17–20) Worksheet 1.2 (*Teacher Guide*, page 20)			
	Day 3	Lesson 1.3 (*Student Textbook*, pages 21–25) Worksheet 1.3 (*Teacher Guide*, pages 21–22)			
	Day 4	Lesson 1.4 (*Student Textbook*, pages 26–28) Worksheet 1.4 (*Teacher Guide*, pages 23–24)			
	Day 5	Lesson 1.5 (*Student Textbook*, pages 29–32) Worksheet 1.5 (*Teacher Guide*, page 25)			
Week 2	Day 6	Lesson 1.6 (*Student Textbook*, pages 33–36) Worksheet 1.6 (*Teacher Guide*, pages 26–27)			
	Day 7	Lesson 1.7 (*Student Textbook*, pages 37–40) Worksheet 1.7 (*Teacher Guide*, pages 28–29)			
	Day 8	Lesson 1.8–1.9 (*Student Textbook*, pages 41–48) Worksheet 1.8 (*Teacher Guide*, pages 30–31)			
	Day 9	Quiz 1 (*Teacher Guide*, pages 361–362)			
	Day 10	Lesson 2.1 (*Student Textbook*, pages 49–53) Worksheet 2.1 (*Teacher Guide*, pages 33–34)			
Week 3	Day 11	Lesson 2.2 (*Student Textbook*, pages 54–57) Worksheet 2.2 (*Teacher Guide*, pages 35–36)			
	Day 12	Lesson 2.3 (*Student Textbook*, pages 58–61) Worksheet 2.3A (*Teacher Guide*, page 37)			
	Day 13	Worksheet 2.3B (*Teacher Guide*, pages 38–39)			
	Day 14	Lesson 2.4 (*Student Textbook*, pages 62–63) Worksheet 2.4 (*Teacher Guide*, pages 40–41)			
	Day 15	Lesson 2.5 (*Student Textbook*, pages 64–67) Worksheet 2.5A (*Teacher Guide*, page 42)			
Week 4	Day 16	Worksheet 2.5B (*Teacher Guide*, pages 43–44)			
	Day 17	Lesson 2.6 (*Student Textbook*, pages 68–71) Worksheet 2.6A (*Teacher Guide*, page 45)			
	Day 18	Worksheet 2.6B (*Teacher Guide*, pages 46–47)			
	Day 19	Lesson 2.7 (*Student Textbook*, pages 72–76) Worksheet 2.7A (*Teacher Guide*, page 48)			
	Day 20	Worksheet 2.7B (*Teacher Guide*, pages 49–50)			

Date	Day	Assignment	Due Date	✓	Grade
Week 5	Day 21	Lesson 2.8 (*Student Textbook*, pages 77–80) Worksheet 2.8 (*Teacher Guide*, page 51)			
	Day 22	Quiz 2 (*Teacher Guide*, page 363–364)			
	Day 23	Lesson 3.1 (*Student Textbook*, pages 81–86) Worksheet 3.1A (*Teacher Guide*, page 53)			
	Day 24	Worksheet 3.1B (*Teacher Guide*, pages 54–55)			
	Day 25	Lesson 3.2 (*Student Textbook*, pages 87–91) Worksheet 3.2A (*Teacher Guide*, page 56)			
Week 6	Day 26	Worksheet 3.2B (*Teacher Guide*, pages 57–58)			
	Day 27	Lesson 3.3 (*Student Textbook*, pages 92–94) Worksheet 3.3A (*Teacher Guide*, page 59)			
	Day 28	Worksheet 3.3B (*Teacher Guide*, pages 60–61)			
	Day 29	Lesson 3.4 (*Student Textbook*, pages 95–99) Worksheet 3.4A (*Teacher Guide*, page 62)			
	Day 30	Worksheet 3.4B (*Teacher Guide*, pages 63–64)			
Week 7	Day 31	Lesson 3.5 (*Student Textbook*, pages 100–102) Worksheet 3.5A (*Teacher Guide*, page 65)			
	Day 32	Worksheet 3.5B (*Teacher Guide*, pages 66–67)			
	Day 33	Lesson 3.6 (*Student Textbook*, pages 103–106) Worksheet 3.6 (*Teacher Guide*, page 68)			
	Day 34	Quiz 3 (*Teacher Guide*, page 365)			
	Day 35	Lesson 4.1 (*Student Textbook*, pages 107–112) Worksheet 4.1 (*Teacher Guide*, pages 69–70)			
Week 8	Day 36	Lesson 4.2 (*Student Textbook*, pages 113–117) Worksheet 4.2 (*Teacher Guide*, page 71)			
	Day 37	Lesson 4.3 (*Student Textbook*, pages 118–123) Worksheet 4.3A (*Teacher Guide*, page 72)			
	Day 38	Worksheet 4.3B (*Teacher Guide*, pages 73–74)			
	Day 39	Lesson 4.4 (*Student Textbook*, pages 124–128) Worksheet 4.4A (*Teacher Guide*, page 75)			
	Day 40	Worksheet 4.4B (*Teacher Guide*, page 76)			
Week 9	Day 41	Lesson 4.5 (*Student Textbook*, pages 129–130) Worksheet 4.5 (*Teacher Guide*, pages 77–78)			
	Day 42	Lesson 4.6 (*Student Textbook*, pages 131–132) Worksheet 4.6 (*Teacher Guide*, pages 79–81)			
	Day 43	Quiz 4 (*Teacher Guide*, pages 367–368)			
	Day 44	Worksheet 4.7 (*Teacher Guide*, pages 82–83)			
	Day 45	Test 1 (*Teacher Guide*, pages 393–394)			

Date	Day	Assignment	Due Date	✓	Grade
		First Semester-Second Quarter			
Week 1	Day 46	Lesson 5.1 (*Student Textbook*, pages 133–137) Worksheet 5.1 (*Teacher Guide*, pages 85–86)			
	Day 47	Lesson 5.2 (*Student Textbook*, pages 138–141) Worksheet 5.2 (*Teacher Guide*, page 87)			
	Day 48	Lesson 5.3 (*Student Textbook*, pages 142–144) Worksheet 5.3 (*Teacher Guide*, page 88)			
	Day 49	Lesson 5.4 (*Student Textbook*, pages 145–148) Worksheet 5.4A (*Teacher Guide*, page 89)			
	Day 50	Worksheet 5.4B (*Teacher Guide*, pages 90–91)			
Week 2	Day 51	Lesson 5.5 (*Student Textbook*, pages 149–152) Worksheet 5.5A (*Teacher Guide*, page 92)			
	Day 52	Worksheet 5.5B (*Teacher Guide*, pages 93–94)			
	Day 53	Lesson 5.6 (*Student Textbook*, pages 153–157) Worksheet 5.6A (*Teacher Guide*, page 95)			
	Day 54	Worksheet 5.6B (*Teacher Guide*, pages 96–97)			
	Day 55	Lesson 5.7 (*Student Textbook*, pages 158–160) Worksheet 5.7 (*Teacher Guide*, page 98)			
Week 3	Day 56	Quiz 5 (*Teacher Guide*, pages 369–370)			
	Day 57	Lesson 6.1 (*Student Textbook*, pages 161–165) Worksheet 6.1A (*Teacher Guide*, page 99)			
	Day 58	Worksheet 6.1B (*Teacher Guide*, pages 100–101)			
	Day 59	Lesson 6.2 (*Student Textbook*, pages 166–169) Worksheet 6.2A (*Teacher Guide*, page 102)			
	Day 60	Worksheet 6.2B (*Teacher Guide*, pages 103–104)			
Week 4	Day 61	Lesson 6.3 (*Student Textbook*, pages 170–174) Worksheet 6.3A (*Teacher Guide*, pages 105–106)			
	Day 62	Worksheet 6.3B (*Teacher Guide*, pages 107–110)			
	Day 63	Lesson 6.4 (*Student Textbook*, pages 175–176) Worksheet 6.4 (*Teacher Guide*, pages 111–112)			
	Day 64	Quiz 6 (*Teacher Guide*, pages 371–372)			
	Day 65	Lesson 7.1 (*Student Textbook*, pages 177–182) Worksheet 7.1A (*Teacher Guide*, page 113)			
Week 5	Day 66	Worksheet 7.1B (*Teacher Guide*, pages 114–117)			
	Day 67	Lesson 7.2 (*Student Textbook*, pages 183–186) Worksheet 7.2A (*Teacher Guide*, page 118)			
	Day 68	Worksheet 7.2B (*Teacher Guide*, pages 119–121)			
	Day 69	Lesson 7.3 (*Student Textbook*, pages 187–193) Worksheet 7.3A (*Teacher Guide*, page 122)			
	Day 70	Worksheet 7.3B (*Teacher Guide*, pages 123–126)			

Date	Day	Assignment	Due Date	✓	Grade
Week 6	Day 71	Lesson 7.4 (*Student Textbook*, pages 194–199) Worksheet 7.4 (*Teacher Guide*, pages 127–128)			
	Day 72	Lesson 7.5 (*Student Textbook*, pages 200–206) Worksheet 7.5 (*Teacher Guide*, pages 129–130)			
	Day 73	Lesson 7.6 (*Student Textbook*, pages 207–211) Worksheet 7.6A (*Teacher Guide*, page 131)			
	Day 74	Worksheet 7.6B (*Teacher Guide*, pages 132–133)			
	Day 75	Lesson 7.7 (*Student Textbook*, pages 212–215) Worksheet 7.7A (*Teacher Guide*, page 134)			
Week 7	Day 76	Worksheet 7.7B (*Teacher Guide*, pages 135–138)			
	Day 77	Lesson 7.8 (*Student Textbook*, pages 216–220) Worksheet 7.8A (*Teacher Guide*, page 139)			
	Day 78	Worksheet 7.8B (*Teacher Guide*, pages 140–142)			
	Day 79	Lesson 7.9 (*Student Textbook*, pages 221–226) Worksheet 7.9 (*Teacher Guide*, pages 143–144)			
	Day 80	Quiz 7 (*Teacher Guide*, pages 373–374)			
Week 8	Day 81	Lesson 8.1 (*Student Textbook*, pages 227–232) Worksheet 8.1 (*Teacher Guide*, pages 145–147)			
	Day 82	Lesson 8.2 (*Student Textbook*, pages 233–239) Worksheet 8.2A (*Teacher Guide*, page 148)			
	Day 83	Worksheet 8.2B (*Teacher Guide*, pages 149–151)			
	Day 84	Lesson 8.3 (*Student Textbook*, pages 240–245) Worksheet 8.3A (*Teacher Guide*, page 152)			
	Day 85	Worksheet 8.3B (*Teacher Guide*, pages 153–155)			
Week 9	Day 86	Lesson 8.4 (*Student Textbook*, pages 246–249) Worksheet 8.4 (*Teacher Guide*, pages 156–157)			
	Day 87	Lesson 8.5 (*Student Textbook*, pages 250–252) Worksheet 8.5 (*Teacher Guide*, pages 158–160)			
	Day 88	Quiz 8 (*Teacher Guide*, pages 375–376)			
	Day 89	Worksheet 8.6 (*Teacher Guide*, pages 161–164)			
	Day 90	Test 2 (*Teacher Guide*, pages 395–397)			
		Mid-Term Grade			

Second Semester Suggested Daily Schedule

Date	Day	Assignment	Due Date	✓	Grade
		Second Semester-Third Quarter			
Week 1	Day 91	Lesson 9.1 (*Student Textbook*, pages 253–261) Worksheet 9.1A (*Teacher Guide*, pages 165–166)			
	Day 92	Worksheet 9.1B (*Teacher Guide*, pages 167–170)			
	Day 93	Lesson 9.2 (*Student Textbook*, pages 262–267) Worksheet 9.2A (*Teacher Guide*, page 171)			
	Day 94	Worksheet 9.2B (*Teacher Guide*, pages 172–174)			
	Day 95	Lesson 9.3 (*Student Textbook*, pages 268–272) Worksheet 9.3A (*Teacher Guide*, pages 175–176)			
Week 2	Day 96	Worksheet 9.3B (*Teacher Guide*, pages 177–178)			
	Day 97	Lesson 9.4 (*Student Textbook*, pages 273–279) Worksheet 9.4A (*Teacher Guide*, page 179)			
	Day 98	Worksheet 9.4B (*Teacher Guide*, pages 180–182)			
	Day 99	Lesson 9.5 (*Student Textbook*, pages 280–282) Worksheet 9.5 (*Teacher Guide*, pages 183–184)			
	Day 100	Lesson 9.6 (*Student Textbook*, pages 283–287) Worksheet 9.6 (*Teacher Guide*, pages 185–187)			
Week 3	Day 101	Lesson 9.7 (*Student Textbook*, pages 288–294) Worksheet 9.7 (*Teacher Guide*, pages 188–190)			
	Day 102	Quiz 9 (*Teacher Guide*, pages 377–378)			
	Day 103	Lesson 10.1 (*Student Textbook*, pages 295–300) Worksheet 10.1A (*Teacher Guide*, page 191)			
	Day 104	Worksheet 10.1B (*Teacher Guide*, pages 192–193)			
	Day 105	Lesson 10.2 (*Student Textbook*, pages 301–305) Worksheet 10.2A (*Teacher Guide*, page 194)			
Week 4	Day 106	Worksheet 10.2B (*Teacher Guide*, pages 195–196)			
	Day 107	Lesson 10.3 (*Student Textbook*, pages 306–314) Worksheet 10.3A (*Teacher Guide*, pages 197–198)			
	Day 108	Worksheet 10.3B (*Teacher Guide*, pages 199–201)			
	Day 109	Lesson 10.4 (*Student Textbook*, pages 315–316) Worksheet 10.4 (*Teacher Guide*, pages 202–204)			
	Day 110	Quiz 10 (*Teacher Guide*, pages 379–380)			
Week 5	Day 111	Lesson 11.1 (*Student Textbook*, pages 317–322) Worksheet 11.1A (*Teacher Guide*, pages 205–207)			
	Day 112	Worksheet 11.1B (*Teacher Guide*, pages 208–210)			
	Day 113	Lesson 11.2 (*Student Textbook*, pages 323–328) Worksheet 11.2A (*Teacher Guide*, page 211)			
	Day 114	Worksheet 11.2B (*Teacher Guide*, pages 212–214)			
	Day 115	Lesson 11.3 (*Student Textbook*, pages 329–334) Worksheet 11.3 (*Teacher Guide*, pages 215–217)			

Date	Day	Assignment	Due Date	✓	Grade
Week 6	Day 116	Lesson 11.4 (*Student Textbook*, pages 335–339) Worksheet 11.4A (*Teacher Guide*, pages 218–219)			
	Day 117	Worksheet 11.4B (*Teacher Guide*, pages 220–222)			
	Day 118	Lesson 11.5 (*Student Textbook*, pages 340–345) Worksheet 11.5A (*Teacher Guide*, pages 223–224)			
	Day 119	Worksheet 11.5B (*Teacher Guide*, pages 225–227)			
	Day 120	Lesson 11.6 (*Student Textbook*, pages 346–348) Worksheet 11.6 (*Teacher Guide*, pages 228–231)			
Week 7	Day 121	Quiz 11 (*Teacher Guide*, pages 381–382)			
	Day 122	Lesson 12.1 (*Student Textbook*, pages 349–353) Worksheet 12.1 (*Teacher Guide*, pages 233–234)			
	Day 123	Lesson 12.2 (*Student Textbook*, pages 354–356) Worksheet 12.2 (*Teacher Guide*, pages 235–237)			
	Day 124	Lesson 12.3 (*Student Textbook*, pages 357–360) Worksheet 12.3A (*Teacher Guide*, page 238)			
	Day 125	Worksheet 12.3B (*Teacher Guide*, pages 239–240)			
Week 8	Day 126	Lesson 12.4 (*Student Textbook*, pages 361–365) Worksheet 12.4A (*Teacher Guide*, page 241)			
	Day 127	Worksheet 12.4B (*Teacher Guide*, pages 242–243)			
	Day 128	Lesson 12.5 (*Student Textbook*, pages 366–370) Worksheet 12.5A (*Teacher Guide*, page 244)			
	Day 129	Worksheet 12.5B (*Teacher Guide*, pages 245–246)			
	Day 130	Lesson 12.6 (*Student Textbook*, pages 371–374) Worksheet 12.6A (*Teacher Guide*, page 247)			
Week 9	Day 131	Worksheet 12.6B (*Teacher Guide*, pages 248–250)			
	Day 132	Lesson 12.7 (*Student Textbook*, pages 375–378) Worksheet 12.7 (*Teacher Guide*, pages 251–253)			
	Day 133	Quiz 12 (*Teacher Guide*, pages 383–384)			
	Day 134	Worksheet 12.8 (*Teacher Guide*, pages 254–257)			
	Day 135	Test 3 (*Teacher Guide*, pages 399–403)			

Date	Day	Assignment	Due Date	✓	Grade
		Second Semester-Fourth Quarter			
Week 1	Day 136	Lesson 13.1 (*Student Textbook*, pages 379–384) Worksheet 13.1 (*Teacher Guide*, pages 259–260)			
	Day 137	Lesson 13.2 (*Student Textbook*, pages 385–388) Worksheet 13.2 (*Teacher Guide*, pages 261–262)			
	Day 138	Lesson 13.3 (*Student Textbook*, pages 389–394) Worksheet 13.3A (*Teacher Guide*, page 263)			
	Day 139	Worksheet 13.3B (*Teacher Guide*, pages 264–265)			
	Day 140	Lesson 13.4 (*Student Textbook*, pages 395–398) Worksheet 13.4A (*Teacher Guide*, pages 266–267)			
Week 2	Day 141	Worksheet 13.4B (*Teacher Guide*, pages 286–269)			
	Day 142	Lesson 13.5 (*Student Textbook*, pages 399–404) Worksheet 13.5A (*Teacher Guide*, page 270)			
	Day 143	Worksheet 13.5B (*Teacher Guide*, pages 271–273)			
	Day 144	Lesson 13.6 (*Student Textbook*, pages 405–413) Worksheet 13.6 (*Teacher Guide*, pages 274–276)			
	Day 145	Lesson 13.7 (*Student Textbook*, pages 414–418) Worksheet 13.7 (*Teacher Guide*, pages 277–279)			
Week 3	Day 146	Lesson 13.8 (*Student Textbook*, pages 418–419) Worksheet 13.8 (*Teacher Guide*, pages 280–282)			
	Day 147	Quiz 13 (*Teacher Guide*, pages 385–386)			
	Day 148	Lesson 14.1 (*Student Textbook*, pages 421–428) Worksheet 14.1A (*Teacher Guide*, pages 283–284)			
	Day 149	Worksheet 14.1B (*Teacher Guide*, pages 285–287)			
	Day 150	Lesson 14.2 (*Student Textbook*, pages 429–439) Worksheet 14.2A (*Teacher Guide*, pages 288–289)			
Week 4	Day 151	Worksheet 14.2B (*Teacher Guide*, pages 290–293)			
	Day 152	Lesson 14.3 (*Student Textbook*, pages 440–446) Worksheet 14.3 (*Teacher Guide*, pages 294–296)			
	Day 153	Lesson 14.4 (*Student Textbook*, pages 447–454) Worksheet 14.4 (*Teacher Guide*, pages 296–297)			
	Day 154	Lesson 14.5 (*Student Textbook*, pages 455–461) Worksheet 14.5A (*Teacher Guide*, pages 298–299)			
	Day 155	Worksheet 14.5B (*Teacher Guide*, pages 300–302)			
Week 5	Day 156	Lesson 14.6 (*Student Textbook*, pages 462–464) Worksheet 14.6 (*Teacher Guide*, pages 303–305)			
	Day 157	Lesson 14.7 (*Student Textbook*, pages 465–469) Worksheet 14.7 (*Teacher Guide*, pages 306–308)			
	Day 158	Lesson 14.8 (*Student Textbook*, pages 470–476) Worksheet 14.8 (*Teacher Guide*, pages 309–313)			
	Day 159	Lesson 14.9 (*Student Textbook*, pages 477–480) Worksheet 14.9 (*Teacher Guide*, pages 314–316)			
	Day 160	Quiz 14 (*Teacher Guide*, pages 387–389)			

Date	Day	Assignment	Due Date	✓	Grade
Week 6	Day 161	Lesson 15.1 (*Student Textbook*, pages 481–484) Worksheet 15.1 (*Teacher Guide*, pages 317–318)			
	Day 162	Lesson 15.2 (*Student Textbook*, pages 485–490) Worksheet 15.2 (*Teacher Guide*, pages 319–321)			
	Day 163	Lesson 15.3 (*Student Textbook*, pages 491–493) Worksheet 15.3 (*Teacher Guide*, pages 322–324)			
	Day 164	Lesson 15.4 (*Student Textbook*, pages 494–499) Worksheet 15.4 (*Teacher Guide*, pages 325–326)			
	Day 165	Lesson 15.5 (*Student Textbook*, pages 500–504) Worksheet 15.5 (*Teacher Guide*, pages 327–329)			
Week 7	Day 166	Lesson 15.6 (*Student Textbook*, pages 505–507) Worksheet 15.6 (*Teacher Guide*, pages 330–332)			
	Day 167	Lesson 15.7 (*Student Textbook*, pages 508–514) Worksheet 15.7A (*Teacher Guide*, pages 333–335)			
	Day 168	Worksheet 15.7B (*Teacher Guide*, pages 336–338)			
	Day 169	Lesson 15.8 (*Student Textbook*, pages 515–520) Worksheet 15.8A (*Teacher Guide*, page 339)			
	Day 170	Worksheet 15.8B (*Teacher Guide*, pages 340–342)			
Week 8	Day 171	Lesson 15.9 (*Student Textbook*, pages 521–528) Worksheet 15.9 (*Teacher Guide*, pages 343–344)			
	Day 172	Lesson 15.10 (*Student Textbook*, pages 529–534) Worksheet 15.10 (*Teacher Guide*, pages 345–347)			
	Day 173	Quiz 15 (*Teacher Guide*, pages 391–392)			
	Day 174	Lesson 16.1 (*Student Textbook*, pages 535–536) Worksheet 16.1 (*Teacher Guide*, pages 348–350)			
	Day 175	Lesson 16.2 (*Student Textbook*, pages 537–541) Worksheet 16.2 (*Teacher Guide*, page 351–355)			
Week 9	Day 176	Lesson 16.3 (*Student Textbook*, pages 542–545) Worksheet 16.3 (*Teacher Guide*, pages 356–358)			
	Day 177	Test 4 (*Teacher Guide*, pages 405–407)			
	Day 178	Study Day			
	Day 179	Study Day			
	Day 180	Test 5 Final Exam (*Teacher Guide*, pages 409–415)			
		Final Grade			

Worksheets

Intentionally left blank

Make sure you know the names of the different properties covered in Lesson 1.1. You may want to make flashcards for any that you do not already know.

Decide how you're going to help yourself learn new concepts and get that set up. You may want to grab a three-ring binder and put paper for taking notes inside it. If you find flashcards helpful, get some blank ones ready to go (or find a way to make them online using a site such as Quizlet). If you ever get confused, go back and review previous concepts. (Notes prove very helpful!)

Solve problems and write your answers in a notebook, as there is not room on the worksheets to write your answers. Be sure to number the problems and circle your final answer to aid in grading.

1. **Term Check** – What is one mathematical *property* covered on pages 3–4 of the *Student Textbook* and what does it mean?

2. **Reviewing Properties and More** – Insert an = sign between any of these expressions that you can absolutely tell are equal. Otherwise, write "can't tell" and explain why.

   Example: $a + c$ $\qquad$ $b + a$

   Answer: Can't tell; depends on what c and b equal. If they are equal, then the expressions are equal. If not, they are not.

   a. $a + b + c$ $\qquad$ $d + b + c$
   b. $2a + b$ $\qquad$ $b + 2a$
   c. $(8 + y) + 3d$ $\qquad$ $8 + (y + 3d)$
   d. $x + 0$ $\qquad$ 0
   e. $a + 0$ $\qquad$ a
   f. $1y$ $\qquad$ y
   g. $8 \div 8$ $\qquad$ 1
   h. A $\qquad$ a

3. **Reviewing Properties**

   a. For which problem in section 2 do you know that the expression on the left equals the expression on the right because of the identity property of multiplication?

   b. For which problem in section 2 do you know that the expression on the left equals the expression on the right because of the associative property of addition?

4. **Thinking It Through** – If we want to divide 5 by $3 - x$, what number can x *not* be and why?

5. **Algebra and Formulas** – Look at the Reference Section (Appendix B in the *Student Textbook*) to find the formulas to solve these problems if they are not ones you know. Be sure to include units of measure in your answers. You should always include a unit of measure in the answer when one is given.

   a. Find the perimeter of a rectangular field that is 60 ft long and 30 ft wide.

   b. Find the circumference of a circular bowl that has a diameter of 7 in.

> *Review the "General Instructions for Students" section on pages 7–8 of this Teacher Guide that contains some general things you need to know in this course. Note that many of the points there are conventions specific to this course! The Student Textbook will go over many of the points as we encounter them for the first time as well, so don't worry if you don't fully understand each one, as we haven't reviewed some of the concepts mentioned. Keep the general instructions somewhere you can reference them later.*

1. **Term Check** – What is one mathematical *convention* covered in Lesson 1.2 and what does it mean?

2. **Comparing** – Draw a >, <, or = sign between these expressions to make a true statement.

   a. $8(8)$ 60

   b. 52   80

   c. xy yx

3. **Simplifying** – Simplify these expressions. Notice how much easier it is to read and compare simplified expressions. Simplifying helps us work with quantities.

   a. $(5\text{ m})(20\text{ kg})$

   b. $4(a)$
   Hint: Remember that we don't need to use parentheses to show multiplication between a numeral and letter.

   c. $(6\text{ m})(15\text{ s})$

4. **Applying Algebra** – Find the circumference of a bowl if it is 5 in across.

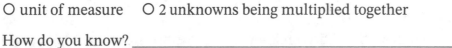

5. **Comprehension Check** – In this course, does kg stand for a unit of measure or 2 unknowns being multiplied together (i.e., k times g)?

   ○ unit of measure   ○ 2 unknowns being multiplied together

   How do you know? _____

6. **Capital and Lowercase Letters** – If a problem gives an unknown using a, and you discover that unknown equals 6, can you list your answer of what a equals as $A = 6$?

   ○ yes   ○ no

   Why or why not? _____

1. **Rewrite as a Fraction** – Rewrite each of these division problems as a fraction. Do not simplify.

   Example: $60 \div 5 = \dfrac{60}{5}$

   a. $11 \div 3$

   b. $\dfrac{1}{5} \div \dfrac{2}{6}$

   c. $8 \div F$

   Example Meaning: A power of 8 watts divided by the force to get the velocity.

   d. $x \div 2y$

   Example Meaning: Your total cost divided by twice the cost for each person.

2. **Thinking It Through** – In the expression $\dfrac{8a}{x-7}$, what number can x not be?

   $x \neq$ _____

   Explain: _____

3. **Multiplicative Inverse** – Write the multiplicative inverse (i.e., the reciprocal) of each of the following fractions.

   a. $\dfrac{5}{9}$

   b. $\dfrac{5a}{2}$

   c. $\dfrac{x}{y}$

4. **Rewriting as a Fraction** – Rewrite the value to the left of the fraction as part of the numerator. Note that both the problem and your answer mean the same thing.

   Example: $x\left(\dfrac{y}{z}\right)$ *Answer:* $\dfrac{xy}{z}$

   a. $5\left(\dfrac{x}{3}\right)$

   b. $y\left(\dfrac{ab}{c}\right)$

5. **Multiplying and Dividing Fractions** – Complete the multiplication or division.

a. $\dfrac{2}{3}\left(\dfrac{1}{5}\right)$

b. $\dfrac{8}{x}\left(\dfrac{y}{3}\right)$

c. $\dfrac{\frac{x}{2}}{\frac{y}{3}}$

d. $\dfrac{\frac{3}{x}}{\frac{2a}{y}}$

e. $\dfrac{\frac{a}{b}}{\frac{3x}{2}}$

6. **Applying Algebra**

a. Suppose that a car gets a gas mileage of 40 miles per gallon. If another car gets a third of that gas mileage, what gas mileage does it get? Leave your answer as an improper fraction.

b. Say that you've been told there's a $\dfrac{2}{3}$-off sale going on at a consignment store. If an item costs $4, what dollar discount would you get? Leave your answer as an improper fraction.

c. If you have 50 yards of fabric and want to cut it into $\dfrac{1}{3}$-yd swatches, how many swatches will you have? Leave off units when solving, as we've not gone over how to simplify the units (they cancel out).

d. Write a formula based on 6c showing how the total yards of fabric (T), portion of a yard you make each swatch (s), and number of swatches (n) compare for any amount of fabric you might want to cut into swatches.

$n = \underline{\qquad}$

7. **Skill Sharpening** – Find 2 kg times 4 m.

Review the "General Instructions for Students" to remind yourself about when to use fractions and how to simplify your fractional answers in this course.

1. **Simplifying Fractions** – Simplify the following fractions.

    a. $\dfrac{88}{22}$

    b. $\dfrac{8a}{3a}$

    c. $\dfrac{2xy}{y}$

2. **Rewrite as a Fraction** – Rewrite these quantities as fractions. Remember that any quantity divided by 1 equals itself.

    Example: 2   *Example:* x

    Answer: $\dfrac{2}{1}$ *Answer:* $\dfrac{x}{1}$

    a. 4

    b. b

3. **Complete the Multiplication** – Simplify into a single fraction.

    a. $4\left(\dfrac{x}{b}\right)$

    b. $b\left(\dfrac{c}{d}\right)$

4. **Combining the Skills** – Simplify the following.

    a. $\dfrac{2}{3}\left(\dfrac{3}{5}\right)$

    Example Meaning: A combined gear ratio for a gear with a gear ratio of $\dfrac{2}{3}$ and one with a gear ratio of $\dfrac{3}{5}$.

    b. $\dfrac{2}{6}\left(\dfrac{1}{3}\right)$

    Example Meaning: If $\dfrac{2}{6}$ of the city's population support a candidate for mayor, and $\dfrac{1}{3}$ of those are strong supporters, what fraction of the city's population are strong supporters?[1]

---

[1]   Example meaning adapted from Katherine Loop, *Principles of Mathematics: Book 2 Teacher Guide* (Green Forest, AZ: Master Books, 2016), Worksheet 4.2.

c. $4\dfrac{x}{2}$

Example Meaning: 4 times the biweekly cost of a magazine divided by the 2 months over which that cost occurs.

d. $\dfrac{\dfrac{2x}{3a}}{\dfrac{b}{3}}$

Example Meaning: $\dfrac{2}{3}$ times the pounds of peaches grown in a year (x) divided by the number of peaches per pound (a), all divided by the total volume of the peaches (b), divided by 3.

5. **Applying Algebra** – Find the area of this triangle using the formula given in Appendix B of the *Student Textbook*. The units are in cm (i.e., centimeters), so your answer will be in cm² (i.e., square centimeters). Be sure to simplify your answer.

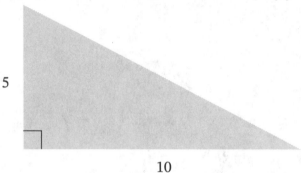

5

10

1. **Ratios** – Represent the following quantities as a ratio. Notice that you could reword each one to include the word *per*. Include units of measure. Do not simplify.

   a. $4 per 3 dozen

   b. 5 for $1

   c. 40 passengers per train

   d. 1 gallon for every 3 trips

2. **Basic Unit Conversion** – Use conversion ratios (see Appendix B of the *Student Textbook* if needed) to complete these conversions.

   a. 4 m to yd

   b. 800 yd to mi

3. **Proportions**

   a. Find x: $\dfrac{4}{10} = \dfrac{x}{20}$

   b. Find x: $\dfrac{2}{x} = \dfrac{10}{20}$

   c. Find x: $\dfrac{8}{22} = \dfrac{x}{11}$

   d. If it took someone 3 days to go 100 miles on horseback, how many miles could they go in 9 days if they travel at the same pace?

   e. If it took someone 3 days to go 100 miles on horseback, how many miles could they go in 2 days if they travel at the same pace?

4. **Applying Algebra**[1] – Using the equation for a combined gear ratio given in the text ($R = \dfrac{g_1 g_3}{g_2 g_4}$), find the combined gear ratio if g_1 equals 4, g_2 equals 15, g_3 equals 8, and g_4 equals 10.

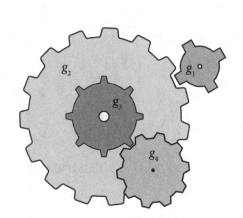

---

1   See PLTW, Inc., *Engineering Formulas (n.p., n.d.), p. 6.*, and Woodgears.ca, *"Gear Ratios and Compound Gear Ratios," (n.d.)*, https://woodgears.ca/gear/ratio.html.

1. **Representing Rates** – Represent the following units of measure using ratios to show units per another unit.

    a. $7 per bushel (bushel is abbreviated bu.)

    b. $7 per 3 bushels

    c. 9 meters per 3 minutes (a speed of 9 meters every 3 minutes)

2. **Simplifying the Rates** – Simplify your answer to 1c to find the meters per each minute.

3. **Unit Conversion** – Let's say you need to convert $3\,\frac{m}{s}$ to $\frac{mi}{hr}$. The following problems break this task down into steps. Use the conversion ratios in Appendix B of the *Student Textbook* to complete the following conversions. **Do not round on problems 3a and 3b,** as they are intermediary steps to solving the problem and rounding intermediary steps will make your answer less precise.

    a. Convert $3\,\frac{m}{s}$ to $\frac{yd}{s}$.

    b. Convert your answer from 3a to $\frac{mi}{s}$.

    c. Convert your answer from 3b to $\frac{mi}{hr}$, rounding your answer this time. Note that you've now successfully converted $3\,\frac{m}{s}$ to $\frac{mi}{hr}$.

4. **Rewriting as a Fraction** – Rewrite the value to the left of the fraction as part of the numerator. Note that both the problem and your answer mean the same thing (i.e., they're equal).

    Example: $4\,\frac{m}{s}$

    Answer: $\frac{4\ m}{s}$

    a. $2\,\frac{m}{s}$

    b. $7\,\frac{ft}{s}$

5. **Units in the Numerator and the Denominator** – Sometimes we have to divide one rate by another! Rewrite the following division using a fraction: $8\,\frac{m}{s} \div 6\,\frac{m}{s}$. You do not need to simplify.

    Example Meaning: One speed divided by another.

6. **Multiplying and Dividing Units** – Simplify.

   a. $\dfrac{8\text{ m}}{4\text{ s}}$

   b. $8\dfrac{\text{ft}}{\text{s}}(2\text{ s})$ *Hint:* Your seconds (s) will cancel out, as you have one in the numerator and one in the denominator. You're really finding your distance, which equals speed times time!

   c. $\dfrac{\dfrac{8\text{ ft}}{\text{s}}}{\dfrac{2\text{ ft}}{\text{s}}}$ *Hint:* Invert and multiply the bottom fraction to complete the division, canceling out your units of measure just as you would unknowns.

7. **Applying Algebra**

   a. If a certain milk sample yields 2.5 lb of butter fat per gallon, how many pounds of butter fat will 100 gallons of such milk yield?

   b. If a change of elevation of about 295 m makes a difference of 1° Centigrade in the boiling point of water, what is the change in boiling point at a place whose elevation is 1.5 mi?
   Hint: Notice that you've been given the ratio between the change in elevation and the change in the boiling point in *meters*, but are asked to find the ratio for 1.5 *miles*.

Review the "General Instructions for Students" to remind yourself about when to use fractions and how to simplify your fractional answers in this course.

1. **Adding and Subtracting Fractions** – Rewrite so you have only one large fraction. You will not be able to actually add the numerators when they are unknowns. Be sure to watch your units!

   a. $\dfrac{4}{b} + \dfrac{2}{c}$

   b. $\dfrac{xy}{2ab} + \dfrac{3y}{b}$

   c. $x + \dfrac{a}{b}$

   d. $7\,\dfrac{m}{s} + 3\,\dfrac{m}{min}$ (Give your answer in $\dfrac{m}{min}$.)

   Hint: Remember, $7\,\dfrac{m}{s}$ can also be written as $\dfrac{7\,m}{s}$.

   e. $6\dfrac{ft}{min} + 5\dfrac{in}{s}$ (Give your answer in $\dfrac{in}{s}$.)

2. **Equality** – Put an $=$ sign between expressions that are equal and a $\neq$ sign between those that are not. On 2a, you can assume $x \neq 0$.

   a. $7x\dfrac{3}{x}$ 21

   b. $\dfrac{5}{2}c$ $\dfrac{5c}{2}$

   c. $\dfrac{5xy}{10}$ $\dfrac{1}{3}xy$

3. **Combining the Tools** – Solve. Remember to simplify your answers!

   a. If a robot can travel at 4.5 meters per second, how many yards can it travel per minute?
   Hint: You can do all of the conversions in one equation — you just need to multiply by a conversion ratio to convert meters to yards, and another to convert from seconds to minutes.

   b. If a robot can travel at 3.2 yards per minute, how many meters per second can it go?

4. **Skill Sharpening** – Find $\dfrac{3\frac{yd}{min}}{\frac{6\,yd}{min}}$.

5. **Applying Algebra** – If Jack can solve algebra problems at an average rate of 4 problems per 20 minutes and Mike can do it an average rate of 5 problems per 30 minutes, how many problems on average can the 2 combined get done in 1 hour? The questions below will help you answer the question.

   a. Write Jack's and Mike's rates.

      Jack's Rate = _____

      Mike's Rate = _____

   b. Convert both rates from minutes to hours.

      Jack's Rate = _____

      Mike's Rate = _____

   c. Use your answer to 5b to figure out how many problems they can both get done in 1 hour.

6. **More Applying Algebra** – Say that you've been told there's a $\frac{2}{3}$-off sale going on at a consignment store. If an item costs $6, how much will the item cost?
   Hint: Notice that you're given the fraction of the discount, not the fraction of the cost you'll actually pay. You need to find the discount and then subtract it from the cost . . . or find the fraction of the cost you'll pay and then calculate that.

Be sure to also review as needed in preparation for the quiz. See the "General Instructions for Students" for some suggestions to help you review.

1. **Negative Numbers** – Simplify. Remember, each negative sign means *the opposite of*!

    a. $-\left(-\left(-\left(-x\right)\right)\right)$

    b. $-\dfrac{b}{-x}$

    c. $-\dfrac{-1}{2}$

    d. $(-a)(-b)(-c)$

    e. $\dfrac{5a}{2} - \dfrac{-3}{2}$

    f. $5 - 7$

    g. $3 - 8$

2. **More with Negative Numbers**

    a. Find $-ax$ if $a = -2$ and $x = 3$.

    b. Rewrite the subtraction as the addition of a negative number: $6 - t$.

    c. Simplify: $t - t$

3. **Applying Algebra** – Remember, we use negative signs to show *the opposite of*. Thus, they come up all over as we look at creation. Here are just a few examples.

    a. If we are traveling 50 miles per hour in the negative direction for 2 hours, how far (and in what direction) will we have traveled?
    Hint: Distance equals speed multiplied by time
    . . . and use a negative number to show the negative direction.

    b. Is a speed of $50 \dfrac{\text{mi}}{\text{hr}}$ faster or slower than a speed of $29 \dfrac{\text{ft}}{\text{s}}$ and by how much? Give how much faster or slower the speed is in $\dfrac{\text{mi}}{\text{hr}}$.

    c. Electricity can flow in different directions . . . and we can use a positive value to show flow in one direction and a negative value in the other! Thus, a negative current means a current that is flowing in the *opposite* direction and a negative voltage means the voltage drops in the *opposite* direction of the net current flow. In an electrical outlet, the power (P) equals the voltage (V) times the current (I), or $P = VI$. If the voltage is $-4\dfrac{\text{J}}{\text{C}}$ and the current is $-5\dfrac{\text{C}}{\text{s}}$, what is the power?
    Note that the C stands for a unit called a coulomb.

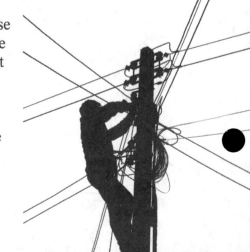

d. If we *owe* $30 per month for a utility, how much will we owe after 1 year? Show amounts owed with negative numbers.

4. **Skill Sharpening** – Simplify. When asked to add fractions, rewrite as a single fraction.

   a. $\dfrac{2x}{y} + \dfrac{-3a}{b}$

   b. $\dfrac{5a}{3}\left(\dfrac{-6}{2a}\right)$ *Hint:* Watch your negative sign!

   c. $\dfrac{-50 \text{ in}}{\dfrac{-5 \text{ in}}{\text{hr}}}$ *Hint:* Invert and multiply, watching your negative signs!

5. **More Skill Sharpening**

   a. Convert $40\dfrac{\text{m}}{\text{s}}$ to $\dfrac{\text{ft}}{\text{min}}$.

   b. Add $30\dfrac{\text{m}}{\text{s}}$ and $50\dfrac{\text{ft}}{\text{min}}$, giving your final answer in $\dfrac{\text{ft}}{\text{min}}$.

6. **Understanding Review**

   a. Rewrite the following expression so that the numerical value is first, and then the letters, in alphabetical order: $zxa8$

   b. What names do we use to describe the consistent way God governs multiplication that allows us to change the order and the grouping of quantities being multiplied, knowing that doing so won't affect the value?

   c. In $\dfrac{a}{2-x}$, what value can x not equal?

   $x \neq$ _____

   Why? _____

Intentionally left blank

1. **Understanding Exponents** – Rewrite using exponents.

   a. $4(4)(4)(4)$

   b. $-4(-4)(-4)$

   c. $xxxxxx$

   Example Meaning: An unknown population that multiplies by itself 6 times.

   d. $(-a)(-a)$

   e. $yyyxx$

   f. x

2. **Reviewing the Order of Operations** – Simplify, watching the order of operations as you do.

   a. $(2^2 + 3 \times 1)^2 \cdot 10$

   b. $(2-1)^3 - 2$

3. **Working with Exponents and Negative Numbers** – Do *not* use a calculator, as the point of these exercises is to make sure you understand how to correctly handle exponents.

   a. Rewrite using exponents: $-a(-a)(-a)$

   b. Simplify if $x = 2 : (-x)^4$

   c. Simplify if $x = 2 : -(x)^4$

   d. Simplify: $-(-2)^2$

   e. Simplify: $(-(-2))^2$

4. **Reviewing the Order of Operations** – Simplify, watching the order of operations as you do.

   a. $(4 + 3 - 2)^2$

   b. $\left(\dfrac{3^2 + 7(3)}{5}\right)^2$

5. **Skill Sharpening** – Simplify the following expressions.

   a. $\dfrac{\frac{2x}{y}}{\frac{x}{4}}$

   b. $\dfrac{6}{b} + \dfrac{-2}{a}$

c. $15\,\dfrac{\text{yd}}{\text{min}} - 5\,\dfrac{\text{ft}}{\text{s}}$. Give your answer in $\dfrac{\text{yd}}{\text{min}}$.

d. $\dfrac{98}{392}$

6. **Applying Algebra**

   a. Given that the power (P) equals the voltage (V) times the current (I), or $P = VI$, and remembering that we use positive numbers to describe flow in one direction and negative in the other, if the voltage is $-3\,\dfrac{\text{J}}{\text{C}}$ and the current is $2\dfrac{\text{C}}{\text{s}}$, what is the power? The C stands for a unit of measure called the coulomb.

   b. A trash can shaped like a cylinder has a height of 0.8 m and a diameter at the base of 0.25 m. What is its volume? Your answer will be in m³. (We'll review how you could have calculated this yourself in a few lessons.)
   Hint: Use the formulas in Appendix B of the *Student Textbook*. Notice the one for finding the volume of a cylinder has an exponent in it! Draw out the problem to help you if needed.

1. **Thinking It Through** – Rewrite the following so each expression contains a negative exponent.

   a. $\dfrac{1}{4^5}$

   b. $\dfrac{1}{4^1}$

   c. $\dfrac{1}{x}$

   d. $\dfrac{m}{s}$

   e. $\dfrac{1}{xxx}$

   Example Meaning: The probability of an event happening 3 out of 3 times, if it has equal probability of happening each time.

2. **Thinking It Through** – Rewrite the following using positive exponents only for each expression.

   a. $\dfrac{1}{x^{-4}}$

   b. $\dfrac{1}{-x^{-4}}$

   c. x^{-9}

   d. $\dfrac{1}{-b}\left(\dfrac{1}{-b}\right)\left(\dfrac{1}{-b}\right)$

   e. $-\dfrac{yyy}{-xxx}$

3. **More Thinking It Through** – When the National Institute of Standards and Technology (NIST) lists the Josephson constant, they list the unit as Hz V^{-1}, which means Hertz times Volts to the negative first, or Hz • V^{-1}. Rewrite these units so as to eliminate the negative exponent.

4. **Scientific Notation** – Rewrite using scientific notation. Do not round. In some cases, units have been omitted for simplicity.

   a. 62,540,000,000 km³

   Volume of Neptune[1]

   b. 0.0000000000012 kg • mol^{-1} (A mol is a unit of measure.)

   Standard uncertainty for the alpha particle molar mass listed by NIST[2]

1 Based on value given by Dr. David Williams, "Neptune Fact Sheet" (NASA, September 27, 2018 update), https://nssdc.gsfc.nasa.gov/planetary/factsheet/neptunefact.html

2 P.J. Mohr, B.N. Taylor, and D.B. Newell (2015), "The 2014 CODATA Recommended Values of the Fundamental Physical Constants," web version 7.0, database developed by J. Baker, M. Douma, and S. Kotochigova (Gaithersburg, MD: National Institute of Standards and Technology), https://physics.nist.gov/constants, accessed 10/27/19.

5. **More Scientific Notation** – Rewrite using standard decimal notation. Do not round.[3] Units (which are in SI base units) have been omitted for simplicity.

a. 4.84×10^{14} Hz • V^{-1}

Approximate Josephson constant

b. $1.00001495 \times 10^{-10}$ m

Angstrom star

c. $6.2 \times 10^7 \ \Omega^{-1}$ • m^{-1} (An Ω is a unit of measure.)

Conductivity of silver[4]

6. **Applying Algebra** – If a computer circuit has a transistor that has an area of 1×10^{-14} m^2, and a company is trying to figure out a way to make it $\frac{1}{4}$ that size, what size does it need to be?

7. **Skill Sharpening**

a. Simplify into a single fraction: $\dfrac{5a}{2c} + \dfrac{2}{x}$

b. Simplify, giving your answer in $\dfrac{\text{ft}}{\text{s}}$: $2\dfrac{\text{ft}}{\text{s}} - 60\dfrac{\text{in}}{\text{s}}$

---

3   Unless otherwise indicated, scientific values quoted are based on P.J. Mohr, B.N. Taylor, and D.B. Newell (2015), "The 2014 CODATA Recommended Values of the Fundamental Physical Constants," web version 7.0, database developed by J. Baker, M. Douma, and S. Kotochigova (Gaithersburg, MD: National Institute of Standards and Technology), https://physics.nist.gov/constants, accessed 10/27/19.

4   Randall D. Knight, *Physics for Scientists and Engineers with Modern Physics: A Strategic Approach* (Pearson, Addison Wesley, NY: 2004), Back Cover Reference Section.

1. **Multiplying and Dividing Exponents** – Simplify these expressions by completing the multiplication or division. Notice how much easier it is to read simplified expressions.

   a. $d^5 d^{-4}$

   b. $y^5 y y^{-9}$

   c. $\dfrac{a^8}{a^4}$

   d. $\dfrac{a^8}{a^{-4}}$

   e. $\dfrac{-4ab^2}{-ab}$

   f. $\dfrac{5x^2}{x^{-9}}$

1. **More Multiplying and Dividing Exponents** – Write an $=$ sign between any two expressions that are equal. For these expressions, assume the variables are not zero.

   a. yy^5 $2y^5$, if $y \neq 2$

   b. d^2d d^3

   c. $\frac{1}{a^2}(a^2)$ 1

   d. $\frac{1}{-a^2}(-a)^2$ 1

   e. $\frac{2ab}{3^2}$ $\frac{2ab}{9}$

2. **Comparing** – Draw a $>$, $<$, or $=$ sign between these expressions to make the statement true.

   a. $\frac{1}{8^2}$ 6^3

   b. 5^1 2^2

   c. $\frac{3^6}{3^2}$ 3^4

   d. $\frac{3^6}{(-3)^2}$ 3^4

   e. $\frac{3^6}{-3^2}$ 3^4

3. **More with Exponents** – Simplify.

   a. $\frac{y^6}{y^2}$

   b. $\frac{3x^{-1}}{x^6}$

   c. $-5ab^2(2a^{-2})$

4. **Thinking It Through** – Why are we able to simplify the multiplication and division in $5ab^2(2a^{-2})$, yet we can't simplify the addition in $5ab^2 + 2a^{-2}$ (unless we knew the value of a and b or had other information)?

5. **Scientific Notation** – Simplify.

   a. $(5.0 \times 10^{-12})(4.0 \times 10^{-6})$

   Example Meaning: Multiplying the mass of two small particles together.

   b. $(3 \times 10^{32})(2 \times 10^6)$

   Example Meaning: Two distances of space multiplied together.

6. **Applying Algebra**

   a. If a 1 mm^2 computer chip contains 1.5×10^8 transistors, how many transistors would a 2 mm^2 chip contain if the ratio were the same?

   b. Rewrite this equation, which is known as Coulomb's Law (it's a useful electrical equation), using a negative exponent rather than a fraction line: $F = k \left(\dfrac{q_1 q_2}{r^2} \right)$.

A note from Dr. Adam: When my college professor taught us Coulomb's Law, the equation given up above, a student asked where it came from.

The professor responded along the lines that people had just figured out the equation from observing how nature worked . . . but I knew it's because God created the equation when He determined how the world worked in regards to electrical charge. That comment was one reason I decided to get my doctorate. I wanted to teach students the truth: the consistencies of creation (which math describes) point to the Creator.

1. **Repeated Multiplications of Exponents** – Simplify.

   a. $(2ac^3)^3$

   b. $\left(\dfrac{1}{x^2}\right)^2$

   c. $(m^{-6})^2$

   d. $\dfrac{(m^{-6})^2}{m^2}$

2. **Seeing the Rule in Action**
   Note: Units of measure have been left off, since we'll review exponents and units in the next lesson.

   a. Find the volume $(V = s^3)$ of a cube, where $s = 4$.

   b. Now find the volume of the same cube when its side is expressed as 2^2 instead of 4, simplifying any terms inside of the parentheses first. Use this equation: $V = (2^2)^3$. *Show your work.*

   c. Now let's say that the side of a cube equals some unknown distance squared, which we'll write as b^2. So $V = (b^2)^3$. Simplify.

   d. Now find the volume using the equation you found in 1c if b equals 2. Notice how what we did in simplifying really did preserve the meaning!

3. **Repeated Multiplications of Exponents** – Simplify.

   a. $(2^{-5})^{-3}$

   b. $\dfrac{(4b^2)^4}{b^6}$

   c. $\left(\dfrac{1}{x^{-2}}\right)^3$

4. **Understanding Check** – Write out this multiplication *without* using exponents: $(2a^3)^2$

   Example: $(5c^2)^4 = (5cc)(5cc)(5cc)(5cc)$ or $625cccccccc$

5. **More with Exponents** – Simplify.

   a. $\dfrac{(-y)^4}{y^2}$ *Hint:* Think this through. We want to multiply $-y$ by itself 4 times. Will that answer be positive or negative?

   b. $\dfrac{-y^4}{y^2}$ *Hint:* Here we're taking the opposite of y^4.

   c. $-\dfrac{-(x^3)^{-3}}{x^4}$ *Hint:* Don't let all the negative signs scare you! You have all the skills you need.

6. **Scientific Notation** – Simplify. Give your answer in scientific notation, with only 1 digit to the left of the decimal point.

   a. $(2.0 \times 10^{-2})(3.0 \times 10^{-1})$

   b. $(7.0 \times 10^{30})(6.0 \times 10^{1})$

7. **Skill Sharpening** – Simplify. Assume $x \neq 0$.

   a. $x^2 x$

   b. $\dfrac{x^2 x}{\dfrac{x^3}{2}}$

8. **Applying Algebra** – Find the volume of ice cream that would be needed to fill an ice cream cone that has a diameter at the base of 1 in and a height of 5 in. Your answer will be in in³. (We'll review how you could have calculated this yourself in the next lesson.)

   Hint: The formula for the volume of a cone is part of Appendix B of the *Student Textbook*.

1. **Unit Conversion with Square and Cubed Units** – Remember to treat units with more than 1 letter as a single entity — in^2 means *inches* squared, not i times n^2.

   a. Convert 4 in^2 to cm^2.

   b. Convert 100 in^3 to ft^3.

2. **Repeated Multiplications of Exponents** – Simplify.

   a. $\left(2\dfrac{\text{ft}}{\text{s}^2}\right)^3$

   b. $\dfrac{\left(2\dfrac{\text{ft}}{\text{s}^2}\right)^3}{-2\ \text{ft}}$ *Hint:* Notice that the numerator is the same as 2a.

   c. $\left(3\dfrac{\text{mi}}{\text{hr}^2}\right)^4$

1. **Simplifying Units of Measure with Division** – Simplify by *inverting and multiplying* the denominators.

   a. $\dfrac{\frac{J}{K}}{\frac{J}{m^3}}$ *Note:* J stands for joules, K for kelvins, and m for meters.

   b. $\dfrac{kg\frac{m}{s^2}}{\frac{m^2}{s^2}}$ *Hint:* Rewrite the numerator as $\dfrac{kg \bullet m}{s^2}$ to avoid confusion.

2. **Applying Algebra** – Use the relationship $P = Fv$ to solve.

   a. If the force (F) is $7\ kg \bullet \dfrac{m}{s^2}$ and the velocity (v) is $6\ \dfrac{m}{s}$, what is the power (P)? Give your answer in a unit that includes kg, m, and s.

   b. Rewrite your answer to 2a using either a newton, watt, or joule (whichever is the appropriate unit to equal the units you had in 2a).

   c. If the force is $6\ kg \bullet \dfrac{m}{s^2}$ and the velocity is $8\ \dfrac{m}{s}$, what is the power?

   d. Rewrite $kg \bullet \dfrac{m^2}{s^3}$ using a negative exponent to show s^{-3}. Note that some materials will write the unit that way.

3. **More Applying Algebra** – Using the gravity formula of $F = G\dfrac{m_1 m_2}{r^2}$ and the gravity constant (G) of $(6.67 \times 10^{-11})\left(\dfrac{m^3}{kg \bullet s^2}\right)$, find the force due to gravity (F) between two objects if the first mass (m_1) is 45 kg, the second mass (m_2) is 2,000 kg, and the radius (r) is 200 m.

   The steps below will help you walk through this problem.

   We'll start by inserting the values given. Since there are more units of measure than normal, this step is done for you.

   $$F = G\left(\frac{m_1 m_2}{r^2}\right)$$

   $$F \approx (6.67 \times 10^{-11})\left(\frac{m^3}{kg \bullet s^2}\right)\left(\frac{45\ kg(2{,}000\ kg)}{(200\ m)^2}\right)$$

   a. Start by simplifying $\dfrac{45\ kg(2{,}000\ kg)}{(200\ m)^2}$.

b. Now multiply your result from 3a by the 6.67×10^{-11}. Remember to keep the units of measure from your result in 3a (we'll deal with the $\dfrac{m^3}{kg\ s^2}$ in a minute). Be sure to write your answer in scientific notation.
Hint: You will need to move the decimal place over and adjust the exponent of 10 accordingly.

c. Multiply your answer to 3b by $\left(\dfrac{m^3}{kg \bullet s^2}\right)$ and simplify to finish finding the force. You will just be multiplying the units of measure and using what you know about multiplying exponents to simplify your result. Your answer will be in $kg \bullet \dfrac{m}{s^2}$, but you need to show how you obtained those units.

d. Rewrite your answer to 3d using either a newton, watt, or joule (whichever is the appropriate unit to equal the units you had in 3c).

Notice how similar the gravity equation $(F = G\dfrac{m_1 m_2}{r^2})$ is to that of Coulomb's Law, the useful electrical equation we looked at a few worksheets ago that's written $F = k\dfrac{q_1 q_2}{r^2}$. Is this just a coincidence? We would argue it's a reminder to us that the same Creator created both the microscopic and the vast distances of space.

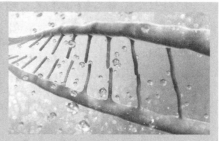

1. **Rewriting Roots as Fractional Exponents** – Rewrite each of these roots using a fractional exponent. Do not simplify.

   Example: $\sqrt{25} = 25^{\frac{1}{2}}$

   a. $\pm\sqrt{16}$

   b. $\sqrt[4]{55}$

   c. $\sqrt[3]{17}$

   d. $\sqrt[5]{30}$

   e. $\sqrt{36}$

   f. $\sqrt[4]{81}$

2. **Finding Roots** – Find the value for each of the roots in problem 1.

   Example: $25^{\frac{1}{2}} = 5$

   Example: $25^{\frac{1}{3}} \approx 2.924$

   a.

   b.

   c.

   d.

   e.

   f.

3. **Negative Fractional Exponents** – Rewrite these fractional exponents using a root sign in the denominator.

   a. $\dfrac{1}{a^{\frac{1}{4}}}$

   b. $\dfrac{3}{5x^{\frac{1}{2}}}$

1. **Roots/Fractional Exponents** – Find the value of these expressions. Remember to follow the order of operations.

   Example: $25^{\frac{1}{2}} = 5$

   Example: $25^{\frac{1}{3}} \approx 2.924$

   a. $\pm 64^{\frac{1}{2}}$

   b. $\sqrt{4+6}$

   c. $(4 + 5 + 234)^{\frac{1}{5}}$

2. **Understanding Check** – While the root symbol $(\sqrt{\ })$ and fractional exponent notation are defined in this course as meaning the positive roots for even roots unless $\pm$ is written in front, it's important to know when using roots for yourself that even roots *can* be either positive *or* negative. Keep this in mind when answering the following questions.

   a. If you were to take the square root of 15 to solve a real-life problem, the answer would be
      ○ positive   ○ negative   ○ either

   b. If you were to take the cubed root of 15 to solve a real-life problem, the answer would be
      ○ positive   ○ negative   ○ either

   c. If you were to take the fourth root of 15 to solve a real-life problem, the answer would be
      ○ positive   ○ negative   ○ either

3. **More with Fractional Exponents** – Solve these without a calculator by first rewriting using a root sign.

   a. $27^{\frac{1}{3}}$

   b. $27^{-\frac{1}{3}}$ (Give your answer as a fraction.)

4. **Applying Algebra**

   a. Rewrite using a fractional exponent: $s = \sqrt{A}$

      Example Meaning: The length of a side of a square equals the square root of the area. (Since the area of a square equals the side length times itself, the side length also equals the square root of the area.)

   b. Rewrite using a fractional exponent: $s = \sqrt[3]{V}$

      Example Meaning: The length of a side of a cube equals the cubed root of the volume. (Since the volume of a cube equals the side length times itself 3 times, the side length also equals the cubed root of the volume.)

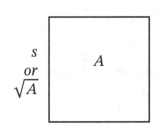

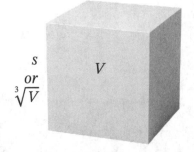

c. Say you want to design a can that has a height (h) of 6 in. If you also want its volume (V) to be 45.36 in³, how much should its radius (r) be

if $r = \left(\dfrac{V}{\pi h}\right)^{\frac{1}{2}}$?

5. **Roots/Fractional Exponents and Unknowns** –
   Rewrite using fractional exponents.

   a. $\sqrt{y}$

   b. $\dfrac{1}{\sqrt{A}}$

   c. $\dfrac{1}{\sqrt[3]{V}}$

6. **Scientific Notation** – Simplify. Give your answer in scientific notation, with only 1 digit to the left of the decimal point.

   a. $(6.0 \times 10^8)(2.0 \times 10^{-15})$

   b. $(4.0 \times 10^{-6})(5.0 \times 10^0)$

7. **Skill Sharpening**

   a. $\left(4\dfrac{ft^2}{s}\right)^2$

   b. $\dfrac{\left(5\dfrac{m^2}{s}\right)^2}{5\ m^2}$

1. **Working with Roots/Fractional Exponents** – Simplify. Remember to follow the *same rules* for working with exponents you have been, coupling them with what you know about working with fractions.

   a. $a^{\frac{1}{3}}a^{\frac{4}{3}}a^2$

   b. $\left(a^{\frac{3}{4}}\right)^2$

   c. $\left(a^2\right)^{\frac{3}{4}}$

   d. $b^{\frac{3}{4}}b^4$

   e. $b^{-\frac{3}{4}}b^4$

   f. $\left(d^{\frac{1}{2}}\right)^3$

   g. $\left(x^4\right)^{\frac{1}{3}}$

   h. $\left(27\ \text{ft}^3\right)^{\frac{1}{3}}$

   i. Solve problem 2f for when *d* is 4.
      Hint: Remember that even roots (such as $\frac{1}{2}$) can be either positive or negative.

1. **Thinking It Through**

    a. Rewrite $4^{\frac{3}{2}}$ using a square root symbol and a whole-number exponent.

    b. Find $16^{\frac{3}{2}}$.
    Hint: Remember, you can input this into your calculator as 16, ^, $(3 \div 2)$.

    c. Simplify by simplifying the fractional exponent as much as possible: $x^{\frac{4}{8}}$.

    d. Rewrite $(\sqrt{9})^3$ using a fractional exponent.

    e. Use your answer to 1d to find $(\sqrt{9})^3$ on a calculator. Then solve without a calculator. You should get the same answer both ways.

    f. Simplify $b^{\frac{1}{2}}b^{\frac{1}{2}}$.

    g. Simplify $\sqrt{b}\sqrt{b}$.

    h. Simplify $b^{\frac{1}{2}}b^{\frac{-1}{2}}$.

    i. Simplify $b^{\frac{1}{2}}b^{\frac{1}{2}}b^{\frac{1}{2}}$.

2. **Roots and Fractional Exponents** – Simplify. Remember to follow the *same rules* for working with exponents you have been, coupling them with what you know about working with fractions.

    a. $y^{\frac{2}{3}}y^4y$

    b. $\left(y^{\frac{2}{3}}\right)^3$

    c. $\left(x^6\right)^{\frac{1}{3}}$

    d. $\left(a^{-2}\right)^{\frac{3}{4}}$

3. **Understanding Time** – Go back to each problem in section 2 and find the answer if a equals 2.

    a.

    b.

    c.

    d.

4. **Applying Algebra**

   a. The area of a regular hexagon equals $A = \left(\dfrac{3\sqrt{3}}{2}\right)s^2$, where s is the length of each side.
      Find the area if the length of the side is 4 mm.
      Hint: Note that mm is a unit of measure here, not m times m.

   b. Rewrite the formula in 4a using a fractional exponent for the square root. Do not simplify.

   c. Using the equation below (notice the fractional exponent!), where b_c equals the current bacteria population, b_0 the initial population, t_c the time since the initial bacteria population was measured, and t_d the doubling time, find the current bacteria population if it has been 17 hours since the initial bacteria population was measured (t_c), the initial bacteria population (b_0) was 800, and the doubling time (t_d) is 10 hr.

   $$b_c = b_0 2^{\frac{t_c}{t_d}}$$

   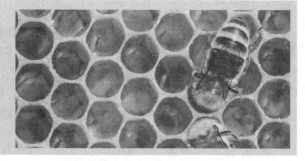

   d. If a box has a volume of 85 in³, what is its volume in cubic feet?

   In 4a, we looked at the area of a regular hexagon. Notice the hexagons in a honeycomb. When we use math to look at the area of honeycombs and compare it to other shapes, such as a square and a triangle, we see the wisdom God placed in bees, as the hexagon has the largest area per perimeter, allowing the bee to use less supplies in building per amount of honey they can store.

This worksheet is designed to help you review the chapter in preparation for the chapter quiz. Be sure to also look over the Key Skills in the Student Textbook *and review as needed. The "General Instructions for Students" section you should have put with your notes includes some study suggestions.*

1. **Understanding Check** – Rewrite using a negative exponent: $\dfrac{1}{x^7}$

2. **Skill Checking** – Simplify or follow instructions in parentheses.

   a. $\dfrac{7y^3}{y^{-2}}$

   b. $\left(b^{\frac{3}{4}}\right)^{-4}$

   c. $(5.0 \times 10^{-8})(6.0 \times 10^{-30})$ (Give your answer in scientific notation.)

   d. $b^{\frac{1}{2}}b^{\frac{2}{3}}$

   e. $\dfrac{\frac{18\ \text{ft}^2}{s}}{-6\ \text{ft}}$

   f. $\sqrt{x}\sqrt{x}$

   g. $\dfrac{1}{x^{\frac{3}{4}}}$ (Rewrite using a negative exponent.)

   h. $-(-a)^2$

   i. $\pm\sqrt{23}$ (Find the value on a calculator.)

   j. $\sqrt{23}$ (Find the value on a calculator.)

   k. $\sqrt{50}$ (Find the value on a calculator.)

   l. $5^{\frac{4}{7}}$ (Find the value on a calculator.)

3. **Applying Algebra**

   a. When you go to move something, it requires effort. To help us quantify that effort, we call it *work*. That work (W) equals the force (F) you have to apply to move the object times the distance (d) you have to move it, or $W = Fd$. Say you apply a force of 7 kg $\cdot \dfrac{m}{s^2}$ and you move it a distance of 40 m. How much work was required?

   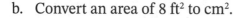

   b. Convert an area of 8 ft² to cm².

   c. Suppose you're trying to carpet a closet that is a rectangular area that is 4 ft by 60 in. How many square inches is this area?

Intentionally left blank

1. **Understanding Sets**

   a. We can use sets outside of math! Let's say I'm trying to organize a junk drawer. What are 3 possible piles, or sets, I could make? For example, you could have a set of all erasers you found in the drawer. Be specific in describing sets that could be found in a junk drawer.

   b. If in my junk drawer I have a set of pencils that I've named P, how could I write that a specific pencil (which I'll call p) is part of (i.e., *an element of*) the set of all pencils (P)?

   p ___ P

1. **Venn Diagrams** – Odd numbers are numbers not evenly divisible by 2; even numbers are numbers that are.

   a. Draw a Venn diagram to show the set of all odd and the set of all even numbers. Use the symbol E to stand for even numbers and O to stand for odd. *Note:* These are not universal symbols — just ones we're using for this problem.

   b. Let's say we have this set: $A = \{5, 11, 15\}$. Draw a circle on the diagram you drew in 1a showing set A.
   Hint: You need to draw the circle so as to show where it fits in relation to the other sets. Is it inside one of them? Inside both of them?

   c. Let's say we have this set: $B = \{5, 6, 10, 15\}$. Draw a circle on the diagram you drew in 1a showing set B.

2. **Understanding Sets**

   a. Use symbols to show that 6 is an element of set B.

   6 _____ B

   b. Use symbols to show that y cannot be an element of set B.

   y _____ B

   c. If set $A = \{4, 7\}$ and $B = \{3, 7\}$, what is set C, if set $C = A \cup B$?

   $C = \{$_____$\}$

   d. If set $A = \{4, 7\}$ and $B = \{3, 7\}$, what is set C, if set $C = A \cap B$?

   $C = \{$_____$\}$

   e. Is $D = \{4\}$ a subset of the set A in problem 2c?

   ○ Yes   ○ No

   If yes, use symbols to show it. _____

   f. Draw a Venn diagram of $A \cap B$ in 2d.
   Hint: Draw a circle for A and one for B and one for C that shows the intersection of the two. Look at the chart in the lesson for help if needed.

   g. If $A = \{2, 3\}$ and $B = \{5, 4\}$, what is $A \cap B$? Give your answer by completing the equation below with the appropriate symbol(s).

   $A \cap B =$ _____

   h. Use symbols to show that the set of small forks (F) is a subset of the set of all silverware (S).

Make flashcards for any of the symbols today you did not know. It's important to understand the "language" side of math.

3. **Skill Sharpening** – Simplify. When asked to add fractions, simplify to a single fraction.

   a. $\left(x^{\frac{1}{4}}\right)^6$

   Meaning: Finding the fourth root and taking that to the sixth power.

   b. $x^{\frac{1}{3}}x$

   Meaning: Multiplying the third root of x by x.

   c. $\dfrac{x^4 x^{-2}}{x^{-5}}$

   d. $\dfrac{2x}{b} + \dfrac{3}{c}$

   e. $2\dfrac{m}{s^2} + 4\dfrac{m}{min^2}$ (Simplify so the units are $\dfrac{m}{min^2}$.) *Hint:* First convert $2\dfrac{m}{s^2}$ to $\dfrac{m}{min^2}$ so you can add these.

   f. $\sqrt{4}\sqrt{4}$

   g. $(-x^2)^2$

4. **Applying Algebra** – Rewrite the Boltzmann constant, a number used in describing gases and in thermodynamics,[1] using a negative exponent so as to avoid having a unit written in the denominator $1.381 \times 10^{-23} \dfrac{J}{K}$. *Note:* The J in the numerator stands for a unit called joules that we use to measure energy, and the K in the denominator is for a unit called kelvin that we use to measure temperature.

5. **More Applying Algebra** – We can describe the consistent way God causes the temperature (T), pressure (P), and number of gas molecules (N) in an ideal gas to relate together using what we call the ideal gas law: $V = k_B NT P^{-1}$, where $k_B = \left(1.381 \times 10^{-23} \dfrac{J}{K}\right)$, the Boltzmann constant. If the number of gas molecules is 1.512×10^{26}, the temperature is 200 K, and the pressure is $100 \dfrac{J}{m^3}$, what is the volume of the gas? The following problems will walk you through answering this.

   a. Rewrite the equation so as to rewrite P^{-1} as P^1 to make it easier when you insert the values.

   b. Insert the values you were given to the equation.

   c. Simplify by completing the multiplication and division of all the known numbers. Your answer now should be in scientific notation (rounded to the 3rd decimal), plus all of the units of measure.

   d. Simplify the units of measure. You can simplify the units in the denominator by treating them like you would variables — invert the fraction and multiply it by the other units, canceling out as you go. If you do the units correctly, you'll end up with a unit for volume — that is, a distance unit cubed.

1   P.J. Mohr, B.N. Taylor, and D.B. Newell (2015), "The 2014 CODATA Recommended Values of the Fundamental Physical Constants," web version 7.0, database developed by J. Baker, M. Douma, and S. Kotochigova (Gaithersburg, MD: National Institute of Standards and Technology), https://physics.nist.gov/constants, accessed 10/27/19.

1. **Number Sets**

   a. If you have a set where $x \in \mathbb{N} \cap x < 8$, can x be 1.56?

   b. Use symbols to show that x must be an element of the set of all complex numbers.

   c. If $x \in \{2, 3, 5\}$, can x equal 4?

      ○ Yes   ○ No

   d. If $x \notin \mathbb{N}$, can x be 5?

      ○ Yes   ○ No

   e. $\mathbb{Q} \subset \mathbb{R}$

      ○ True   ○ False

1. **Number Sets**

   a. What kind of number is $\frac{2}{3}$? List all the sets that were in the chart in Lesson 3.2 of which it's a member.

   b. Use symbols to specify that for a problem y must be a natural number greater than 3.

   y _____ $\cap$ $y >$ _____

   c. What does $z \in \mathbb{Q}$ mean?

   d. Use words to explain what this means: $\mathbb{Q} \cup \mathbb{P} = \mathbb{R}$.

   e. Use words to explain what this means: $\mathbb{Q} \cap \mathbb{P} = \varnothing$.

2. **Mastering the Greek**

   a. Write down the symbol for and the value of (rounded to the fifth decimal place) pi.

   b. Write down the symbol for and the value of (rounded to the fifth decimal place) Euler's number.

   c. Write down the symbol for and the value of (rounded to the fifth decimal place) phi, the golden ratio.

   d. Search online for "Greek alphabet song" to familiarize yourself with how to pronounce different letters. Write out the pronunciation of ρ (or say it to your parent/teacher).

3. **Algebra Applied** – The fascinating thing about π, e, and ϕ is that they help us describe so many different aspects of God's creation. Much like an artist whose specific trademarks or hidden signature tell us that various works had the same designer,[1] it's as if these numbers show us that the same designer created each aspect of creation. We'll encounter all of them a lot as we go forward, but today we'll look at an example of how two of them apply in the least-likely place you might expect: when describing the consistencies God placed in electrical charges.

   a. Back on Worksheet 2.3B, you rewrote an equation known as Coulomb's Law, a useful electrical equation: $F = k \left(\frac{q_1 q_2}{r^2} \right)$.

   Well, the k in that equation equals[2] $\frac{1}{4 \pi \varepsilon_0}$. Notice the π in this equation! Given that $\varepsilon_0 = 8.85 \times 10^{-12} \frac{C^2}{N \cdot m^2}$, calculate k, using the equation $k = \frac{1}{4 \pi \varepsilon_0}$. Give your answer in scientific notation. The unit C here is the coulomb, the unit of charge.

---

1   Answers in Genesis often points out how similarities throughout creation, including within animals, point to a common designer — see "Common Ancestor or Common Designer?" (Answers in Genesis, 2007), https://answersingenesis.org/theory-of-evolution/evidence/common-ancestor-or-common-designer/

2   The surface area of a sphere is $4 \pi r^2$, so really the electrical force is inversely proportional to the surface area of a sphere surrounding one of the charges q_1 or q_2.

b. Like pi, Euler's constant also shows up when working with electrical charges.[3] The equation $V_c = V_s e^{\frac{-t}{RC}}$ helps us describe how capacitors ("basically a device to store charge"[4] — most electronic devices have one) discharge in a circuit with a resistor. The V_c stands for the capacitor's voltage, the V_s for the voltage of whatever is supplying the capacitor with electricity, the t for the time that has passed, and RC is basically a measurement of how long it takes the capacitor to discharge (R is the resistance of a resistor in the circuit and C the capacitance of the capacitor). Notice the e in the equation; it stands for Euler's number! If the source voltage is 120 Volts (V), the time that has passed is 4 seconds (s), and RC is 5 seconds (s), what is the capacitor's voltage?

4. **Skill Sharpening and Negative Number Review** – Simplify. When asked to add fractions, simplify to a single fraction.

a. $\left(b^{\frac{2}{3}}\right)^{-2}$

b. $(-b)^4$

c. $-\left(\dfrac{8}{x} + \dfrac{3}{a}\right)$

d. $-\dfrac{-\left(x^2\right)}{-\left(x^9\right)}$

e. $--a^8 a^{-2}$

f. $\sqrt{16}\sqrt{16}$

g. $y^{-\frac{2}{3}} y^3$

Make flashcards for any symbols for number sets that were new for you and continue reviewing your flashcards from Lesson 3.1B.

---

3   Equation from Electronics Tutorials, "RC Discharging Circuit" (AspenCore) https://www.electronics-tutorials.ws/rc/rc_2.html.

4   W. Thomas Griffith and Juliet Brosing, *The Physics of Everyday Phenomena: A Conceptual Introduction to Physics*, 6th ed. (New York: McGraw-Hill, 2009), p. 249.

1. **Rewriting Roots** – Rewrite these roots so as to be a whole (i.e., natural) number multiplied by a square root.

    Example: $\sqrt{24} = \sqrt{4}\sqrt{6} = 2\sqrt{6}$

    a. $\sqrt{12}$

    b. $32^{\frac{1}{2}}$

    c. $45^{\frac{1}{2}}$

2. **More Rewriting Roots** – Use a single root to simplify each of these expressions.

    a. $\sqrt{2}\sqrt{3}$

    b. $\sqrt{-1}\sqrt{5}$
    Hint: We'll look at negative square roots in the next lesson. But yes, you can have a square root of a negative number!

    c. $\dfrac{\sqrt{100}}{\sqrt{10}}$

    d. $\dfrac{8^{\frac{1}{4}}}{2^{\frac{1}{4}}}$

1. **Rewriting Roots: Multiplication** – Rewrite these roots so as to be a whole (i.e., natural) number multiplied by a square root.

   Example: $\sqrt{24} = \sqrt{4}\sqrt{6} = 2\sqrt{6}$

   a. $54^{\frac{1}{2}}$

   b. $(16x)^{\frac{1}{2}}$

2. **More Rewriting Roots** – Put an equal sign between any 2 expressions you know are equal.

   a. $\sqrt{8}$ $\qquad$ $\dfrac{\sqrt{16}}{\sqrt{2}}$

   b. $8^{\frac{1}{2}}$ $\qquad$ $\dfrac{16^{\frac{1}{2}}}{2^{\frac{1}{3}}}$

   c. $\sqrt{x^3}$ $\qquad$ $x\sqrt{x}$

3. **Using a Single Root** – Use a single root to simplify each of these expressions.

   a. $\dfrac{\sqrt{5}}{\sqrt{10}}$

   b. $\dfrac{\sqrt{15}}{\sqrt{3}}$

4. **Simplifying** – Use what you've learned so far to simplify this to a single value that doesn't have an exponent or root.

   a. $\sqrt{3}\sqrt{3}$

   b. $\sqrt{a}\sqrt{a}$

   c. $a^{\frac{1}{2}}a^{\frac{1}{2}}$

5. **Applying Algebra** – Take a look at the picture shown of a rectangle. We know the area of the rectangle equals the length times the width, or $A = lw$.

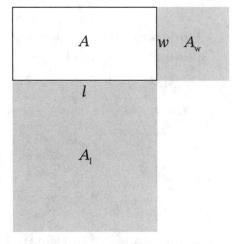

But now let's suppose that we don't know the length and the width (lw). But we do know the area of squares built off the length and width, which we've represented by A_w and A_l.

Can we describe how to find the area of the main rectangle (A) in terms of A_w and A_l? Yes! Since A_l and A_w are the area of squares and the area of a square equals its side squared, the width would equal the square root of A_w! So now we know that $w = \sqrt{A_w}$. The same reasoning holds for the length (l); $l = \sqrt{A_l}$. So we could rewrite $A = lw$ as $A = \sqrt{A_l}\sqrt{A_w}$. Rewrite this as a formula containing only *one* square root sign.

6. **Skill Sharpening**

   a. If $A = \{15, 25\}$ and B $= \{25, 40\}$, what is $A \cap B$?

   $A \cap B = \{_____\}$

   b. If $s \in \mathbb{N}$, can s be $\dfrac{5}{6}$?

   ○ Yes   ○ No

   c. Simplify: $(-x)^2 x^3 x x^{\frac{1}{2}}$

   d. Simplify: $-\dfrac{-(x^3)^2}{x}$

Continue reviewing the flashcards you made in Lessons 3.1 and 3.2.

1. **Understanding Imaginary Numbers** – Rewrite each square root as a multiplication of a positive square root by $\sqrt{-1}$.

   Example: $\sqrt{-4}$

   Answer: $\sqrt{4}\sqrt{-1}$

   a. $\sqrt{-16}$

   b. $\sqrt{-9}$

   c. $\sqrt{-(x^2)}$

2. **Understanding Imaginary Numbers, Part 2** – Rewrite your answer to problem 1 by finding the positive square roots and using an *i* to stand for the $\sqrt{-1}$. Notice how much easier it is to write *i* than $\sqrt{-1}$.

   Example: $\sqrt{4}\sqrt{-1}$

   Answer: 2*i*

   a.

   b.

   c.

1. **Understanding Imaginary Numbers** – Rewrite each square root using an imaginary number, simplifying where you can using what you learned in the last lesson as well.

   Example: $\sqrt{-20} = \sqrt{4}\sqrt{5}\sqrt{-1} = 2\sqrt{5}i$

   a. $\sqrt{-17}$

   b. $\sqrt{-a^2}$

   c. $\sqrt{-18}$

   d. $\sqrt{-x}$

   e. $(-24)^{\frac{1}{2}}$

2. **Understanding Complex Numbers** – Rewrite your answers to section 1 with a $0 +$ before the imaginary part to show that its real part is 0.

   Example: $\sqrt{15}i$

   Answer: $0 + \sqrt{15}i$

   a.

   b.

   c.

   d.

   e.

Continue reviewing the flashcards you made in Lesson 3.1 and 3.2; add flashcards for $\mathbb{I}$ and $\mathbb{C}$.

3. **Applying Imaginary and Complex Numbers** – Use complex numbers to describe these points on the graph. Notice that one point is done for you as an example.

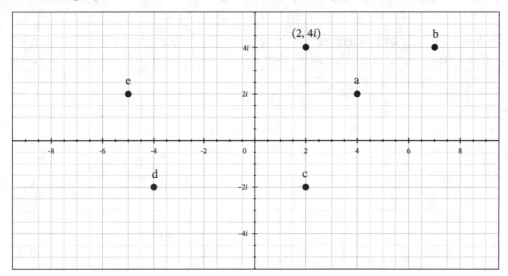

a.

b.

c.

d.

e.

4. **Understanding Check** – When we find even roots of negative numbers, we get an imaginary number, while odd roots yield a negative number, since a negative number multiplied by itself an odd number of times results in a negative number. Keeping that in mind, find the following roots.

    a. $\sqrt[3]{-27}$

    b. $\sqrt[3]{-55}$

    c. $\sqrt[3]{-48}$

5. **Skill Sharpening**

    d. If $x \in \mathbb{Z} \cup x \in \mathbb{I}$, can x be $4i$?

        ○ Yes   ○ No

    e. Is $\mathbb{Q} \subset \mathbb{R}$?

        ○ Yes   ○ No

    f. If $A = \{b, c, d\}$ and $B = \{a, d, e\}$, what is $A \cap B$?

        $A \cap B =$ _____

    g. If $A = \{b, c, d\}$ and $B = \{a, d, e\}$, what is $A \cup B$?

        $A \cup B =$ _____

1. **Simplifying Imaginary Numbers** – Use the knowledge that $\sqrt{-1}$ *times* $\sqrt{-1}$ equals -1 (that is, that i times i, or i^2, equals -1) to simplify these problems.

   Example: $4i(2i) = 8i^2 = 8(-1) = -8$

   a. $8i(3i)$

   b. $24i^4$ *Hint:* Think through what i^4 means: $\sqrt{-1}\,\sqrt{-1}\,\sqrt{-1}\,\sqrt{-1}$.

   c. $24i^5$

   d. $24i^6$

1. **Simplifying Imaginary Numbers** – Use the knowledge that $\sqrt{-1}$ *times* $\sqrt{-1}$ equals -1 (that is, that i times i, or i^2, equals -1) to simplify these problems.

   Example: $4i(2i) = 8i^2 = 8(-1) = -8$

   a. $\dfrac{5i^2}{i^3}$

   b. $3i^3 i^{-2}$

   c. $\dfrac{6i^5}{2i^3}$

   d. $-4i^2$

2. **Simplifying Roots** – Simplify without a calculator. Note that you will need to use what you reviewed in Lesson 3.3 about rewriting square roots and what you know about working with imaginary numbers.

   Example: $\sqrt{-12}\sqrt{-4} = \sqrt{12}i\sqrt{4}i = \sqrt{4}\sqrt{3}\sqrt{4}\,i^2 = 4\sqrt{3}i^2 = -4\sqrt{3}$

   a. $\sqrt{-40}\sqrt{-16}$

   b. $\sqrt{-8}\sqrt{2}$

   c. $\sqrt{-3}\sqrt{-27}$

   d. $\dfrac{\sqrt{-8}}{\sqrt{-2}}$

   e. $\dfrac{\sqrt{6}}{\sqrt{-3}}$

   f. $\dfrac{\sqrt{-7}}{\sqrt{14}}$

3. **Applying Algebra** – Say we're designing a picture and we could use a variety of different sized papers angled different ways. Our options for paper A are a width of either 8.5 in or 11 in; paper B gives us an option of either 11 in or 17 in. We could write these options out as sets: $A = \{8.5 \text{ in}, 11 \text{ in}\}$ and $B = \{11 \text{ in}, 17 \text{ in}\}$. The union of the two sets represents all of our possible widths. What is that union, that is, what is $A \cup B$? *Note:* Of course, you wouldn't bother to write out sets when picking a paper width. But there are much more complicated scenarios where writing out options like this proves helpful.

4. **Skill Sharpening** – Simplify. When asked to add fractions, simplify to a single fraction.

a. $\dfrac{x^3y}{5} + 2x$

b. $\dfrac{2x^4y}{b} + \dfrac{-a}{3}$

c. $-\dfrac{x^3x^{-2}}{-x^4}$

d. $(-y)^5$

e. $(-y)^6$

f. $\sqrt{25}\sqrt{25}$

g. $\sqrt{b}\sqrt{b}$

h. $y^{\frac{2}{3}}y^4y^{\frac{1}{2}}$

i. $\left(y^{\frac{2}{3}}\right)^4$

Continue reviewing the flashcards you have made this chapter.

1. **Skill Review**

   a. What number set does $\mathbb{R} - \mathbb{Q}$ equal? Use a symbol to answer.
      Hint: Look at the chart in Lesson 3.2. The $\equiv$ means "is defined as"; since the sets are not numbers but collections of them, we have to use a different symbol than the equal sign when defining a new set in terms of other sets.

      $\mathbb{R} - \mathbb{Q} \equiv$ _____

   b. If set $A = \{3, 5\}$ and set $B = \{1, 3, 5, 7\}$, what is $A \cup B$?

      $A \cup B = \{$ _____ $\}$

   c. If set $A = \{3, 5\}$ and set $B = \{1, 3, 5, 7\}$, what is $A \cap B$?

      $A \cap B = \{$ _____ $\}$

   d. Use symbols to specify that for a problem y must be a real number less than 2.

      y _____ $\cap\ y <$ _____

   e. Simplify $\sqrt{-63}$ without a calculator.

   f. Rewrite $\dfrac{\sqrt{-70}}{\sqrt{7}}$ as a single square root multiplied by i.

   g. Rewrite $\dfrac{x^{\frac{1}{4}}}{b^{\frac{1}{4}}}$ as a fraction raised to a single fractional exponent.

   h. Find $\sqrt{y}\sqrt{-y}$

   i. Rewrite as an imaginary number: $(-25)^{\frac{1}{2}}$

   j. Simplify: $3i(i^2)\left(\dfrac{1}{2i}\right)$

   k. Simplify without a calculator: $\sqrt{-18}\,\sqrt{-2}$

2. 🎯 **Challenge Problem: Language Learning Challenge** – While you do not need to fully learn the set-builder and interval notations mentioned in Lesson 3.6, the following problems will help build your language skills by forcing you to engage with these notations and figure out what is meant. Basically, you get to be a math detective! Try to guess what each one means and write down the meaning using words or a notation you know — or simply explain the meaning to your parent or teacher.

   a. $\{x \mid x \in \mathbb{I}\}$

   b. $[-2, 3)$

   c. $(5, 10]$

Continue reviewing the flashcards you have made this chapter.

1. **Using Equalities to Solve Problems** – Solve for the unknown. Remember to follow the order of operations, simplifying exponents and roots first.

   a. $9 = 3x$

   Example Meaning: If the power produced is $9\ \dfrac{\text{kg} \bullet \text{m}^2}{\text{s}^3}$ and the force applied to an object is $3\ \dfrac{\text{kg} \bullet \text{m}}{\text{s}^2}$, what must the velocity be?

   b. $9 = -3x$

   Example Meaning: If the power produced is $9\ \dfrac{\text{kg} \bullet \text{m}^2}{\text{s}^3}$ and the force applied to an object is $3\ \dfrac{\text{kg} \bullet \text{m}}{\text{s}^2}$ in the *opposite direction,* what must the velocity be?

   c. $-120 = -12x$

   Example Meaning: If you travel a distance of 120 miles in the negative direction at a speed of 12 miles per hour, how long will it take you? *Note:* Negative speeds means speed in the *opposite direction.* If we're viewing north as positive, than –7 miles per hour would be 7 miles per hour southwards.

   d. $15 = x + 6$

   Example Meaning: Your total pay per hour equals the $6 salary plus your tips. If it totaled $15 one hour, how much did you get in tips?

   e. $\dfrac{2}{5} = \dfrac{1}{2}x$

   f. $\dfrac{3}{4}i^2 = x + \dfrac{2}{3}$ *Hint: i* is representing the imaginary unit, $\sqrt{-1}$.

   g. $\dfrac{1}{2}x^6 x^{-5} x^{\frac{1}{3}} x^{-\frac{1}{3}} = 2$

   h. $\sqrt{-16}\sqrt{-25} = 5x$

Checking Your Work – *Go back and plug in the value you got for x into the original equation instead of x. When you simplify, do you end up with equal amounts on both sides of the equation? If not, you know you need to rework that problem. Note: You can check simple problems in your head — it's not necessary to write out the answers, only to get in the habit of checking your work.*

2. **Applying Algebra** – Use what you know about equalities to solve these problems for the unknown. Be sure to watch your units of measure and include the unit in your answer! Also, you'll make it easier on yourself if you solve for the unknown you need to find first, *and then* plug in the values given.

   a. If the power produced equals the force applied to an object times the velocity ($P = Fv$) and the velocity (v) is $\dfrac{10 \text{ m}}{\text{s}}$ and the power (P) is 50 kg$\dfrac{\text{m}^2}{\text{s}^3}$, what is the force ($F$)?

   b. If you're traveling at 50 $\dfrac{\text{mi}}{\text{hr}}$ in one direction and need to travel 300 mi in the opposite direction, how long will it take you? *Distance = speed(time)*, or *d = st*.
   Hint: Use negative numbers for distances in the opposite direction.

   c. Solve $P = Fv$ for the velocity (v).

   d. The consistent way God causes gravity to operate can be expressed like this: $F = G\dfrac{m_1 m_2}{r^2}$. Let's say we know that m_1 is 300 kg. You know that G is $(6.67 \times 10^{-11}) \left(\dfrac{\text{m}^3}{\text{kg} \cdot \text{s}^2}\right)$, that the fore ($F$) is 90,000 kg $\cdot \dfrac{\text{m}}{\text{s}^2}$, and that r is 200 m. What is m_2?

3. **Skill Sharpening** – Simplify without a calculator.

   a. $\dfrac{\sqrt{10}}{\sqrt{-5}}$

   b. $\sqrt{-y^2}$

1. **Equalities and Roots** – Solve for the unknown. **Remember, even roots can be either positive or negative, so be sure to include ± before your answer when working with even roots!**

   a. $8x^2 = 512$

   b. $5x^2 = 500 \text{ ft}^2$

   c. $2 = \dfrac{32}{r^2}$

   Example Meaning: If the force on an object is 2 and equals 32 divided by the square of the absolute value of the distance between it and the center of the mass exerting a pull on it, what is that distance?

   Hint: Remember that the fraction sign means *divide by*. To undo this division, you have to *multiply* both sides by the same amount, r^2 . . . and then you'll need to find the square root.

   d. $90 = 3x^2$

   e. $6 = \dfrac{24 \text{ in}^2}{x^2}$

   f. $x^3 = 56$

   g. $x^5 = 40$

   h. $x^4 = 40$

2. **Applying Algebra** – Remember to include your units of measure!

   a. Let's say you need to design a square garden with an area of 144 ft². How long should you make the sides? The area of a square equals the length of the sides squared, or $A = s^2$.

   b. Let's say you need to design a cubic container with a volume of 125 in³. How long should you make each side if the volume (V) equals the length of each side (s) cubed?
   Hint: The equation is $V = s^3$. Take the *cubed root* of both sides! You can find the cubed root of 125 by finding $125^{\frac{1}{3}}$. Remember, fractional exponents are another way of showing roots.

3. **Skill Sharpening** – Simplify without a calculator.

   a. $\sqrt{-4}\sqrt{-2}\sqrt{-6}$

   b. $\dfrac{3i^2}{i}$

1. **Inequalities** – Solve for the unknown. **Put the unknown to the *left* of the inequality sign in your final answer.**

    Example: $4 > 3 + x$

    $1 > x$ (subtracted 3 from both sides)

    $x < 1$ (reversed sides, being careful to keep the meaning of the inequality by keeping the larger side of the sign with the greater number)

    a. $8 > 2 + x$

    Example Meaning: You have to have less than 8 people playing a game. If you already have 2, how many more can play?

    b. $98 \leq x + 70$

    Example Meaning: If your score has to be greater than or equal to 98 on a test to pass, where each correct problem is worth a point and you already got 70 right, how many more must you get right?

    c. $30 > 15x$

    d. $30 > -15x$

1. **Inequalities** – Solve for the unknown. **Put the unknown on the *left* of the inequality sign in your final answer.**

   a. $\$14 \geq \$5 - x$

   b. $-5x \leq -45$

   c. $\frac{2}{3}x > -\frac{4}{5}$

   d. $-\frac{2}{3}x > -\frac{4}{5}$

2. **Inequalities**

   a. If in a situation we need $x > 10$, and you have found 2 possible solutions for x, one of 5 and one of 15, which solution is the one needed?

   b. Show what the speed (s) of a robot must be if you need it to be greater than or equal to $10 \frac{mi}{hr}$ to win a competition.

3. **Algebra in Action** – On Quiz 2, we looked at the equation for centripetal acceleration: $a_c = \frac{v^2}{r}$. Let's say that you know the centripetal acceleration is $5 \frac{m}{s^2}$ and that the velocity is $3 \frac{m}{s}$. What is the radius (r) the object is traveling?
   Hint: Remember to solve for the unknown you're trying to find first!

4. **More Algebra in Action** – Let's say there's a device where the energy (U) put into it is 6 J. If the work it produces can be described by the entropy[1] (S) times the change in temperature (ΔT), then the energy put in must be less than or equal to the entropy times the change in temperature, or $U \leq S\Delta T$. If the change in temperature (ΔT) is 3 K, what are the values the entropy (S) can be?

   Δ is a symbol meaning "change in." Treat ΔT as a single unknown standing for the change in the temperature.

   a. Substitute the values you've been given for U and ΔT into the inequality $U \leq S\Delta T$. (Since we're dealing with an inequality, we're going to substitute first in case any values are negative.)

   b. Solve the inequality from 4a to isolate S. Be sure to watch your units of measure!

   c. Rewrite the inequality you solved in 4b so that S is on the left of the inequality.

---

1 To keep things simple, "entropy can be thought of as a measure of the disorder of a system." W. Thomas Griffith and Juliet Brosing, *The Physics of Everyday Phenomena: A Conceptual Introduction to Physics*, 6th ed. (New York: McGraw-Hill, 2009), p. 229. In this problem, the inequality comes from assuming a system where the entropy is constant but the temperature changes.

5. **Skill Sharpening**

   a. Simplify as much as possible without using a calculator: $\sqrt{-22}\ \sqrt{-24}\ \sqrt{-3}$

   b. Simplify: $5i^3 3i^2$

   c. If $x \in \mathbb{N} \cap x > 5$, can x equal 3?

      O Yes   O No

6. ◎ **Challenge Problem: Exploring the Second Law of Thermodynamics** – Search online at answersingenesis.org for the "second law of thermodynamics" and read one of the articles you find, writing a paragraph summarizing the main point.

Note that while many of these problems require more arithmetic concepts than algebra, thinking them through will help prepare you for solving algebraic problems.

Remember to always include units of measure in your answer when units are part of the problem.

See Appendix B in the Student Textbook for unit conversion ratios.

1. **Thinking Through Word Problems** – Be sure to show enough steps that someone can see how you obtained your answer!

   a. 📖[1] A map of Kansas is made on a scale where 1 inch represents 100 miles. The map measures 4 inches by 2 inches. Find the area of Kansas in square miles, assuming it is basically a rectangle.

   b. 📖 Suppose someone decides to walk around the inside of a rectangular field that is 200 ft by 400 ft. The person walks 5 ft inside the edge for a total of 4 laps. How many steps does it take if he or she averages 2.5 ft a step?

   c. 📖 If 110 college seniors adorn themselves with ribbon streamers in the class colors (red and white) using $\frac{3}{4}$ of a yard of each color, what will be the total cost of the ribbon if it costs 20 cents a yard?

   d. 📖 When a man runs at a speed of 100 yards in 9.4 seconds, how many feet does he travel in one second?

   e. 📖 In the scenario described in 1d, what is the man's speed in miles per hour?

---

1 The 📖 symbol means the problem is adapted from Eugene Henry Barker, *Applied Mathematics for Junior High Schools and High Schools* (Boston: Allyn and Bacon, 1920). Available on Google Books, http://books.google.com/books?id=-t5EAAAAIAAJ.

1. **Problem-Solving Practice** – *Solve. Be sure to show your work.*

   a. What is the value of a 160-acre cotton crop if 2 bales are raised to the acre, cotton is worth $0.40 a pound, and a bale of cotton weighs 500 lb?

   b. The estimated value of a crop of grapes is $450 per acre. Thorough spraying costs $9 per acre. If, without spraying, 30% of the crop is lost, what is the net value of spraying 10 acres (i.e., how much more value do you get by spraying, even with the cost of spraying, than you would if you didn't spray)?

   c. In finance, businesses use lots of formulas to evaluate their finances. One such formula is this: $R_E = R_A + (R_A - R_D)\left(\dfrac{D}{E}\right)$. This formula helps firms know what their rate of return on equity is, considering their return on their assets and debt and the ratio between their debt and equity.[1] (Don't worry if that didn't make complete sense — you'll learn about all those terms if you study finance. The point here is that men can use math to help them in business . . . whatever field God calls you to, math helps in completing tasks.) Find R_E if R_A *is* 0.05, R_D is 0.09, D is $56,000, and E is $60,000. Remember to use your calculator to avoid rounding until the end.

2. **Breaking Problems Down** – Determine the cost of materials and labor to enclose a 10-acre field in the form of a square with a 3-rail fence (i.e., a fence with three pieces of wood across it) with posts every 5 ft if the posts cost 10 cents a piece, the wood for the fence costs 10 cents for 4 ft, labor costs $3 for a day's labor, and one man can build 200 ft of fence per day (all 3 rails together). *Hint:* As with many real-life problems, there are a lot of steps to solving this problem! The following questions will help you solve it step by step.

   a. Start by figuring out the area of the field that needs to be enclosed. Then solve for the length of a side of the square fence. Give your answer in feet, as the rest of the measurements are given in feet. Appendix B in the *Student Textbook* lists the conversion factor from acres to square feet.

   b. Using your answer to 2a to help you, determine the wood and posts needed for the fence, along with how many days labor is needed.

   c. Using your answers to 2b to help you, calculate the total cost.

3. **Skill Sharpening**

   a. Solve for x: $\sqrt{-4}\,\sqrt{-4}\,x = 24$

   b. Simplify without using a calculator: $\dfrac{\sqrt{-24}}{\sqrt{-8}}$

4. **Worldview Building** – Look up "Bible verses on work" online. Write down 5 references and a couple of sentences about something you noticed in the verses about what the Bible teaches us about work. After all, math helps us with the work God has given us . . . so understanding how to view work biblically will help you apply math with joy in your work.

---

1   Formula from Ross Westerfield Jordan, *Essentials of Corporate Finance,* 6th ed. (New York: McGraw-Hill, 2008), p. 411.

1. **Understanding and Applying Substitution**

   a. If the total you make per week equals the total you make per day times 5 ($W = 5d$), and the total you make per day equals $11 times the hours you work ($d = \$11h$), write an equation showing the total you make per week in terms of the hours you work.

   b. The weight of an object equals its mass times the acceleration due to gravity (g), which we can express like this: $W = mg$. The mass (m) of an object equals its volume times its density, which we can express like this: $m = V\rho$. Write an equation showing what weight (W) equals that does not require knowing the mass (m) to solve.

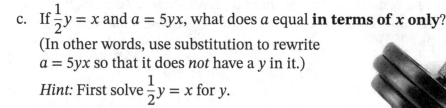

   c. If $\frac{1}{2}y = x$ and $a = 5yx$, what does a equal **in terms of x only**? (In other words, use substitution to rewrite $a = 5yx$ so that it does *not* have a y in it.)

   Hint: First solve $\frac{1}{2}y = x$ for y.

   d. Say a certain field of land is being divided evenly into smaller sections. Its area divided by the number of sections will tell you the area of each section ($a = \frac{A}{n}$). Let's say you don't know the area of the field, but you do know its length and that it's a rectangle, and you know that the area of a rectangle equals the length times the width ($A = lw$). Rewrite the $a = \frac{A}{n}$ so that A is not used.

   e. Rewrite $y = 2ab^2$ so as to eliminate b, if $\frac{1}{3}b = a$. (In other words, solve for y in terms of a only. There should *not* be a b in your answer.) Simplify.

2. **Algebra Applied**

   a. Say you know that the weight of an object is 80 kg $\frac{m}{s^2}$. Rewrite this in newtons.

   b. Say you know that the weight of an object is 80 N, the local constant of gravity 9.8 $\frac{m}{s^2}$, and the volume 6 m³. What is its density (ρ)? Use the knowledge that $W = V\rho g$ to find; be sure to substitute kg $\cdot \frac{m}{s^2}$ for N at the end to simplify the units. Give your answer as a rounded decimal.

3. 📖 **More Algebra Applied: Breaking Problems Down** – How many feet of wire will be required to fence (three wires all around) a 12-acre field if it is a rectangle that is twice as long as it is wide? The problems below will help you break this down.

   a. To solve this, you need to find the perimeter, or distance around, the rectangle. But you don't know the length or width! However, you *do* know the area and how the length relates to the width (you were told the rectangle is twice as long as wide) . . . and you can find the formula for the area of a rectangle in Appendix B in the *Student Textbook* if you don't know it. Find the width of the rectangle in feet. Do not round, as this is really just a step in a larger problem.
   Hint: Start by converting your area to feet.

   b. Now, how do you find your perimeter? Well, you now know the width . . . and you know how the width relates to the length. Use substitution to rewrite the formula for finding the perimeter of a rectangle (see Appendix B in the *Student Textbook* if you don't remember it) in terms of width only and then calculate it. Do not round, as this is still just a step in a larger problem.

   c. Use your answer to 3b to calculate the total length of wire needed.

4. **Skill Sharpening**

   a. Solve for x: $-5x^2 = 40$ *Hint:* Your answer will be an imaginary number!

   b. Simplify without a calculator: $\sqrt{-14}\,\sqrt{-7}\,\sqrt{-2}$

Rather than a typical worksheet, this worksheet is designed to allow you to apply what you're learning to explore an aspect of God's creation: blood pressure. Note that it may take you a little longer to solve, but we hope you enjoy getting to apply your skills! And note that the quiz will not be this involved.

First off, here's a basic definition of blood pressure: "When your heart beats, it pumps blood round your body to give it the energy and oxygen it needs. As the blood moves, it pushes against the sides of the blood vessels. The strength of this pushing is your blood pressure."[1]

Whatever the pressure is at our heart, the density, gravitational acceleration, and distance from the heart will cause that pressure to change at different parts of our body. We can represent the *approximate* pressure at any point in our body using a formula![2]

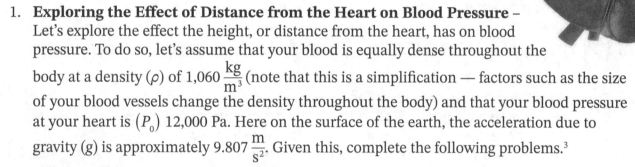

$P = P_0 + \rho g h$

P_0 = *the pressure at the heart*

ρ = *density*

g = *the acceleration due to gravity*

h = *the height below the heart (meaning a negative height is above the heart)*

1. **Exploring the Effect of Distance from the Heart on Blood Pressure** –
   Let's explore the effect the height, or distance from the heart, has on blood pressure. To do so, let's assume that your blood is equally dense throughout the body at a density (ρ) of 1,060 $\frac{\text{kg}}{\text{m}^3}$ (note that this is a simplification — factors such as the size of your blood vessels change the density throughout the body) and that your blood pressure at your heart is (P_0) 12,000 Pa. Here on the surface of the earth, the acceleration due to gravity (g) is approximately 9.807 $\frac{\text{m}}{\text{s}^2}$. Given this, complete the following problems.[3]

   a. Plug in all the values you've been given into the equation $P = P_0 + \rho g h$.

   b. Notice that in the equation you wrote in 1a, you have units of m, kg, s, and Pa. So that your units will work out when you simplify, rewrite the equation you wrote in 1a, replacing Pa with $\frac{\text{kg}}{\text{m} \cdot \text{s}^2}$ since 1 Pa equals 1 $\frac{\text{kg}}{\text{m} \cdot \text{s}^2}$.

   c. Suppose you were to stand up and take your blood pressure at your ankle. If your ankle is 1.2 m (about 4 ft — but use the 1.2 m so your units will work out) under your heart, what will your blood pressure be measured there? Note that heights under the heart are considered positive, so you can find this by inserting 1.2 m for *h* into the equation you wrote in 1b and simplifying.

1 "What is blood pressure?" Blood Pressure UK, (England, 2008), http://www.bloodpressureuk.org/BloodPressureandyou /Thebasics/Bloodpressure, s.v., "Blood Pressure."

2 See William & Mary, *107 Manual: Chapter 11* (Williamsburg, VA). Found on physics.wm.edu/~labs/107_manual/ch11.pdf. See also Lumen, "Physics: Pressures in the Body," https://courses.lumenlearning.com/physics/chapter/11-9-pressures-in-the-body/. Note that throughout this worksheet, we are ignoring any changes due to the density of blood by assuming a constant density even though the density is not necessarily constant. However, by assuming a constant density, we could look at what effect just the height would have on blood pressure.

3 Blood pressure is normally given in mm Hg (this would be about 90 mm Hg); we've saved you a step, though, and converted to pascals to make it easier to solve.

d. Suppose you were to elevate your feet so they were 0.5 m *above* your heart and then take your blood pressure. What would your blood pressure be at your feet? Since heights under the heart are considered positive, this height would be considered negative, making –0.5 m the number you need to use for h in the equation you wrote in 1b.

e. Looking at your answers to 1c and 1d, is your blood pressure higher or lower when it's taken at a part of the body below the heart?

   ○ Higher   ○ Lower

f. Looking at your answers to 1c and 1d, is your blood pressure higher or lower when it's taken at a part of the body above the heart?

   ○ Higher   ○ Lower

g. Substitute ΔP for ρgh in the formula $P = P_0 + \rho gh$. ΔP is a single unknown we're using to stand for the result of ρgh — that is, the *change in* pressure from whatever it is at the heart. After all, it's this amount that gets added to the blood pressure at the heart P_0 in order to figure out the blood pressure anywhere in the body. When this value is positive, then the pressure is greater than that at the heart (P_0); when it's negative, it's less.

Note: The symbol Δ is one commonly used in upper math to mean "change in."

2. **Exploring Blood Pressure in Giraffes** – Use the formula $\Delta P = \rho gh$ for these problems (we're just looking at the change to the pressure at the heart, regardless of what the pressure is at the heart). As we did with problem 1, assume the blood is equally dense throughout the body at a density (ρ) of 1,060 $\frac{\text{kg}}{\text{m}^3}$ and that the acceleration due to gravity (g) is 9.807 $\frac{\text{m}}{\text{s}^2}$.

a. Say the top of a person's head is 0.508 m above his heart (about 1.67 ft). What would the approximate blood pressure be at the top of the person's head due to the distance from the heart *when he bends down and touches his head to the floor*?
   This answer can be found by substituting 0.508 m for h and the value for ρ and g given above into $\Delta P = \rho gh$, as we're asked to find just the change due to the distance from the heart, which is what ΔP tells us.

b. Say a giraffe's neck is about 1.829 m above its heart (about 6 ft).[4] What would its blood pressure be at the top of its head due to the distance from the heart *when it bends down for a drink*? This can be found by substituting 1.829 m into the formula for ΔP, along with the values for ρ and g given.

c. How many times greater was the pressure due to the distance from the heart on the giraffe's head than the person's?

When they bend, giraffes have a much higher blood pressure rushing to their heads due to how far away the head is from their heart! But God specially designed the giraffe to handle this pressure!

Evolutionists also encounter a design dilemma for the evolution of a long neck. That six-foot neck requires an intricate blood vessel system to maintain proper blood pressure between the heart and brain. A giraffe bending its neck down to drink water is a marvelous display of design. The 25-pound heart that pumps blood way up that neck against gravity suddenly pumps down with gravity, which should cause the delicate brain to explode. But the blood vessels are uniquely designed with reinforced walls, bypass valves, a cushioning web, and sensor signals to moderate the pressure when the giraffe bends its neck down.

The reverse of this intricate system happens when the giraffe raises its head so that the pressure is regained and the giraffe doesn't pass out. In addition, the tight skin on giraffe legs has been compared to an astronaut's G-suit because it prevents high blood pressure from pressing blood out of the capillaries. – Karin Viet, Answers in Genesis[5]

Giraffes were given just what they need — G-suit and all — to be able to handle the higher pressure caused by their long necks. God is an amazing engineer.[6]

4   Based on a neck of 6 ft, as shared by the San Diego Zoo, "Giraffe," https://animals.sandiegozoo.org/animals/giraffe, and the fact that its heart is located in the giraffe's chest.

5   Karin Viet, "Giraffes: Towering Testimonies to God's Design" (Answers in Genesis, 2017), https://answersingenesis.org/mammals/giraffes-towering-testimonies-to-gods-design/

6   See also Brett Petrillo, "Why Giraffes Don't Have Brain Damage" (BP's Fuel for Thought, 2012), https://bpsfuelforthought.wordpress.com/2012/08/14/why-giraffes-dont-have-brain-damage/, for more details.

Study Suggestion: *Review Quizzes 1–3 and the Key Skills from Chapters 1–4. The quiz will cover Chapter 4, but the test will cover Chapters 1–4. (The "General Instructions for Students" section that you should have put with your notes gives some study tips.)*

Remember to check your work!

1. **Reviewing Sets and Imaginary Numbers**

   a. Given that $x \in \mathbb{N}$, solve for x: $\frac{1}{3}x^2 = 192$

   b. Is π a member of the set of $\mathbb{Q} \cap \mathbb{P}$?

   ○ Yes   ○ No

   c. Finish the statement: $\mathbb{Q} \cap \mathbb{P} =$

   d. Simplify: $3i^2 + 2i^3$

   e. Simplify without a calculator: $\sqrt{-12}\sqrt{-14}$

   f. Simplify without a calculator: $\dfrac{\sqrt{15}}{\sqrt{-5}}$

2. **Miscellaneous Review**

   a. Simplify: $\dfrac{\left(2\frac{m}{s^2}\right)^4}{4 \, m^2}$

   b. Simplify: $\left(\dfrac{5x^3y^{-7}}{yx^{-5}}\right)\left(\dfrac{2x^{-2}}{y^3}\right)$

   c. Simplify: $-2\left(\dfrac{4r^{\frac{5}{2}}}{2r^{-2}}\right)$

   d. Simplify the following expression, simplifying as much as possible along the way and only using positive exponents. Keep terms with different powers of x separate.

   $$\dfrac{-\left(x^8y\right)^{-2}}{-2y^{-2}} - \dfrac{-3}{x^{-1}}$$

   e. Simplify: $\sqrt{\dfrac{200\frac{m}{s}}{\frac{2 \, m \cdot s}{kg^2}}}$

   f. Solve for b in terms of y if $a = -3$: $\;3b = ay^2$

3. **Understanding Check** – List the order of operations.

4. **Solving for an Unknown** – Solve for x.

   a. $-16x = -4x^{\frac{1}{2}}x^{-\frac{1}{2}}$ *Hint:* Simplify the exponents first!

   b. $-2x = -\dfrac{-3}{2}$

   c. $7x^2 = -63$

   d. $-\dfrac{3}{2}x > \dfrac{27}{2}$

   e. $-\dfrac{x}{2} < 4$

5. **Algebra Applied**[1] – Have you ever wondered how shipbuilders know if a ship will float before they build it? Because of the consistent way God governs all things, they can use algebra! To float, the density of the object (ρ), which is found by dividing the mass by the volume $\left(\dfrac{m}{V}\right)$, has to be less than the density of the liquid in which it's resting, or $\dfrac{m}{V} < \rho_{liquid}$. If the volume ($V$) of an object is 30 m³ and the object is resting in water, which has a density (ρ_{liquid}) of about $1{,}000{,}000 \dfrac{g}{1\,m^3}$ at 39.2°F, what must the mass (m) of the object be less than for the object to still float? You can answer this question by substituting the known values into $\dfrac{m}{V} < \rho_{liquid}$ and solving for m, the mass. Since this is an inequality, you will want to substitute first and then solve.[2]

6. **More Algebra Applied**

   a. If you can type a 9,000 word document in 3 *hours*, what is your typing speed in words per *minute*?

   b. 🎯 **Challenge Problem:** Find m_3 if $-\dfrac{F_t r^2}{G m_1} + m_2 = m_3$ if m_2 is 100 kg, r is 100 m, m_1 is 300 kg, G is $6.674 \times 10^{-11} \dfrac{m^3}{kg \bullet s^2}$, and F_t is 7.105×10^{-11} N.

      Hint: Substitute kg $\bullet \dfrac{m}{s^2}$ for N in order to simplify the units.

   c. Suppose you want to figure out the surface area of a toy ball. You use a ruler to measure the diameter and find it to be about 10 in. What is its surface area in square feet?

---

1   See Randall D. Knight, *Physics for Scientists and Engineers with Modern Physics: A Strategic Approach* (Pearson, Addison Wesley, NY: 2004), p. 461.
2   Water density based on value given by USGS, "Water Density," https://www.usgs.gov/special-topic/water-science-school /science/water-density?qt-science_center_objects=0#qt-science_center_objects

Intentionally left blank

1. **Understanding Terms** – Rewrite these expressions and then circle each term in these expressions. On fractions with more than 1 term in either the numerator or the denominator, also circle each "subterm" within the fraction itself — that is, circle anything within the fraction that is separated by a plus or minus sign.

   a. $2y + \dfrac{xy}{2}(cb) + 2x$

   b. $\dfrac{5}{y}$

   c. y

   d. $3xyz - 85a$

   e. $\dfrac{x^3y}{5} + 2x$

   f. $\dfrac{2x^4y}{b} + \dfrac{a}{3}$

   g. $7x$

   h. $xy + \dfrac{3+x}{4} + z$

2. **Combining Like Terms** – Combine like terms.

   a. $9x - 3x$

   b. $5ab + 3ab$

   c. $\dfrac{1}{2}a + \dfrac{2}{3}a$

   d. $3x^3 - 2x^2 + 3a^2 - 2x^2$

   e. $2\sqrt{2} + 4\sqrt{2}$ *Hint:* You can treat 2 and 4 as coefficients and combine these like terms, treating $\sqrt{2}$ as you would an unknown. After all, they are multiplications of the *same amount.*

   f. $10x^2y + 5xy^2z + 12x^2y + 8x^2z$

   g. $2ab + 3a^2b + ab$

   h. $4\sqrt{3} - 2\sqrt{3}$

3. **Solving Equations with More Than One Term**

   a. Solve for x: $\frac{4}{5}x + 2 = 4$

   b. Solve for x: $\frac{2}{3}x + \frac{1}{8} = \frac{3}{8}$

   c. Solve for x: $\frac{2}{3}x + 3 = \frac{3}{8}$

   d. Convert 68 degrees Fahrenheit (°F) to Celsius (°C) given that $F = \frac{9°F}{5°C}C + 32°F$, where we have used F to represent the temperature in Fahrenheit and C the temperature in Celsius.

   Hint: Be sure to include the unit of measure in your answer! Don't confuse the unknowns F and C with units of measure; we're using F and C here as unknowns, while when we mean degrees Fahrenheit or degrees Celsius we put a degree sign in front like this °F and °C.

4. **Applying Algebra**

   a. When looking at an electrical circuit, we can examine something called the resistance to the flow of electricity.[1] Let's say the circuit has 4 different resistance elements (called resistors) that are arranged in what we call a parallel arrangement. Because of the consistent way God holds all things together, we can describe the equivalent or total resistance like this:

   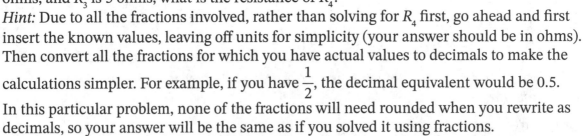

   $$\frac{1}{R_{total}} = \frac{1}{R_1} + \frac{1}{R_2} + \frac{1}{R_3} + \frac{1}{R_4}.$$ If the total
   resistance R_{total} is $\frac{5}{4}$ ohms, R_1 is 4 ohms, R_2 is 4 ohms, and R_3 is 5 ohms, what is the resistance of R_4?

   Hint: Due to all the fractions involved, rather than solving for R_4 first, go ahead and first insert the known values, leaving off units for simplicity (your answer should be in ohms). Then convert all the fractions for which you have actual values to decimals to make the calculations simpler. For example, if you have $\frac{1}{2}$, the decimal equivalent would be 0.5. In this particular problem, none of the fractions will need rounded when you rewrite as decimals, so your answer will be the same as if you solved it using fractions.

   b. The total area of two rectangles equals the area of the first plus the area of the second, or $A_{total} = A_1 + A_2$. Suppose the length and width of each rectangle are the same. We could rewrite the equation like this: $A_{total} = lw + lw$. Simplify $A_{total} = lw + lw$ by combining like terms.

---

1   Equation is from W. Thomas Griffith and Juliet Brosing, *The Physics of Everyday Phenomena: A Conceptual Introduction to Physics*, 6th ed. (New York: McGraw-Hill, 2009), p. 267.

Remember, don't use a calculator to simplify algebraic expressions.

1. **Simplifying Fractions** – Simplify. If you cannot simplify, write "cannot simplify."

   a. $\dfrac{4a + 2a + 3}{2}$

   b. $\dfrac{3a + 3b + a}{5}$

   c. $4\left(\dfrac{a + 2}{8a}\right)$

   d. $\dfrac{3a}{6 + a}$

   e. $\dfrac{4x}{x^3} + 3x^{-2}$

2. **More Simplifying Fractions** – Simplify. Don't let the complexity scare you — just take each problem step by step.

   a. $2ax^3y - y\dfrac{5ax}{x^{-2}}$

   b. $2x^2 - 3x - 2x + \dfrac{5a}{2a + 3a}$

   c. $7ab + \dfrac{2a^2 + 3a^2}{5a^5}$

   d. $\dfrac{25a^2y^3}{5ay^2} - 3ay + 2a^2y^3$

1. **Solving Problems, Remembering to Divide Each Term** – Solve each equation for x. Note that your answer may still contain an unknown. If you can, rewrite subterms as their own fraction and simplify.

    a. $3y + 2x = 14$

    b. $5y - 3x = 21$

    c. $\dfrac{1}{2}x = 6 - b$

    d. $2x = 3 - a$

Remember to check your work by plugging in your answer for the unknown! This will help you avoid careless errors — and on simple problems, you can check your work in your head.

2. **Simplifying Fractions with Multiple Terms** – Rewrite each subterm as its own fraction and simplify, if possible.

    a. $\dfrac{2a - 3d}{d}$

    b. $\dfrac{x - 2y}{2}$

    c. $\dfrac{y + 6}{6 - x}$

1. **Performing Several Operations** – Solve each equation for x.

   a. $2\left(\dfrac{x-2}{3}\right) = 20$

   b. $4\left(\dfrac{x+1}{-3}\right) = -8$

2. **Multiplying *Both Sides* of an Equation by Multiple Terms** – Solve each equation for x. Note that your answer may still contain an unknown.

   a. $4\left(\dfrac{x}{8x-3}\right) = 2$

   b. $-3\left(\dfrac{x}{2b+3}\right) = -6$

1. **Solving Problems** – Solve each equation for x. Note that your answer may still contain an unknown.

   a. $\dfrac{2(x-1)}{5} = 3$

   b. $5x + 3a = 17a$

   c. $8 = a\left(\dfrac{x-2}{3}\right)$

   d. $b = y\left(\dfrac{x-3}{c}\right)$

   e. $\dfrac{2}{x} + \dfrac{3}{y} = 15$

   f. $\dfrac{a}{x+2} = 3$

   Remember to check your work by plugging in your answer for the unknown! This will help you avoid careless errors — and on simple problems, you can check your work in your head.

2. **Simplifying Fractions with Multiple Terms** – Simplify these fractions by first rewriting each term as its own fraction.

   a. $\dfrac{a + 2x^2}{x}$

   b. $\dfrac{xy + 5}{5}$

3. **Applying Algebra**

   a. Solve this formula for m_3, which is based on the gravity formula (you'll see more in a few lessons): $F_t = Gm_2 \dfrac{m_3 - m_1}{r^2}$.

   b. Using the formula you found in 3a, find the approximate value of m_3 if the force (F) equals 2.967×10^{-9} N, G equals $6.674 \times 10^{-11} \dfrac{m^3}{kg \cdot s^2}$, $m_1 = 70$ kg, $m_2 = 80$ kg, and $r = 3$ m.

   Hint: Remember that a newton (N) equals $\dfrac{kg \cdot m}{s^2}$.

c. 🎯 **Challenge Problem:** Businessmen use all sorts of different formulas to help determine where to invest money. Here's one equation from Investopedia[1]: $ER_i = R_f + \beta_i\left(ER_m - R_f\right)$. Let's say you want a return of 6% on your money $\left(ER_i\right)$. The beta (β_i — basically, a measure of how risky the investment is) you're willing to accept is 2, and the "risk-free rate"[2] $\left(R_f\right)$ is 3%. What does the "expected return of market"[3] $\left(ER_m\right)$ need to be for this to happen? *Note:* In finance, we sometimes use multiple letters to stand for a single unknown. Treat ER_m as a single unknown.

Hint: Due to the fractions involved, this will be easiest to solve if you start by inserting the values given and then solve for ER_m.

Think It Through

Many of math's applications involve money. Knowing how to use math to make financial decisions can be a blessing, as God has given us the opportunity to steward finances (and for some people, to earn a living through working in finance). Always remember, though, that the love of money leads us astray. Keep loving God with all your heart, not money.

> *For the love of money is the root of all evil: which while some coveted after, they have erred from the faith, and pierced themselves through with many sorrows. (1 Timothy 6:10)*

---

d. 📖 If sound travels 1,100 feet per second, how far distant was a rifle whose discharge was heard 4 seconds after firing? Show your work.
Hint: Distance equals speed times time.

4. **Skill Sharpening** – Solve for y if x equals $2y$: $\dfrac{2}{y} + \dfrac{3}{x} = 20$

Hint: We're combining quite a few skills here! But you have all of the skills you need.

1   Will Kenton, "Capital Asset Pricing Model (CAPM)" (Investopedia: 2019), https://www.investopedia.com/terms/c/capm.asp
2   Ibid.
3   Ibid.

1. **Working with the Distributive Property** – Use the distributive property to distribute this multiplication and then simplify; show your work.

   a. $y(3 + 2x)$

   Example Meaning: The total paid in sales tax, where y represents the state tax rate and x the cost of an item of which you bought 2. The addition of 3 is to account for another $3 item purchased.

   b. $\frac{1}{2}h(y + 8)$

   Example Meaning: Area of a triangle if the base equals $y + 8$.

   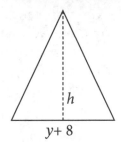

   c. $5(2 - b)$

   Example Meaning: The total cost if you bought 5 of something that was 2 minus some consistent per-item discount.

   d. $(x - 4)(x - 2)$

   Example Meaning: The area of the rectangular portion of the figure shown.

   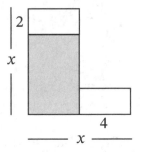

   e. $20 - (x - 2)$

   f. $t\left(-\frac{g}{2}t^2 + 2t + b\right)$

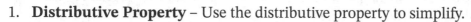

Remember on problems where you solve for an unknown to check your work by plugging in your answer for the unknown! This will help you avoid careless errors.

1. **Distributive Property** – Use the distributive property to simplify.

    a. $\frac{1}{2}(50\text{ ft})(x + 5\text{ ft})$

    Example Meaning: Area of a triangle if the height equals $x + 5$ ft.

    b. $(x + 7)(x - 4)$

    c. $5 - (a + 3)$

    d. $A^4\left(A^{\frac{1}{2}} - h\right)$

    e. $(a + 2)(a + 3)$

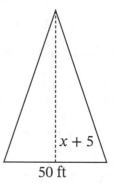

$x + 5$

50 ft

2. **Practicing Skills** – Practice some skills you'll need for problems later in this course by completing the following. **Show your work.**

    a. Distribute the multiplication, giving your answer as two separate fractions: $3\left(\dfrac{5a - 3}{2}\right)$

    b. Divide both sides of $2a + 3b = 10$ by 2 and solve for a.

    c. Multiply both sides of $2a + 3b = 10$ by 2, distributing the multiplication; then solve for a.

3. **Solving Problems** – Solve for the unknown. You'll need to use a variety of skills you've learned!

    a. $18 = 5 - (x - 2)$

    b. $3\left(\dfrac{5a - 2a}{3}\right) = 4$

    c. $(x + 2)(x + 5) = 26 + 7x$

    d. $(y + 4)(y - 4) = 0$

4. **Applying Algebra**

    a. One formula used in finance is called the "dividend growth model,"[1] and it "determines the current price of a stock (P_0) as its dividend next period [which, in this model, is found by taking the last dividend (D_0) times 1 plus the growth rate (g)] divided by the discounted rate less the dividend growth rate $(R - g)$."[2] Here's the equation in the way the finance book gives: $P_0 = \dfrac{D_0(1 + g)}{R - g}$. Solve this equation for the growth rate g in terms of the other unknowns.

    b. Using the equation you solved in 4a, find g if P_0 is \$311.50, D_0 is \$12.45, and R is 0.06.

---

1   Ross Westerfield Jordan, *Essentials of Corporate Finance* (New York: McGraw-Hill/Irwin, 2008), pp. 206.
2   Ibid.

c. If the weight of oak ashes is 3% of the weight of the oak wood burned, and the weight of carbonate of potash (a particular ash chemical) contained in the ashes is 3.5% of the weight of the ashes, how many pounds of carbonate of potash are there in the ashes when 4,000 lb of oak wood is burned?

5. **More Skill Sharpening**

a. Solve for x: $\dfrac{1}{4}x + \dfrac{1}{5}y = \dfrac{2}{3}$ *Hint:* Your answer will still contain an unknown (y).

b. Solve for x if $y = \dfrac{1}{3}x$: $\dfrac{2}{3}x + \dfrac{5}{6}y = \dfrac{1}{2}$

1. **Factoring** – Factor out all common factors in the following expressions.

   Example: $2x + 3ax$

   Answer: $x(2 + 3a)$

   a. $7y + 2xy$

   b. $20xy + 10x$

   c. $2abc + 3ab - ab^2$

   d. $b^2 + 3b + bc$

Remember on problems where you solve for an unknown to check your work by plugging in your answer for the unknown! This will help you avoid careless errors.

1. **Factoring** – Simplify, factoring out any common factors. You may also need to use other skills in addition to factoring to do so (we built some of your "Skill Sharpening" section into these problems)! Remember, the purpose of these problems is to make sure you're equipped to solve any real-life problem you encounter.

   a. $3x + 6xy + 12x^2$

   b. $7x^{\frac{1}{2}}x^{\frac{4}{2}} + 8x + 5xy$

   c. $5y + 10x + 20y^2$, if $x = 2y$ (simplify in terms of y — in other words, substitute $2y$ for the x in $5y + 10x + 20y^2$ and simplify)

   d. $6i^2y + 8i^2 + 10x$ *Hint:* The i represents the imaginary number, $\sqrt{-1}$.

   e. $6x^2y + 8x^2 + 10x$

   f. $(-3x)^3 y + \left(x^{\frac{1}{3}}\right)^{\frac{27}{3}}$

2. **Applying Algebra**

   a. Solve $F_t = G m_2 \dfrac{m_3 - m_1}{r^2}$ for m_1. Notice that this is the formula we found in the lesson text, and also the same one we used on Worksheet 5.4B. Note that unlike on Worksheet 5.4B, though, you're finding m_1 instead of m_3.

   b. The area of a rectangle equals 2 times the length plus 2 times the width: $A = 2l + 2w$. If the area equals 40 ft², use factoring to simplify the equation as much as possible.

   c. 📖 If the cost of labor is $6 for spraying 4 acres, what will it cost altogether to spray 40 acres of grapes if the spraying mixture costs $6 per 100 gallons and it takes 150 gallons for 1 acre?

3. **Skill Sharpening** – Use the distributive property to complete the multiplication.

   a. $(x + 2)(x + 3)$

   b. $(y - x)(y + x)$

4. **More Skill Sharpening** – Solve for x.

   a. $\dfrac{10}{x} + \dfrac{3}{y} = 15$

   b. $\dfrac{8x - 3}{8} = 10$ *Hint:* There's more than one way to solve this. But notice that if you separate the terms in the fraction on the left into $\dfrac{8x}{8} - \dfrac{3}{8}, \dfrac{8x}{8}$ will simplify to x.

5. **Skill Expanding** – If $y - 5x = c$ and $x - 3c = y$, find an equation for y that only includes the unknowns y and c and does *not* include x. (This skill is the one you'd need to use if you knew the value of y and c but didn't know the value of x.)
   Hint: Solve the second equation for x (the unknown you're wanting to remove from the equation) and substitute that value into the first equation, solving it for y. Make sure you understand this problem — it applies many different skills you've been learning all at once!

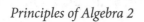
1. **Reviewing Chapter 5**

    a. Solve for x and simplify: $\dfrac{x}{2} < \dfrac{3(2y - y)}{2} + \dfrac{1}{2}y$. Put x to the *left* of the inequality sign in your final answer.

    b. Simplify by factoring out common factors: $5xy^3 - 10xy - 15y$

    c. Simplify: $x(7 - 2y + 3z) - y(2 - 2x - z) + 5(3z - x)$

    d. Simplify : $\dfrac{3a + x}{b} + \dfrac{5ab}{ba}$

    e. Solve for x: $\dfrac{3}{2x + 3} = \dfrac{1}{3}$

    f. Solve for x : $\dfrac{3}{4}x + \dfrac{1}{8}y = 10$

    g. If $a + 3b = c$ and $8a - 4b = 0$, find an equation for a that only includes the unknowns a and c and does *not* include b.

2. **Algebra Applied** – If the blood pressure equaled a specific amount at our heart (which we'll call P_0),[1] then the approximate blood pressure at another part of our body (P) could be found by this formula, where height is the distance from the heart:

$$P = P_0 + \rho g h$$

Using this formula, find the distance from the heart (h) if P_0 is

$7{,}521.68 \ \dfrac{\text{kg}}{\text{s}^2 \cdot \text{m}}$,

ρ (an approximate density of blood) is $1{,}060 \ \dfrac{\text{kg}}{\text{m}^3}$, and P (the pressure

reading taken on the ankle)[2] is $20{,}000 \ \dfrac{\text{kg}}{\text{s}^2 \cdot \text{m}}$. Assume the person is

on earth where g is $9.807 \ \dfrac{\text{m}}{\text{s}^2}$.

Hint: Insert the known values first here, as that will make this particular problem simpler. **Be sure to include the unit of measure.**

Notice how much higher the blood pressure is just a short distance from the heart! This reiterates what we saw at a simpler level (since we hadn't gone over as much math) in Lesson 4.6 about how critical it is for the giraffe, which has such a long neck, to be designed the way God designed it in order to survive.

---

1   See William & Mary, *107 Manual: Chapter 11* (Williamsburg, VA). Found on physics.wm.edu/~labs/107_manual /ch11.pdf. See also Lumen, "Physics: Pressures in the Body," https://courses.lumenlearning.com/physics /chapter/11-9-pressures-in-the-body/

2   "Ankle Blood Pressure as a Predictor of Total and Cardiovascular Mortality," Heikki Hietanen, Rauni Pääkkkönen, and Veikko Salomaa, found in *BMC Cardiovascular Disorders* 8 (BMC, 2008), found on https://bmccardiovascdisord.biomedcentral.com/articles/10.1186/1471-2261-8-3

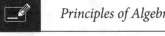
Many of the systems of equations you'll be solving in both this chapter and the next are adapted from a textbook written in the 1800s called The Franklin Elementary Algebra.

*Unlike many modern textbooks, math books back then tended to teach math more as a real-life tool. As the preface says: "The method of teaching algebra set forth in this book assumes as a leading principle that algebraic language, like other language, is best acquired, not through definitions and formal rules, but rather through **actual use** of the language itself as an instrument of thought"[1] [emphasis added]. This is consistent with a biblical worldview, in which math is a way of describing God's creation. So after a few abstract problems today to help you practice the skill, the next worksheet will focus on applying systems of equations to solving actual settings.*

1. **Solving Systems of Equations by Substitution** – Solve the following (i.e., find both x and y) using the substitution method taught in Lesson 6.1. You can start by solving either equation for either unknown — in the *Solutions Manual*, we started by solving the second equation for b on problem 1a, and solving the first equation for x first on problems 1b and 1c. You should get the same answer if you solve starting with the other equation, but if you want to be able to follow the *Solutions Manual*'s solutions, you'll want to take that same approach.

   a. $5b + 6c = \$27$

       $2b + 2c = \$10$

       Note: This is the ground beef and chicken problem we first introduced back in Lesson 5.3. The b stands for pounds of ground beef and the c for pounds of chicken.

       $b = $ _____ $c = $ _____

   b. ⊞ $3x + 5y = 8$

       $4x + 3y = 7$

       $x = $ _____ $y = $ _____

   c. ⊞ $2x - 7y = 8$

       $4y - 9x = 19$

       $x = $ _____ $y = $ _____

Go back and check your answers by making sure the values you found really do work in both equations!

---

1   Edwin Seaver and George Walton, *The Franklin Elementary Algebra* (Boston: William War & Co., 1882), p. iii.

Rather than just solving more abstract problems, today you're going to get to solve some real-life systems of equations! Remember to check your work, plugging your answer back into the original equations. And check that you have the correct original equations by thinking through if your answers make sense!

1. ⊞ **Applying Algebra**

   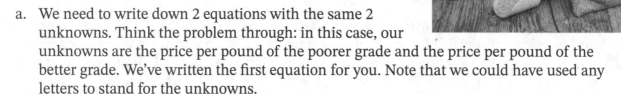

   A grocer has two grades of sugar. If he mixes 3 pounds of the poorer grade with 5 pounds of the better grade, the mixture will be worth $1.30 a pound; if he mixes 5 pounds of the poorer grade with 3 pounds of the better grade, the mixture will only be worth $1.10 a pound. How much is each grade of sugar worth?

   a. We need to write down 2 equations with the same 2 unknowns. Think the problem through: in this case, our unknowns are the price per pound of the poorer grade and the price per pound of the better grade. We've written the first equation for you. Note that we could have used any letters to stand for the unknowns.

   $3p + 5b = \$1.30$

   Write down another equation using those same 2 unknowns:

   _____ + _____ = _____

   b. Using the equations you wrote in 1a, find the value of each grade of sugar (i.e., of p and b). You can use substitution to find the answer! Note that the *Solutions Manual* solved the first equation for p to start.

   $p =$ _____ $b =$ _____

2. ⊞ **More Applying Algebra**

   a. The income from a certain farm exceeds the expenses by $2,000. However, two years ago the income was 20% of the current income and the expenses were 25% of the current expenses, and the income *was less than the expenses by $900. What are the current income and expenses?*

   income = _____

   expenses = _____

   b. A tank is supplied by two pumps. One day the tank was half filled by working both pumps 3 hours, and on the next day it was two-thirds filled by working the larger pump two hours and the smaller seven hours. At what rate does each pump fill the tank? *Hint:* Omit units of measure while solving, but remember time is being tracked in hours when you list your answer.

   Rate of small pump = _____

   Rate of large pump = _____

3. **Skill Sharpening**

  a. Simplify: $x^3x^2y^{-1} + \dfrac{x^{-1}}{x^{-6}y} + 2i^2x^2$ *Hint:* Remember that i represents $\sqrt{-1}$.

  b. Solve this formula for converting between Celsius and Fahrenheit for F so as to more easily use it to convert from Fahrenheit to Celsius: $C = \dfrac{5}{9}\left(F - 32\right)$.

  c. Factor out an x: $7x^{-2} + 2x$
  Hint: Just think about what you'd have to change the exponent in x^{-2} to in order to have it equal x^{-2} when multiplied by x.

  d. ◎ ▦ **Challenge Problem:** Solve for the values of x and y in these two equations:

  $$\frac{6}{x} + \frac{5}{y} = 4$$

  $$\frac{8}{x} - \frac{15}{y} = 1$$

  $x = $ _____ $y = $ _____

  Hint: Pick either equation and solve for an unknown (we solved the second equation for x in the *Solutions Manual*). You will need to combine your tools, using factoring and remembering that you can divide *both sides* by multiple terms.

1. **Solving Systems of Equations by Addition or Subtraction** – Solve for both the unknowns using the method taught in Lesson 6.2. Note that these are the same problems you solved on Worksheet 6.1A using substitution, so you should obtain the same answers! **Be sure to show your work — you must show how you found the answer by addition or subtraction of the two equations.**

    a. $5b + 6c = \$27$

    $2b + 2c = \$10$

    $b =$ _____ $c =$ _____

    b. $3x + 5y = 8$

    $4x + 3y = 7$

    $x =$ _____ $y =$ _____

    c. $2x - 7y = 8$

    $4y - 9x = 19$

    $x =$ _____ $y =$ _____

1. **Solving Systems of Equations by Addition or Subtraction** – Solve these problems using the method taught in Lesson 6.2. **Be sure to show your work.**

   a. $2x - 2y = -10$

   $3x + 4y = -1$

   $x =$ _____ $y =$ _____

   b. $3x + 2y = \dfrac{7}{4}$

   $\dfrac{1}{3}x + 5y = \dfrac{31}{12}$

   $x =$ _____ $y =$ _____

   c. $\dfrac{6}{x} + \dfrac{5}{y} = 4$

   $\dfrac{8}{x} - \dfrac{15}{y} = 1$

   $x =$ _____ $y =$ _____

Note that problem 1c is the same problem as the challenge problem (3d) on Worksheet 6.1B, but that the method we learned today makes it much easier! Some problems are decidedly easier using one method over another. Both ways give you the same answer because of how God faithfully upholds the laws of mathematics, but God also gives us wisdom and discernment to choose the better way for the situation.

2. ⊞ **Algebra Applied** – Hiero, king of Syracuse, is said to have given his goldsmith gold with which to make a crown. The king, suspecting that the finished crown had been alloyed with silver (alloying means mixing different metals together), consulted Archimedes. While the crown weighed the same amount as the gold the king had given the goldsmith, this philosopher detected the fraud by plunging the crown in water. If he knew that pure gold displaces 0.05 of its weight and pure silver 0.10 of its weight of water, but the crown didn't displace 0.05 of its weight of water like the pure gold, he would have known the crown wasn't pure gold. Let's say the crown displaced 0.0625 of its total weight of 20 pounds of water. What was the weight of gold and the weight of silver in the crown, assuming that no other metals were used in the alloy? The following problems will help you answer this.[1]

a. Write down 2 equations with 2 unknowns that describe this situation. *Hint:* Be sure to track your units of measure. They will help you figure out the correct equations. Remember that the total weight of the crown can only come from the weight of the gold and the silver.

_____

_____

b. How much did the gold and silver in the crown weigh? You can use either method for solving a system of equations, although the solution is shown using substitution.

Weight of gold ≈ _____

Weight of silver ≈ _____

3. **Skill Sharpening** – Simplify, factoring out common factors, including a factor of x:

$$3\left(x^{\frac{3}{5}}\right)^{-5} + \frac{6}{x^3} + 12x^2 + 9x.$$

Remember to check your work!

Solving Systems of Equations Using Matrices – *Solve for both the unknowns using the matrix method taught in Lesson 6.3. Note that these are the same problems you solved on Worksheet 6.1A and 6.1B, so you should obtain the same answers!* **The goal of these problems is to give you familiar problems on which to make sure you understand how to solve systems of equations using matrices.** *Keep playing with them until you get the same answers you got before!*

1. $5b + 6c = \$27$

   $2b + 2c = \$10$

   a. Write matrix A showing the coefficients of the unknowns. The first row is done for you.

   $$A = \begin{bmatrix} 5 & 6 \\ \square & \square \end{bmatrix}$$

   b. Write matrix B with the *right side* of the equations. The first row is done for you.

   $$B = \begin{bmatrix} \$27 \\ \square \end{bmatrix}$$

   c. How many rows and how many columns does matrix A have?

   $$\underline{\hspace{2cm}} \times \underline{\hspace{2cm}}$$
   rows × columns

   d. How many rows and how many columns does matrix B have?

   $$\underline{\hspace{2cm}} \times \underline{\hspace{2cm}}$$
   rows × columns

   e. Use a calculator to calculate $A^{-1}B$ and find the value for b and c. Double check yourself by looking back at your answers to 6.1A, 1a or 6.2A, 1a. Did you get the same answer using all 3 methods? You should have!

   $b = \underline{\hspace{2cm}} \quad c = \underline{\hspace{2cm}}$

2. 🏫 $3x + 5y = 8$
   $4x + 3y = 7$

   a. Write matrix A showing the coefficients of the unknowns.

   $$A = \begin{bmatrix} \square & \square \\ \square & \square \end{bmatrix}$$

   b. Write matrix B with the *right side* of the equations.

   $$B = \begin{bmatrix} \square \\ \square \end{bmatrix}$$

   c. Use a calculator to calculate $A^{-1}B$. Write your answers below. Double check yourself by looking back at your answers to 6.1A, 1a or 6.2A, 1a. Did you get the same answer using all 3 methods? You should have!

   $x = $ _____ $y = $ _____

3. 🏫 $2x - 7y = 8$
   $4y - 9x = 19$

   a. Write matrix A showing the coefficients of the unknowns.
   Hint: Be sure to list the first equation on the first row, and the second equation on the second row, in the same order as you did the first row (in this case, x then y). **Note that this is not the order in which they're written!** To avoid errors, first rewrite the second equation so $-9x$ is first. Be careful about your negative signs — **you must include the negative sign when you list the coefficient following it.** For example, the coefficient of x in the second equation is -9.

   If your calculator gives you difficulty inputting a negative sign, make sure you're using the negative sign button and not just the minus sign. Some calculators have different ones.

   $$A = \begin{bmatrix} \square & \square \\ \square & \square \end{bmatrix}$$

   b. Write matrix B with the *right side* of the equations.

   $$B = \begin{bmatrix} \square \\ \square \end{bmatrix}$$

   c. Use a calculator to calculate $A^{-1}B$. Write your answers below. Double check yourself by looking back at your answers to 6.1A, 1a or 6.2A, 1a. Did you get the same answer using all 3 methods? You should have!

   $x = $ _____ $y = $ _____

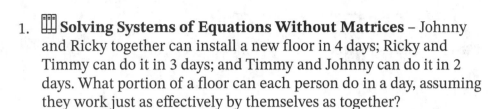

1. ⊞ **Solving Systems of Equations Without Matrices** – Johnny and Ricky together can install a new floor in 4 days; Ricky and Timmy can do it in 3 days; and Timmy and Johnny can do it in 2 days. What portion of a floor can each person do in a day, assuming they work just as effectively by themselves as together?

   This situation can be described by the following relationship:

   $$J\frac{\text{floors}}{\text{day}} + R\frac{\text{floors}}{\text{day}} + T\frac{\text{floors}}{\text{day}} = Total\frac{\text{floors}}{\text{day}}$$

   Leaving off the units of measure $\left(\dfrac{\text{floors}}{\text{day}}\right)$ for simplicity and plugging in the values given, we'd have the following system of equations:

   $$J + R + 0T = \frac{1}{4} \qquad 0J + R + T = \frac{1}{3} \qquad J + 0R + T = \frac{1}{2}$$

   Note: Notice that we added $0T$ to show that Timmy was not working at all in the first situation, $0J$ to show that Johnny was not working in the second, and $0R$ in the third to show that Ricky was not working. We got the $\dfrac{1}{4}$ because Johnny and Ricky can do 1 floor per 4 days, or $\dfrac{1 \text{ floor}}{4 \text{ days}}$; leaving units off gives us $\dfrac{1}{4}$. Similar logic applies to the other 2 equations.

   To make this problem easier to work with, we'll now eliminate the fractions by converting to decimals, rounding $\dfrac{1}{3}$ to 0.333. Although we will still use equals signs to keep things simple, this rounding will make our answers all approximate (if we cared about more accuracy, we'd have to solve the problem using fractions — but decimals make it easier).

   $J + R + 0T = 0.25 \qquad 0J + R + T = 0.333 \qquad J + 0R + T = 0.5$

   Use either the substitution or addition/subtraction method from Lessons 6.1 or 6.2 to find the value of *J*, *R*, and *T*. The *Solutions Manual* starts by solving the first equation for *J*. Note that your answer is the floors per day each can do. **Do not round.**

   $$J = \underline{\hspace{2cm}} \frac{\text{floors}}{\text{day}} \quad R = \underline{\hspace{2cm}} \frac{\text{floors}}{\text{day}} \quad T = \underline{\hspace{2cm}} \frac{\text{floors}}{\text{day}}$$

2. **Solving Systems of Equations with Matrices, Part 1** – Solve the final decimal equations from problem 1a again (which are listed again below) using the matrix method discussed in Lesson 6.3.

$$J + R + 0T = 0.25 \qquad 0J + R + T = 0.333 \qquad J + 0R + T = 0.5$$

a. Write matrix A so each row shows the coefficients of one equation.

$$A = \begin{bmatrix} 1 & 1 & 0 \\ \square & \square & \square \\ \square & \square & \square \end{bmatrix}$$

b. Write matrix B to show the values on the right side of the equations.

$$B = \begin{bmatrix} 0.25 \\ \square \\ \square \end{bmatrix}$$

c. Find the values of J, R, and T by using a calculator to find $A^{-1}B$. List your answer as matrix C. (*Hint:* When plugging in fractions on your calculator, you can use the division sign. $\frac{1}{3}$ is $1 \div 3$.) Write your results as a matrix. **Do not round.** Note that here the first row represents the value for J, the next the value for R, and the last the value for T. Notice also that all the values are the same as you found in problem 1b using another method!

$$C = \begin{bmatrix} \square \\ \square \\ \square \end{bmatrix}$$

3. **Solving Systems of Equations with Matrices, Part 2** – Below are the 6 systems of equations we showed at the beginning of Lesson 6.3. You now know all you need to know to solve them!

$$6x + 2y + 3z + 4q + 2r + 3s = 31$$
$$x + 3y + z + r + 5s = 23$$
$$y + 3z + q - r + s = 0$$
$$2x + 3y + 10z + q - 3r - 3s = -15$$
$$5x + y - z + 3q + 2r + 2s = 27$$
$$3x + 2y - 2z + 2q + r + s = 21$$

a. Write matrix A so each row shows the coefficients of one equation. The first column should be the coefficients of x, then of y, then of z, then of q, then of r, then of s (we chose this order since that is the order in which the equations were written). The coefficient may be 0 if that unknown is not in that equation . . . or a negative number if there's a negative sign in front of that unknown. Remember that the unknown by itself can be thought of as having a coefficient of 1, since any number times 1 equals itself. To get you started, the first 3 rows are given for you.

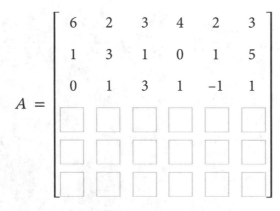

$$A = \begin{bmatrix} 6 & 2 & 3 & 4 & 2 & 3 \\ 1 & 3 & 1 & 0 & 1 & 5 \\ 0 & 1 & 3 & 1 & -1 & 1 \\ \square & \square & \square & \square & \square & \square \\ \square & \square & \square & \square & \square & \square \\ \square & \square & \square & \square & \square & \square \end{bmatrix}$$

b. How many rows and how many columns does matrix A have? Write your answer in the format of rows × columns.

c. Finish writing matrix B to show the values on the right side of the equations. The first 3 rows are given for you.

$$B = \begin{bmatrix} 31 \\ 23 \\ 0 \\ \square \\ \square \\ \square \end{bmatrix}$$

d. How many rows and how many columns does matrix B have? Write your answer in the format of rows × columns.

e. Find the values of x, y, z, q, r, and s by using a calculator to find $A^{-1}B$. Write your results as matrix C. Note that here the first row represents the value for x, the next the value for y, and so forth. You can round your answers to the nearest whole number.

$$C = \begin{bmatrix} \square \\ \square \\ \square \\ \square \\ \square \\ \square \end{bmatrix}$$

f. What was the value for s? *Hint:* The values are listed in the same order from top to bottom as you inputted them from left to right. You can check to make sure you have the right value for the right unknown by substituting them back into one of the equations.

Notice how much easier it was to solve this system of equations using matrices than it would have been to solve it using one of the other methods!

4. ⊞ **Solving Systems of Equations with Matrices, Part 3**

At a fruit stand (that happens to be a real bargain of a fruit stand — this problem was written back in the 1800s), one girl bought 3 peaches, 2 pears, and 8 apples for 20 cents; another bought 4 peaches, 5 pears, and 6 apples for 29 cents; and another bought 5 peaches, 7 pears, and 10 apples for 41 cents. What was the price of a peach, of a pear, and of an apple?

a. Write 3 equations in 3 unknowns to describe this situation.

_____

_____

_____

b. Write matrix A showing the coefficients in your equations.

$$A = \begin{bmatrix} \square & \square & \square \\ \square & \square & \square \\ \square & \square & \square \end{bmatrix}$$

c. Write B as a 3×1 matrix showing the quantities to the right of the equals sign.

$$B = \begin{bmatrix} \square \\ \square \\ \square \end{bmatrix}$$

d. Find $A^{-1}B$ in order to find your unknowns.

$$A^{-1}B = \begin{bmatrix} \square \\ \square \\ \square \end{bmatrix}$$

e. What was the price of a peach?

f. What was the price of a pear?

g. What was the price of an apple?

1. ⊞ **Applying Systems of Equations**
   Each problem is worth 15 points.

   a. A certain sum of money (P) at simple interest grows to \$1,375 (P) in 15 months (T), and to \$1,425 (P_f) in 21 months (T). Find the initial sum of money (P_i) and the rate of interest (r). Note that $P = P_i(1 + rt)$. Write 2 equations, both of which have the unknowns (P_i) and (r) in them.

   b. Use any of the methods from this chapter to solve the system of equations you wrote in 1a to find P and r. Leave your answers to r in fractional form.

   $P_i = $ _____

   $r = $ _____

2. ◎ ⊞ **Challenge Problem: Applying Algebra**
   A certain sum of money (P_i) at simple interest will amount to a dollars in m months and to b dollars in n months. Substituting a for P and m for t into the formula $P = P_i(1 + rt)$ gives us $a = P_i(1 + rm)$ and substituting b for P and n for t into the same formula gives us $b = P_i(1 + rn)$.

   Use the system of equations given to find the initial sum of money (P_i) and the interest rate (r) in terms of a, m, b, and n. Note that you will be doing the same thing you did in problem 1b, only with letters standing for values.

   $P_i = $ _____

   $r = $ _____

There's a reason we need to know multiple ways of solving a problem — each proves useful. While you might settle on a method for solving most systems of equations you prefer (and that's fine!), it's important to be aware of all the different tools so you're equipped for various situations.

3. **Matrix Solving** – Solve this system of equations using matrices. The questions below will help you.

$$4x + 2y + z = 9$$

$$\frac{1}{2}x + y - z = -3$$

$$6x + 6y - 2z = 0$$

a. Write matrix A showing the coefficients in your equations.

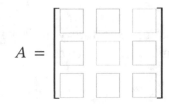

$$A =$$

b. Write B as a 3×1 matrix showing the quantities to the right of the equals sign.

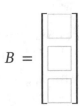

$$B =$$

c. Find $A^{-1}B$ in order to find your unknowns.

$$A^{-1}B =$$

d. List the value of each unknown. Test to make sure you have the correct value for the unknowns by plugging them back into one of the equations.

$$x = \underline{\hspace{2cm}}$$

$$y = \underline{\hspace{2cm}}$$

$$z = \underline{\hspace{2cm}}$$

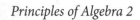

1. **Inputs and Outputs** – In previous chapters, we've looked at the relationship $F = ma$ (force equals mass times acceleration). For these problems, assume we're looking at a situation where the mass is a constant 70 kg and we want to see how force varies based on the acceleration.

   a. What are we viewing as the dependent variable?

   b. What are we viewing as the independent variable?

   c. What is the constant?

   d. Is the relationship a function?

   ○ yes   ○ no

   e. Explain your answer to 1d.

Note: You may ask your parent/teacher if you can answer 1e, 2e, 3b, and 3d orally with them. Be prepared to defend why the relationship is or isn't a function!

1. **Inputs and Outputs** – In previous chapters, we've looked at the relationship $P = VI$ (power equals voltage times current). For these problems, assume we're looking at a situation where the voltage (V) is a constant 120 volts and we want to see how power (P) varies based on the current (I).

   a. What are we viewing as the dependent variable?

   b. What are we viewing as the independent variable?

   c. What is the constant?

   d. Is the relationship a function?

      O yes   O no

   e. Explain your answer to 1d.

2. **More Inputs and Outputs** – In the situation in problems 1a–1e, suppose that instead we want to see how current depends on power. We don't know the exact voltage, but we're viewing it as a constant.

   a. Rewrite the equation $P = VI$ so that current (I) is on a side by itself in order to make the relationship easier to see.

   b. What are we viewing as the dependent variable now?

   c. What are we viewing as the independent variable?

   d. Is the relationship a function?

      O yes   O no

   e. Explain your answer to 2d.

3. **Understanding Check**

   a. In the equation $B = t^2$, can we look at B as a function of t?

      O yes   O no

   b. Explain your answer to 3a.

   c. In $y = \pm\sqrt{x}$, can we look at y as a function of x?

      O yes   O no

   d. Explain your answer to 3c.

4. **Algebra in Action: Hot Air Balloons** – It's incredible to watch hot air balloons float up and down by increasing or decreasing a flame of fire at the base. But you know what's even more amazing? The fact that day in and day out, the air in these balloons responds consistently to the heat from the flame used to control their movement. Let's use math for a minute to look at some consistencies God both created and sustains in the atmosphere — consistencies that make hot air balloons possible.

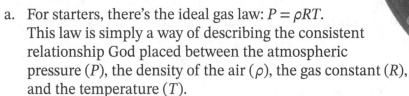

a. For starters, there's the ideal gas law: $P = \rho RT$. This law is simply a way of describing the consistent relationship God placed between the atmospheric pressure (P), the density of the air (ρ), the gas constant (R), and the temperature (T).

   Solve the ideal gas law for ρ, the density of the air. Arrange the equation so ρ is on the left.

Look closely at the equation you wrote in 4a. Notice that the density of air (ρ) — how close together the molecules are — depends on the atmospheric pressure (P), the gas constant (R), and the temperature (T). Since the atmospheric pressure and gas constant are constant for a specific area on earth, we can view the pressure and gas as constants and look at the density (ρ) as a function of the temperature (T). As the temperature (T) changes, the density (ρ) will too!

b. In the function you wrote in 4a, think about what happens to the density of the air (ρ) when the temperature (T) increases, assuming the atmospheric pressure (P) and gas constant (R) stay the same. If P and R are constant, as the temperature increases, does the density increase or decrease?
   Hint: Set P and R each equal to 1 and calculate the density (ρ) when the temperature (T) is 2 and then when the temperature increases to 20. Look at whether the density (ρ) increased or decreased when you increased the temperature from 2 to 20.

   ○ increase   ○ decrease

c. The buoyancy force (the force that makes the balloon float) changes as the density of the air inside the balloon changes . . . meaning that we can use temperature to change a balloon's ability to float! Here's the equation showing the relationship:

$$F_{B} = (\rho_{a} - \rho)Vg$$

   In words: The buoyancy force (F_{B}) of a hot air balloon equals the difference between the density of the air outside of the balloon (ρ_{a}) and that inside (ρ), times the volume of the balloon (V), times the local acceleration due to gravity (g).

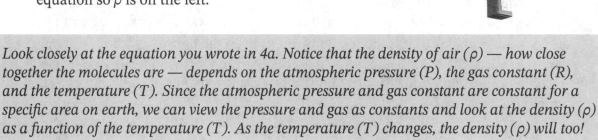

Look closely at this relationship. If the air outside of the balloon (ρ_a) and the volume (V) and gravity (g) remain constant and the density (ρ) decreases, does the buoyancy force (F_B) increase or decrease?

Hint: Insert a 1 for the values you were told remain constant and then play with different values for ρ (evaluate when ρ also equals 1 . . . and then see what happens to the buoyancy force when you *decrease* ρ to 0.5).

○ increase   ○ decrease

d. A hot air balloon will float when its buoyancy force (F_B) is greater than the force of gravity (F_g), or $F_B > F_g$. Knowing this and thinking about your answers to 4b and 4c, in order to get a balloon to float, which would we do to the temperature (T): increase it or decrease it?

○ increase   ○ decrease

e. Look again at the equation $F_B = (\rho_a - \rho)Vg$. Not only can we look at the buoyancy force as a function of the density (ρ), but we could also look at it as a function of the volume (V). After all, while we can't change the force of gravity (g) or the pressure outside of a balloon (ρ_a), we *can* change the size we make the balloon. If we view everything else as constant and look at just the relationship between the buoyancy force (F_B) and the volume (V), as the volume increases, does the buoyancy force increase or decrease?

Hint: Set $\rho_a - \rho$ and g equal to 1 so that you can easily look just at the changes in the volume.

○ increase   ○ decrease

f. Assuming the volume (V) is the only difference, which balloon will have a greater buoyancy force: a larger balloon or a smaller balloon?

○ a larger balloon   ○ a smaller balloon

Hot air balloons are one example of how men, using their God-given abilities to explore God's creation, have utilized the consistencies God created and sustains around us to develop a useful device (in this case, a balloon that floats). But don't miss the miracle of our ability to use hot air balloons. We can only get in a hot air balloon with confidence because atmospheric pressure and buoyancy operates in a consistent way, day after day, year after year. While individual balloons may have different volumes, densities, masses, and forces, the relationship between them stays the same no matter what the individual values. Without the consistencies of creation, we would be unable to use hot air balloons. It's this consistency of creation that makes modern science (and hot air balloons) — as well as algebra — useful.

Yet why is creation so consistent that we can describe how it will operate with letters and know that the relationships will hold true, no matter the actual values we plug in?

The Bible gives us an answer: because of the biblical, consistent, faithful God. Jesus is faithfully upholding all things. We have a faithful Creator God.

He is the radiance of the glory of God and the exact imprint of his nature, and he upholds the universe by the word of his power. After making purification for sins, he sat down at the right hand of the Majesty on high . . . (Hebrews 1:3; ESV)

5. **Skill Sharpening**

   a. 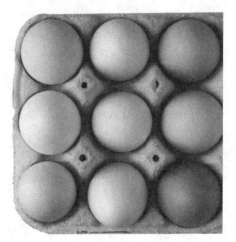 A woman bought a certain number of hen eggs at the rate of 3 cents for 2 (i.e., $0.015 per hen egg), and a certain number of duck eggs at the rate of 2 cents for 3 (i.e., approximately $0.00667 per duck egg), paying $2.83 for all. She afterwards sold the same number of hen eggs and duck eggs she bought, gaining $0.005 on each hen egg and $0.005 on each duck egg, for a total gain of $1.50. Write 2 equations, both of which have the unknowns h (for the number of hen eggs) and d (for the number duck eggs) in them.

   _____

   _____

   b. Use any method you like to solve the system of equations you wrote in 5a to find how many of each kind of egg was purchased. Round your answers to the nearest whole number, as you can't buy a portion of an egg.

   Number of hen eggs ≈ _____

   Number of duck eggs ≈ _____

1. **Function Notation**

   Example: Rewrite $d = 2t$ to show y as a function of x.

   Answer: $d(t) = 2t$

   a. Use function notation to rewrite $t = \dfrac{d}{s}$ to show t as a function of s.

   b. Use function notation to rewrite $P = VI$ to show P as a function of I.

1. **Using Function Notation** – Give all of your answers in function notation.

    Example: Rewrite $d = 2t$ to show y as a function of x.

    Answer: $d(t) = 2t$

    a. Rewrite $F = G\left(\dfrac{m_1 m_2}{r^2}\right)$ to show F as a function of r; treat the rest of the unknowns as constants. *Note:* We would want to look at it this way when looking at the force between objects when the distance between them — the r — could change.

    b. Rewrite the doubling time formula to show b_c as a function of t_c.

    $$b_c = b_0 2^{\frac{t_c}{t_d}}$$

    c. Given that $W = Fd$ (that is, that work equals force times distance), rewrite the equation to show d as a function of F.
    Hint: First solve the equation for d; then rewrite in function notation.

    d. Distribute the multiplication on the right-hand side of this function:

    $$f(x) = (x + 3)(x - 2)$$

2. **Evaluating Functions for Specific Values**

    Example: If $f(x) = 2x$, find $f(3)$.

    Answer: $f(3) = 2(3) = 6$

    a. If $d(s) = 10s$, find $d(2)$.

    b. If $f(a) = 8a + 10$, find $f(6)$.

3. **Understanding Domains and Ranges**
    Hint: Remember that we can't divide by 0. So the domain can't include any value that would have us divide by 0.

    a. In the function $y(x) = \dfrac{1}{x} + 2$, what is the domain? Remember, all real numbers is assumed, so you only have to specify any real numbers x does not equal.

    b. In the function $y(x) = \dfrac{2}{x + 3}$, what is the domain?

    c. Given the function $P(I) = (120 \text{ volts})I$, suppose in a situation the current (I) has to be either 10 amps or 20 amps. Your answer should be in the form of $I \in \{\_\_\_\_,\_\_\_\_\}$, with the correct values filled in.

    d. Show the range of the function described in 3c if the domain is the one specified in 3c. Since a volt times an amp equals a watt, your unit of measure for P will be a watt.
    Hint: Look at what the output would be for each element in the domain. Those are your possible outputs, or your range! Your answer should be in the form of $P \in \{\_\_\_\_,\_\_\_\_\}$, with the correct values filled in.

e. Given the domain and range shown, is this relation a function?

Domain (i.e., inputs)	Range (i.e., outputs)
3	6, 5
4	2

○ yes   ○ no

f. Explain your answer to 3e.

g. Show the domain of the relation in 3e. Your answer should be in the form of $x \in \{\_\_\_\_\_,\_\_\_\_\_\}$, with the correct values filled in.

h. Given the domain and range shown, is this relation a function?

Domain (i.e., inputs)	Range (i.e., outputs)
1	3
2	5
3	4
4	3

○ yes   ○ no

i. Explain your answer to 3h.

j. Specify the domain in $f(x) = \dfrac{8}{x^2 - 9}$. Part of the domain is given below, but be sure to rewrite the part given when you write your answer.

$x \neq \quad \cap x \neq$

k. How would we show that x could be any real number? Note that this is generally an unwritten assumption.

4. **Applying Algebra: Hot Air Balloons**

a. Rewrite your answer to Worksheet 7.1B, problem 4a, in function notation to show ρ as a function of T.

b. Rewrite $F_B = (\rho_a - \rho)Vg$ (the buoyancy force equation we looked at on Worksheet 7.1B) to show the buoyancy force (F_B) as a function of ρ.

c. Rewrite $F_B = (\rho_a - \rho)Vg$ to show the buoyancy force (F_B) as a function of V.

5. **Skill Sharpening** – Solve this system of equations using any method you like.
   Hint: We would suggest using matrices — write a 3×3 matrix (Matrix A) showing the coefficients, a 3×1 matrix (Matrix B) showing the quantities to the right of the equals sign, and then find $A^{-1}B$.

$$x + 3y + 2z = 2$$

$$\frac{1}{3}x + y - z = 3$$

$$2x - \frac{1}{2}y + z = 11$$

$x =$ _____ $y =$ _____ $z =$ _____

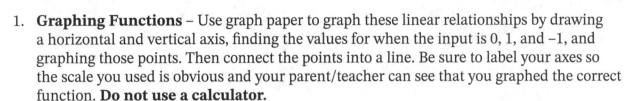

1. **Graphing Functions** – Use graph paper to graph these linear relationships by drawing a horizontal and vertical axis, finding the values for when the input is 0, 1, and –1, and graphing those points. Then connect the points into a line. Be sure to label your axes so the scale you used is obvious and your parent/teacher can see that you graphed the correct function. **Do not use a calculator.**

   a. $f(d) = 5d$ (This is the equation $W = Fd$, or work equals force times distance, when F equals 5 Newtons.)

   b. $y = x + 2$

2. **Graphing Functions on a Calculator** – Play around with your graphing calculator, learning and making sure you know how to input functions. Use the example given in the lesson, trying it out yourself. Experiment with different scales, as explained in the box. Show your parent or teacher that you were able to correctly graph the equation shown in the example in the lesson $\left(y = -\dfrac{1}{2}x^2 \right)$ on your calculator; then show him or her that you can successfully change the scale to the graph as well.

   Hint: Getting familiar with your calculator will save yourself a *lot* of time in the long run. We highly suggest looking at your calculator's user manual too in order to make sure you know the most efficient way to graph, zoom, etc., on it. Many user manuals are available online if you don't have a physical copy.

Important graphing note! *When asked to draw the general or basic shape of the graph from your calculator, you do not need to worry about being precise like you do when asked to graph a function using actual data points. The point is simply to make sure you graphed it on your calculator correctly — not to actually manually graph the function. Thus* **you don't need to use graphing paper — just draw the general shape in your notebook.**

1. **Applying Algebra: Hot Air Balloons**[1] – For these problems, use the function $F_B(\rho) = (\rho_a - \rho)Vg$ when the density outside the balloon (ρ_a) is $1.225\dfrac{\text{kg}}{\text{m}^3}$ (the approximate atmospheric density at sea level and 59°F), the volume of the balloon (V) is 200 m³, and the force due to gravity (g) is $9.8\dfrac{\text{m}}{\text{s}^2}$.

    a. What is the output for the function described when the input (i.e., the ρ) is $0.9\dfrac{\text{kg}}{\text{m}^3}$?
        Be sure to watch your units!

    b. In 1a, you calculated F_B for a specific density (ρ). Now let's see if that balloon would float when the air is at that density! The force due to gravity (F_g) equals the mass (m) of the balloon (including its basket and everything in it) times g, or $F_g = mg$. If the balloon's mass is 400 kg, will it float?
        Hint: It will float if $F_B > F_g$.

        ○ yes   ○ no

2. **Graphing Functions on a Graphing Calculator** – Use a graphing calculator to graph the following functions. Draw a rough sketch of the graph in your notebook. Remember that you may need to adjust the scale in order to see enough of the function. Notice the astronomy functions![2]
    Hint: You can usually use the standard zoom (choose "ZStandard" on your calculator — see the "Zooming In and Out with Calculators" box in Lesson 7.3) in these problems.

    a. $f(x) = \dfrac{1}{x}$

    b. $f(a) = \dfrac{4\pi^2 a^3}{24.398}$

    Example Meaning: Using Kepler's 3rd Law of Planetary motion to calculate the mass of a star in kg if its planet orbits in 1 week based on its semimajor axis measured in meters.

1   Anne Marie Helmenstine, "What Is the Density of Air at STP? (ThoughtCo., 08/10/19 update), https://www.thoughtco.com/density-of-air-at-stp-607546
2   See David Halliday, Robert Resnick, and Jearl Walker, *Fundamentals of Physics,* 7th ed. (USA: John Wiley & Sons, 2005), p. 345, for more about the relationships from which these problems are based.

c. $f(r) = -\dfrac{1.2}{r}$

Example Meaning: A scaled-down version of $f(r) = -\dfrac{1.2}{r}(10^{36})$,

which would be calculating the potential energy of a system with a hypothetical planet and a moon orbiting that hypothetical planet based on the distance from the planet the moon orbits. Each block on the graph represents 10^{36}.

> *Have you ever wondered how we measure the size of the planet and moons? We use math, relying on the consistent relationships we observe about gravity, etc., to help us determine what the size must be to produce the orbit, etc., we see. And we likewise use math to design satellites to orbit the earth.*
>
> *Indeed, we live in an amazing, consistent universe held together by a powerful God . . . a God who yet loved His creation enough to become a man and die for us!*
>
> > *O LORD, our Lord, how majestic is your name in all the earth! You have set your glory above the heavens . . . . When I look at your heavens, the work of your fingers, the moon and the stars, which you have set in place, what is man that you are mindful of him, and the son of man that you care for him? (Psalm 8:1, 3; ESV)*

3. **Domains and Ranges on Graphs** – Specify the domain for the graph on problem 2a.

4. **Identifying the Intersection Point** – Graph $y(x) = 6x$ and $y(x) = 2x + 10$ on the *same graph* (see the instructions in the box in today's lesson if needed) and list the intersection point.

5. **Our Moon – Just What We Need**

   Look carefully at the gravity equation, $F = G\left(\dfrac{m_1 m_2}{r^2}\right)$. We can use this equation to help

   us better appreciate how perfectly God created both the size and the position of the moon. Notice that the force (F) between two objects is affected by both the mass of the objects $(m_1 m_2)$ and the distance between them (r). According to NASA,[3] the moon (which we'll view as m_2) has a mass of 0.07346×10^{24} kg and the earth (which we'll view as m_1) of 5.9724×10^{24} kg. While the distance between them (r) varies throughout the year, they are

   approximately 3.78×10^5 km apart from each other. G is a constant, $(6.67 \times 10^{-11})\left(\dfrac{m^3}{kg \cdot s^2}\right)$.

   a. Calculate the force (F) between the earth and the moon.
      Hint: First convert 3.78×10^5 km to m so that your units will cancel out.

> *The force between the earth and the moon is just right for what we need. It gives us tides without flooding us with water. It regulates the earth's tilt. (See the article A Perfect Partner by Dr. Faulkner on the Answers in Genesis site.)*

---

3   David Williams, "Moon Fact Sheet," (NASA, 2017 update), https://nssdc.gsfc.nasa.gov/planetary/factsheet/moonfact.html

b. To better appreciate God's design, let's look at how the force *depends on* the mass of the moon (m_2), assuming the distance (r) and size of the earth stay the same. Insert the values given for G and m_1 into the equation

$F = G\left(\dfrac{m_1 m_2}{r^2}\right)$, leaving m_2 and F as your variables. You

may ignore units, although **be sure to plug in the value for r in meters, not kilometers.** Simplify the resulting equation as much as possible (i.e., perform all of the multiplication and division you can), but do not round.

$F(m_2) =$ _____

c. In order to make the equation you wrote in 5b easier to graph, multiply the right-hand side of your equation from 5b by 1,000.

Equation from 5b with right hand multiplied by 1,000: _____

Note: When multiplying the right side by 1,000, we're essentially just changing the unit of measure.

d. Now graph it on a graphing calculator, drawing a rough sketch in your notebook. Keep in mind that each change on the graph now represents a change of 1,000 kg in the mass.

e. To see even more of God's design, let's look at how the force *depends on* the distance between the earth and the moon (r), assuming the size of both stay the same. Once

again, we'll use $F = G\left(\dfrac{m_1 m_2}{r^2}\right)$ to find it. This time, we'll leave F and r as the variables

and scale it so that we can look at just how the force changes based on the distance between the earth and the moon (r). While we won't go into the details of the process, the result is $F(r) = \dfrac{2.926}{r^2}$. **Graph $F(r) = \dfrac{2.926}{r^2}$, where $r > 0$** (negative distances between the earth and moon don't make sense . . . and r can't equal 0, as that would make the denominator equal 0, and we can't divide by 0) and draw the basic shape in your notebook. Notice that after a certain distance, the force the moon exerts on the earth would be almost negligible, while for any distances very close, it will be super large. But guess what? God put the moon at just the right distance for the ocean tides we need!

f. If $f(r) = \dfrac{2.926}{r^2}$, find $f(100)$. Do not round your answer.

6. **Function Identification** – Look carefully at the graphs below. List any graphs that are not functions.

 Hint: Look to see if for any input (i.e., horizontal value) there are 2 outputs. If not, it's a function; if there are, it's not.

Graph A	Graph B	Graph C

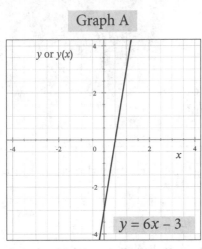

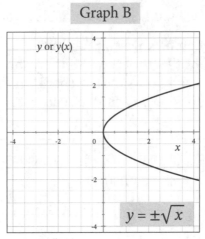

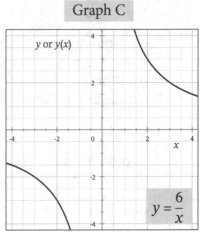

7. **Quadrants**

   a. In what quadrants does the last graph (Graph C) in problem 6 have values?
      (List as many as apply.)

      ○ I   ○ II   ○ III   ○ IV

   b. In what quadrants does the graph in the middle (Graph B) in problem 6 have values?
      (List as many as apply.)

      ○ I   ○ II   ○ III   ○ IV

1. **Intercepts**

    a. If $W(F) = -3F + 6$, find $W(0)$.

    b. If $W(F) = 3F$, find $W(0)$.

    c. Graph both $W(F) = -3F + 6$ and $W(F) = 3F$ on a single graph **without using a calculator**. Use graphing paper, as you need to accurately draw the lines (you will be answering questions based on them) rather than just the general shape.

    d. Do the output values you found for 1a and 1b match any of the vertical coordinates of any of the intercepts shown on the graph in 1c?

       O yes   O no

       If you answered yes, why do you think that is? _____

    e. Solve $W(F) = -3F + 6$ for when the *output* — that is, $W(F)$ — is 0. What is the value of F that gives an output of 0?

    f. What is the value of F that gives an output of 0 for $W(F) = 3F$?
       Hint: Solve $W = 3F$ for when $W(F)$ is 0.

    g. Look back at the graph from 1c. Do your answers to 1e and 1f match the horizontal coordinates of any of the horizontal coordinates of any of the intercepts shown on the graph?

       O yes   O no

       If you answered yes, why do you think that is? _____

    h. Find the *y*-intercept of $f(x) = x^2 + 6x + 20$.
       Hint: The *y*-intercept is the point at which the line or curve intersects the *y*-axis, which occurs when $x = 0$. Your answer should be listed as an ordered pair (i.e., (x, y)).

2. **Asymptote**

    a. At what x value would the asymptote(s) of $y = \dfrac{3}{x}$ be?

    b. What are the values that x cannot equal in the function $f(x) = \dfrac{2}{x^2 - 4}$? Your answer should be in the format of $x \notin \{$____, ____$\}$, except there should be values where the ___ are. Note that you're really specifying the domain of the function.

    c. At what x value would the asymptote(s) of $g(x) = \dfrac{4}{x - 2}$ be?

3. **Minimum and Maximum Values** – Below is a computer graph of an audio signal as a function of time (this is the type of signal music-editing software show). Show your parent/ teacher where the global maximum and global minimum are.

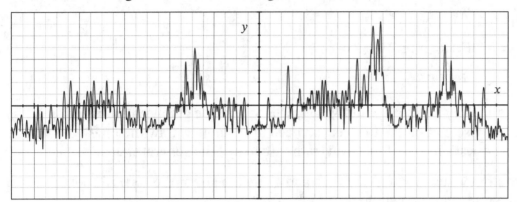

4. **Applying Algebra** – Suppose you are on a boat and start at a place 8 miles from your dock. You continue heading away from the dock. You are traveling at a speed of $5 \frac{mi}{hr}$.

   a. Describe the distance you go as a function of time going forward; consider time 0 as your starting time. Remember to include the fact that you are already 8 mi from the dock when you start.

   b. Graph the function you wrote in 4a on a calculator (you do not need to draw the shape). What is the *y*-intercept of the function? What does the *y*-intercept tell you?

   y-intercept = _____

   Meaning:_____

We've covered a lot of terms so far in this chapter. Use the "Functions – Key Attributes" in Lesson 7.9, which highlights them in outline form, to help you keep track of them. Make flashcards for terms you don't know, or find another way to study these terms until you feel comfortable with them.

Reminder on Graphing: *Unless specifically told to, you do not have to draw the graphs you are asked to find on a calculator. And if you do draw them, you're only expected to draw the general shape in your notebook without worrying about scale, unless otherwise specified.*

1. **Convexity**

   a. Graph $y_1(v) = \frac{1}{2}v^2 + 2v + 6$ on a calculator. Is the function concave down or concave up?

      ○ concave down (∧)   ○ concave up (∨)

   b. What is the y-intercept of the function in 1a?

   c. Graph $y_2(v) = -\frac{1}{2}v^2 + 2v + 6$ on a calculator. Is the function concave down or concave up?

      ○ concave down (∧)   ○ concave up (∨)

   d. What are the x-intercepts of the function in 1c?

   e. At what point is the maximum value of the function in 1c (list both the horizontal and vertical coordinates)?

   f. Which graph — 1a or 1c — looks more like the motion of something thrown into the air that falls back down due to gravity?

   g. Using the function in 1c, find $y_2(3)$.

2. **Even and Odd**

   a. Graph $f(x) = 7x$ on a calculator. Is it even or odd or neither?

      ○ odd   ○ even   ○ neither

   b. Graph $f(x) = 7x^2$. Is it even or odd or neither?

      ○ odd   ○ even   ○ neither

   c. Were the graphs in 1a and 1c even or odd or neither?

      ○ odd   ○ even   ○ neither

d. Use what you know about even and odd functions to finish graphing $f(x) = 2x^2 + 3$ by drawing what the rest of the shape would look like in your notebook..

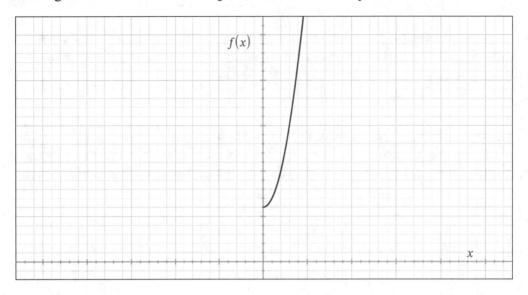

3. **Skill Sharpening** – Distribute the multiplication on the right side of the function:

$$g(x) = (x + 6)(x - 3)$$

4. **More Skill Sharpening** – (This problem is adapted from one in an ancient Babylonian tablet, as shared in *Matrix Algebra for Beginners, Part 1*[1].) There are two fields whose total area is 1,800 square yards. One produces grain at the rate of 2 bushels per 3 square yards while the other produces grain at the rate of a bushel per 2 square yards. If the total yield is 1,100 bushels, what is the size of each field?

Hint: Start by writing down 2 equations, where the unknowns are the size of each field.

Size of field that produces grain at a rate of $\dfrac{2 \text{ bu}}{3 \text{ yd}^2}$ = _____

Size of field that produces grain at a rate of $\dfrac{1 \text{ bu}}{2 \text{ yd}^2}$ = _____

1   Jeremy Gunawardena, *Matrix Algebra for Beginners, Part 1* (Cambridge, MA: Harvard Medical School, 2006), p. 2, http://vcp.med.harvard.edu/papers/matrices-1.pdf and http://vcp.med.harvard.edu/teaching.html.

1. **Operations with Functions** – Perform the requested operations. Be sure to simplify as much as possible. Remember, all you're doing is basic substitution and then simplifying.

   Example: Find $f(x) + g(x)$, if $f(x) = 2x$ and $g(x) = 8x$

   Answer: $f(x) + g(x) = 2x + 8x = 10x$

   a. Find $f(x) + g(x)$, if $f(x) = 5x$ and $g(x) = \frac{1}{2}x - 9$.

   b. Find $f(x)g(x)$, if $f(x) = 3x$ and $g(x) = \frac{3}{x^2}$.

   c. Find $\frac{y(x)}{z(x)}$, if $y(x) = 3x$ and $z(x) = \frac{3}{x^2}$.

   d. Find $a_c(v) - a_{c2}(v)$, if $a_c(v) = \frac{v^2}{20}$ and $a_{c2}(v) = \frac{v^2}{5}$.

   Example Meaning: Subtracting one centripetal acceleration (the kind you get when the motion is in a circle) from another.

1. **Operations with Functions** – Be sure to simplify your answers.

   a. $y(x) + z(x)$, if $y(x) = ax^7$ and $z(x) = \dfrac{3a}{x^{-7}}$

   b. $f(x)g(x)$ if $f(x) = \dfrac{1}{2}x$ and $g(x) = -3x$

   c. Graph $f(x)g(x)$ and $g(x)$ from problem 1b on a single graph using a calculator. How did the shape of $g(x)$ change when it was multiplied by $f(x)$?

   d. At what points do $f(x)g(x)$ and $g(x)$ intercept?
      Hint: Simply look at the graph from 1c and find the point(s).

   Key Observation: *When we combine functions by adding, subtracting, multiplying, or dividing them, their shape may change, as we then have a new function.*

2. **Applying Algebra** – Let's say that a stock's value as a function of time for the last 5 years can be approximated by $v_1(t) = \dfrac{t}{\$19} + \$100$. Another stock's growth as a function of time for the last 5 years can be approximated by $v_2(t) = \dfrac{t}{\$50} + \$150$. t is measured in days, and $t = 0$ corresponds to today.

   a. If you've owned both these stocks for the last 5 years, write a function to show the total value of them both as a function of time. Your answer should still contain a fraction.

   b. Can we use these functions to figure out the stocks' value 6 years ago?

      ◯ yes   ◯ no

      Explain your answer: _____

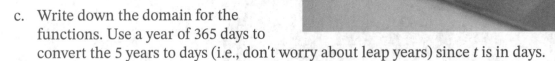

   c. Write down the domain for the functions. Use a year of 365 days to convert the 5 years to days (i.e., don't worry about leap years) since t is in days.

   d. Use a calculator to graph the functions of both of the individual stocks over time. What are the y-intercepts of the functions?

      y-intercepts: _____ and _____

   e. What are the x-intercepts or roots (if any) of the functions you graphed in 2d? Note that while the calculator will still graph them (unless you change the domain on your calculator), you should ignore any values for these functions that are not in the domain.

      x-intercept(s) in domain (if any): _____

f. If the stocks' value continue to grow at the same rate (which is a big assumption!), will there ever be a time in the next 10 years when the 2 stocks will have the same value?

g. Are the functions even, odd, or neither?

    ○ odd   ○ even   ○ neither

h. Find $v_1(10\,\text{yr})$. Round to the nearest cent.

    $v_1(10\,\text{yr}) = $ _____

    Hint: Convert 10 yr to days first, as the t in the function represents days.

i. What does $v_1(10\,\text{yr})$ tell you about how the stocks' value will have changed 5 years from now if this relationship continues?

3. **More Skill Sharpening** – Suppose you have a book reselling business. One time, you sell 5 fiction, 3 nonfiction, and 2 children's books for $51.50 total. Another time, you sell 4 fiction, 6 nonfiction, and 2 children's books for $62 total. Yet another time, you sell 3 fiction books and take back a return of 2 nonfiction books (i.e., –2 books) for a total of $3.50 (that is, you gained $3.50, even after the refund). Find the average price for which you've sold fiction, nonfiction, and children's books. You can use any method you like.
    Hint: If you use a matrix, remember when setting up the equation to include the fact that you sold 0 children's books the 3rd time — you must have each unknown listed in each equation for the matrix to work.

    average fiction price = _____

    average nonfiction price = _____

    average children's book price = _____

Term Review – *Review the "Functions – Key Attributes" section at the end of Chapter 7 (Lesson 7.9) in the vocabulary in the* Student Textbook.

1. **Composite Functions** – Find these composite functions. Be sure to simplify.

   Example: Find $g(f(x))$ if $g(x) = \dfrac{1}{2x}$ and $f(x) = 3x$.

   Answer: $g(f(x)) = \dfrac{1}{2(f(x))}$ (We used the output of $f(x)$ as the input to the function $g(x)$.)

   $g(3x) = \dfrac{1}{2(3x)} = \dfrac{1}{6x}$ (We inserted the value of $f(x)$ and simplified.)

   a. Find $g(f(x))$ if $g(a) = 15a$ and $f(x) = 5x$.

   b. Find $g(f(x))$ if $g(x) = x^2$ and $f(x) = \dfrac{1}{2}x$.

1. **Composite Functions** – Be sure to simplify the final equations.

   Example: Find $g(f(x))$ if $g(x) = \dfrac{1}{2x}$ and $f(x) = 3x$.

   Answer: $g(f(x)) = \dfrac{1}{2(f(x))}$ (We used the output of $f(x)$ as the input to the function $g(x)$.)

   $g(3x) = \dfrac{1}{2(3x)} = \dfrac{1}{6x}$ (We inserted value of $f(x)$ and simplified.)

   a. Find $g(f(x))$ if $g(x) = x^{-2} + 5$ and $f(x) = \dfrac{1}{x^2}$.

   b. Look carefully at $g(f(x))$ and $f(x)$ from problem 1a. What was the domain of $f(x)$ and what was the domain of $g(f(x))$? The first part is given to you, but be sure to include the entire domain as your answer (including the $x \neq$ and $x \in$).
   Hint: Remember that we assume a function's domain is the set of all real numbers unless something in the problem or application limits it.

   In $f(x) : x \neq$ _____

   In $g(f(x)) : x \in$ _____

   When we find a composite function, the domain can sometimes change! Be careful to keep the application context of a problem in mind, though. Sometimes you will need to still keep the old domain, as other values won't make sense for that application.

   c. Find $g(f(y))$ if $g(x) = 2x^2$ and $f(y) = 3y$.

2. **Applying Algebra: Bonuses** – Be sure to simplify as much as you can. Leave off the units of measure.

   a. Let's say that you make \$15 an hour. Finish writing your salary as a function of the number of hours you work (h).

   $s(h) =$ _____

   b. Let's say that you earned a bonus of 30% of your salary. Finish writing a function showing your bonus as a function of your salary.

   $b(s) =$ _____

   c. Finish rewriting the functions from 2a and 2b into 1 composite function that shows your bonus as a function of the hours you worked.

   $b(s(h)) =$ _____

d. Let's say that you have to pay taxes on the bonus at a rate of 10% of your bonus, or $t(b) = 0.1b$. Finish compositing this function with $b(s(h))$ to find your taxes as a function of the hours you work.
Hint: Yes, we can take composites of composite functions! Just view $b(s(h))$ as the input to $t(b)$.

$t(b(s(h))) =$ _____

e. Now let's say that you want to find the total you made, including the bonus and your salary. Add $s(h)$ and $b(s(h))$ to find this.

f. Graph the function you finished writing in 2a on a calculator to answer and list the x-intercept.

g. Given the scenario the function describes, what does the x-intercept tell you about your salary and the hours you work?

h. Suppose that due to personal reasons and your boss's needs, you can only work either 15, 20, or 40 hours. Using them as the domain, calculate what the range will be (i.e., what are the outputs for those hours) and finish filling out the table for the function $b(s(h))$ that you composited back on 2c to find the bonus for each option.

Domain (i.e., inputs)	Range (i.e., outputs)
15	
20	
40	

3. **Applying Algebra: Hot Air Balloons**

a. As we've already seen back on Worksheet 7.1B, the buoyancy force of a balloon (F_B) can be looked at as a *function of* the density (ρ) like this: $F_B(\rho) = (\rho_a - \rho)Vg$. The gravity force is $F_g = mg$. The net force on the balloon as a function of ρ will be $F_{net}(\rho) = F_B(\rho) - F_g$. (We subtract F_g because that force is pulling down, while the buoyancy force is pulling up.)

Plug in the values for $F_B(\rho)$ and F_g into $F_{net}(\rho) = F_B(\rho) - F_g$ and simplify.

b. Substitute the values for ρ and ρ_a into the equation you simplified in 3a given that $\rho(T) = \dfrac{P}{RT}$ and $\rho_a(T_a) = \dfrac{P}{RT_a}$ to finish writing $F_{net}(\rho(T))$.

Note that this final equation is really a function showing the total force on the balloon as a function of the temperature; we've put $\rho(T)$ as the input to show this.

$F_{net}(\rho(T)) =$ _____

4. **Applying Algebra: Planetary Motion**[1]

   a. One of the equations[2] Johannes Kepler discovered to describe the consistent way God keeps planets orbiting is this one: $T^2 = \left(\dfrac{4\pi^2}{GM}\right)r^3$. Solve this equation for T.

   b. Rewrite the equation you solved for T in 4a to show T as a function of r. Basically, just use function notation and use only the positive solution of the square root so that it is a function (plus, the time of a period should be positive — it doesn't take negative time to travel around the sun).

   c. Let's say that $\dfrac{4\pi^2}{GM} = x$. We'd then have this function: $T(r) = \sqrt{xr^3}$. If we scale this by $\sqrt{\dfrac{1}{x}}$ (making each value on the graph $\sqrt{\dfrac{1}{x}}$ of the actual value), we'd have

   $T(r) = \sqrt{xr^3\left(\dfrac{1}{x}\right)} = \sqrt{r^3}$, which we could rewrite as $T(r) = r^{\frac{3}{2}}$. Graph $T(r) = r^{\frac{3}{2}}$ on a calculator and draw the general shape in your notebook. Note that your graph shows the general shape of the relationship between T and r but is scaled so the values are not the actual values.

   Note that the function in 3c is neither odd nor even because the square root function, which is what the 2 in the fractional exponent $r^{\frac{3}{2}}$ shows, can only be positive. Thus there are no negative output values!

   d. The distance between Mercury and the sun (r) is approximately 36 million miles. If we divide that value by the distance between the earth and the sun (approximately 93 million miles) to look at its relative distance, we get approximately 0.3870967742. Given the formula $T(r) = r^{\frac{3}{2}}$, find $T(0.3870967742)$.

   e. Mercury orbits the sun in about 88 earth days. Divide this by 365.25 (the days in a year) to see what portion of a year it takes.

   portion of a year Mercury takes to orbit the sun $\approx$ _____

   Compare your result with your answer to 4d. What do you notice?

   _____

---

1   Values for Mercury from NASA, "Planet Mercury," https://solarsystem.nasa.gov/planets/mercury/ (accessed 10/29/19); values for Neptune based on NASA Science, "Neptune: The Windiest Planet," https://solarsystem.nasa.gov/planets/neptune/ (accessed 10/29/19)

2   If you're curious, T represents "the period of the motion," G the gravitational constant $6.67 \times 10^{-11}\dfrac{m^3}{kg \cdot s^2}$, M the mass around which the planet is orbiting, and r the distance between the planet and the mass it is orbiting. T is the time it takes to complete an orbit (i.e., the length of a year for that planet). David Halliday, Robert Resnick, and Jearl Walker, *Fundamentals of Physics*, 7th ed. (USA: John Wiley & Sons, 2005), p. 343-344.

f. The distance between Neptune and the sun (r) is approximately 2,795 million miles. If we divide that value by the distance between the earth and the sun to look at its relative distance, we get 30.05376344. Given the formula $T(r) = r^{\frac{3}{2}}$, find $T(30.05376344)$.

g. Neptune orbits the sun in approximately 60,190 days. Divide this by 365.25 (the days in a year) to see how many years it takes.

Years Neptune takes to orbit the sun $\approx$ _____

Compare your result with your answer to 3f. What do you notice?

_____

You just explored what is known as Kepler's Third Law, which "many consider . . . to be one of the most elegant results in all of astronomy."[3] This law describes how the speed at which a planet orbits the sun is always consistently related to the distance away from the sun it is! Planets don't orbit at random speeds; instead, there's order and design that can be described mathematically. We see evidence of order and design throughout the heavens.

"I had the intention of becoming a theologian . . . but now I see how God is, by my endeavors, also glorified in astronomy, for 'the heavens declare the glory of God.'" – Johannes Kepler[4]

3 Johannes Kepler and the Door to Science, "Kepler's Harmonices Mundi," https://www.keplersdiscovery.com/Harmonies.html

4 Johannes Kepler, *Conversation with Galileo's Sidereal Messenger*; as cited in Clifford Pickover, *Archimedes to Hawking: Laws of Science and the Great Minds Behind Them* (New York: Oxford University Press, 2008), p. 7.

1. **Finding the Inverse** – Find the inverse of these functions. Give your answer in function notation, using the same letters as the original functions.

   Example: $F(a) = 10a$

   Answer: $a(F) = \dfrac{F}{10}$

   a. $y(x) = 8x$

   b. $s(t) = \dfrac{d}{t}$

   Hint: t is the input, so we want to make t the output. We know that d is a constant, since function notation makes it clear what our input and output are! You might recognize this as $speed = \dfrac{distance}{time}$, where we're viewing distance as the constant and speed as dependent on time (which it could be for a rocket, for instance, as it changes its speed over time).

   c. $P(I) = VI$

   Hint: I is the input, so that means we're looking at V as a constant.

2. **Checking Your Work** – Go back to the inverses you found in 1a, 1b, and 1c and show how you can check your work.

   a.

   b.

   c.

3. **Rewriting the Functions** – Rewrite each original function in problems 1a–1c *and* each inverse you found in those problems following the convention to use x for the input and f for the output, with f^{-1} differentiating the inverse function.

   Example: $F(a) = 10a$ and $a(F) = \dfrac{F}{10}$ get rewritten as $f(x) = 10x$ and $f^{-1}(x) = \dfrac{x}{10}$

   a.

   b.

   c.

4. **More with Inverses** – Find the requested inverses. If the inverse is not a function, write "not a function" as your answer. Write your answer using the convention of x standing for the input.

   a. Find $f^{-1}(x)$ if $f(x) = -\dfrac{1}{2}x$.

   b. Find $f^{-1}(x)$ if $f(x) = 2x + 6$.

   c. Find $f^{-1}(x)$ if $f(x) = 10x^2$.

1. **Finding the Inverse** – Find the inverse of these functions. Give your answer in function notation, using the same letters as the original functions.

   a. $W(m) = adm$ (work as a function of mass (m); a stands for acceleration, and d for distance displaced, which we're viewing as constants)

   b. $f(x) = 5x + 10$

   c. Draw the inverse of the function shown on graphing paper.

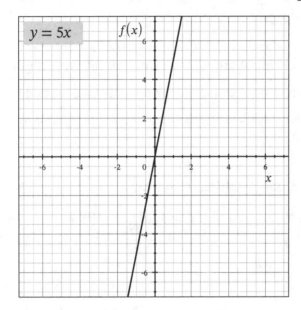

2. **Checking Your Work** – Go back to the inverses you found in 1a and 1b and show how you can check your work.

   a.

   b.

3. **Rewriting the Functions** – Rewrite each original function from problems 1a and 1b *and* each inverse you found following the convention to use x for the input and f for the output, with f^{-1} differentiating the inverse function.

   a.

   b.

4. **More with Inverses** – Find the requested inverses. If the inverse is not a function, write "not a function." Write your answer using the convention of x standing for the input.

   a. Find $f^{-1}(x)$ if $f(x) = \dfrac{x}{8} + 3$.

   b. Find $f^{-1}(x)$ if $f(x) = 10x$.

   c. Find $f^{-1}(x)$ if $f(x) = x^2 + 2$.

5. **Finding the Ranges**

   a. Find the range of $f(x) = 5x + 10$. Your answer should start "$f(x) \in$."
      Hint: The range of the function is what the output could be . . . which you can find by finding the inverse, and then looking at the inverse's domain. So just find the domain of the inverse you found in 1b, as this is the same function you worked with there! If there's no limitations, then the domain is all real numbers.

   b. In the function $y(x) = \dfrac{1}{x} + 2$, what can the range not include? Your answer should start "$y \neq$."
      Hint: To find this, rewrite without function notation and solve the equation for x. You'll see that there is a specific value the output cannot be. The range is any value *but* that one.

6. **Applying Algebra** – Let's say a ball's vertical trajectory through the air can be described by this function: $y(t) = -\dfrac{9.8(t^2)}{2} + 5t$, where $y(t)$ is the vertical position of the ball in air and the initial velocity upwards is $5\,\dfrac{\text{m}}{\text{s}}$ (we omitted the units in the equation for simplicity).

   a. Graph the function on a calculator; is the curve of $y(t) = -\dfrac{9.8(t^2)}{2} + 5t$ concave up or concave down?

      ○ concave down (∩)   ○ concave up (∪)

   b. Looking at the graph, what is the domain of $y(t) = -\dfrac{9.8(t^2)}{2} + 5t$, given that any negative position (i.e., output) is unphysical since that means the ball goes into the ground? Rewrite the part that's given you so as to express the entire domain in your answer.

      $t \geq$ _____ ∩ $t \leq$ _____

   c. Is the function in 6a an even or odd function . . . or neither?

      ○ even   ○ odd   ○ neither

   d. Looking at the graph, what are the x-intercepts of the function in 6a?

7. **Skill Sharpening** – Perform the requested operations. Be sure to simplify.

   a. $\dfrac{f(x)}{g(x)}$, if $f(x) = \dfrac{2 + 2x}{4x^2}$ and $g(x) = \dfrac{1}{x^2} - 2$

   b. $g(f(x))$ if $g(x) = 17x$ and $f(x) = x^3 x^{-2} y^{-1} y$

   c. $g(f(x))$ if $g(x) = 3x^2$ and $f(x) = 2x$

8. **More Skill Sharpening and Applying Algebra** – Let's say one train travels for 5 hours at an average speed of s_1; it then travels at a slower average speed, s_2, due to having more stops, for another 3 hours. Altogether, it covers 500 miles. On another route, a train travels with an average speed of s_1 for 2 hours, and then travels at the slower speed of s_2 for an hour, traversing a total of 190 miles. What is s_1 and s_2?

Hint: Leave the units off when solving. The speed will be in $\frac{\text{mi}}{\text{hr}}$.

$s_1 = $ _____

$s_2 = $ _____

Study Suggestion: Look at "Functions – Key Attributes" in Lesson 7.9 of the Student Textbook *to help review.*

1. **Exploring Functions**

   a. Rewrite $a = \dfrac{y}{x}$ to show that y is a *function of x*.

   b. Show the domain of the function $f(x) = \dfrac{a}{x}$. Your answer should start "$x \neq$."

   c. Show the range of the function $f(x) = \dfrac{a}{x}$. Your answer should start "$f(x) \neq$."

   d. Is the a in the function in 1a a variable or a constant?

      ○ variable   ○ constant

   e. Graph the function $y(x) = 8x$ without a calculator on graph paper. Be sure to label your axes and make sure you have accurately described the function.

   f. If $f(x) = \dfrac{a}{x}$, find $f^{-1}(x)$ or explain that the inverse is not a function.

   g. If $f(x) = 3x^2$, find $f^{-1}(x)$ or explain that the inverse is not a function.

   h. If $f(x) = -x$, find $f^{-1}(x)$ or explain that the inverse is not a function.

2. **More Exploring Functions** – Use a graphing calculator to graph the function $y = \dfrac{2}{x}$.

   a. In what 2 quadrants does the function have values?

      ○ I   ○ II   ○ III   ○ IV

   b. At what value(s) of x is/are the vertical asymptote(s)?

      $x =$_____

   c. Is the function even, odd, or neither?

      ○ even   ○ odd   ○ neither

3. **Even More Exploring Functions** – Use a graphing calculator to graph the function $f(x) = x^2 + 2x - 3$.

   a. What are the x-intercept(s) — that is, the point(s) at which the output is 0?

   b. Is the function concave up or concave down?

      ○ concave down (∧)   ○ concave up (∨)

4. **Functioning with Functions** – For these problems, $y(x) = 2x^2$ and $z(x) = 6x^{-2}$.

   a. Find $y(x) + z(x)$.

   b. Find $\dfrac{y(x)}{z(x)}$.

   c. Find $y(z(x))$.

5. **More Functioning with Functions** – For these problems, $f(x) = 2x^2 + 3$ and $g(x) = 3x^2$.

   a. Find $f(x)g(x)$.

   b. Find $g(x) - f(x)$.

   c. Find $f(g(x))$.

6. **Algebra Applied – Marathon Donation** – Suppose an organization offers to donate to a charity for each runner who completes a marathon; the donation will be \$5,000 divided by the number of minutes it took them to complete the marathon. The runner's time depends on their average speed, as the distance is a set 42.195 kilometers.

   a. Set up a function showing how the donation depends on the time (in minutes).

   b. Set up a function showing how the time depends on the average speed.
     Hint: Distance equals speed multiplied by time.

   c. Set up a composite function showing the donation as a function of the runner's average speed — that is, how the donation depends on the speed. Note that for this function to hold true, the speed must be given in km per minute, since minutes are the unit of time used in the function written in 6a.

   d. Use your answer to 6c to find the donation amount if the runner runs at an average speed of $0.2 \dfrac{\text{km}}{\text{min}}$. Round to the nearest cent.

1. **Term Time** – Are these expressions polynomials? Answer yes or no. Treat all letters as variables.

   a. a^{-3} ○ Yes ○ No

   b. $\dfrac{4x}{3} + 2$ ○ Yes ○ No

   c. $\dfrac{7x^2}{x} + 3$ ○ Yes ○ No

   d. $2x$ ○ Yes ○ No

   e. $7b^{\frac{3}{2}} + b$ ○ Yes ○ No

2. **Categorizing Polynomials** – Name each polynomial function by the highest degree (1st, 2nd, 3rd, etc.) to which the input is raised.
   Hint: Be sure to simplify first.

   a. $f(x) = x^7$

   b. $f(s) = 4s^2 + 3^3 s$

   c. $g(t) = \dfrac{5t^5}{t} + \dfrac{1}{2}t^2$

   d. $f(x) = 7x^4 + 3x^3 + 1$

3. **More Categorizing Polynomials** – Go back and categorize the polynomials in problems 2a–2d based on the number of terms each has.

   a. ○ monomial ○ binomial ○ trinomial

   b. ○ monomial ○ binomial ○ trinomial

   c. ○ monomial ○ binomial ○ trinomial

   d. ○ monomial ○ binomial ○ trinomial

4. **Even, Odd, or Neither** – Go back and identify if the functions in problems 2a–2d were even, odd, or neither.

   a. ○ Even ○ Odd ○ Neither

   b. ○ Even ○ Odd ○ Neither

   c. ○ Even ○ Odd ○ Neither

   d. ○ Even ○ Odd ○ Neither

5. **Graphing** – Go back and graph the functions in problems 2a–2d on a calculator, sketching their general shape in your notebook.

Look carefully at how the graphs in problems 5a–5d look. For the even functions, you should see that the graph mirrors itself across the y-axis — that's because every output is the same for both positive and negative inputs. For the odd functions, you should see that the output is the same, only the sign is different. For those functions that are neither odd nor even, the graph looks different (even if slightly) for positive and negative inputs; this is because the positive and negative inputs don't yield the same outputs.

6. **Putting Odd and Even to Work** – Using your knowledge about odd and even and what the box above explained, finish these graphs on graph paper. Do not use a graphing calculator.

   a. $y = x^2 + 5$ b. $f(x) = x^8 + 6x^2$

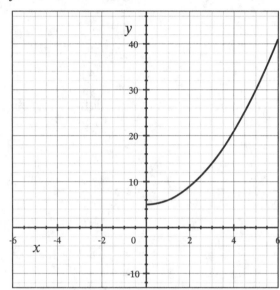   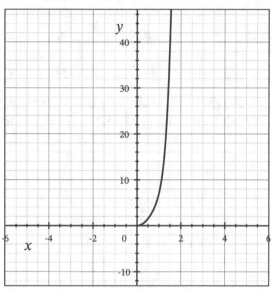

   c. $f(x) = 2x^3 + x$

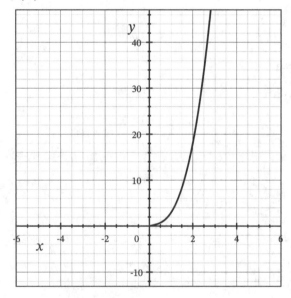

7. **Skill Sharpening** – What are the *x*-intercepts of the function shown?
   Hint: Remember, the *x*-axis refers to the horizontal axis, regardless of its label.

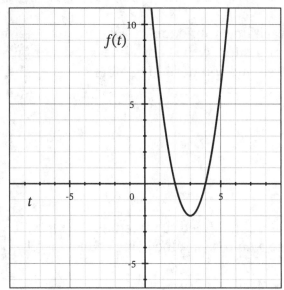

Make flashcards for any terms from Lesson 8.1 you did not already know.

1. **Identifying Linear Functions** – Rewrite each linear function in slope-intercept form: $f(x) = mx + b$. If the function is not a linear function, write "not a linear function." For this exercise, write the values of $m = 1$ and $b = 0$ should you need to in order to match the form $f(x) = mx + b$.

   Hint: Remember to simplify first!

   Example: $y = 3\left(\dfrac{1}{4}\right)x$

   Answer: $y(x) = \dfrac{3}{4}x + 0$

   (Notice that we rewrote in function notation, simplified so there was just *one* value being multiplied by x, and added a zero so there would be a value being added, thereby having the same structure as the slope-intercept form.)

   a. $y(x) = \dfrac{4x}{2}$

   b. $t = \dfrac{4}{d}$, where t is a function of d

   c. $y(x) = \dfrac{1}{4}8x + \dfrac{2}{3} + \dfrac{1}{3}$

   d. $d = \dfrac{s}{2} + 13$, where d is a function of s

2. **Identifying m** – Knowing that the general form of a linear function is $f(x) = mx + b$, identify what the value of m, the slope, is for each function.

   a. $f(t) = t + 3$

   b. $f(x) = -2x - 4$

   c. $f(a) = \dfrac{1}{2}a$

3. **Identifying b** – Knowing that the general form of a linear function is $f(x) = mx + b$, identify what the value of b is for each function.

   a. $f(t) = t + 3$

   b. $f(x) = -2x - 4$

   c. $f(a) = \dfrac{1}{2}a$

4. **Connecting with Graphing** – Given the value of b you found in 3a–3c and knowing that value is the vertical coordinate of the y-intercept, write the y-intercepts of each of the functions given in 3a–3c. For example, if b in the equation was 10, then the y-intercept would be at (0, 10).

   a.

   b.

   c.

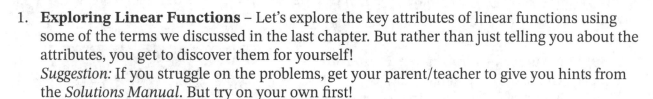

1. **Exploring Linear Functions** – Let's explore the key attributes of linear functions using some of the terms we discussed in the last chapter. But rather than just telling you about the attributes, you get to discover them for yourself!

   Suggestion: If you struggle on the problems, get your parent/teacher to give you hints from the *Solutions Manual.* But try on your own first!

   a. Look carefully at $f(x) = mx + b$. Assuming there are no restraints due to the application in a specific problem, identify the correct statement about the domain of all linear functions. Answer this question by thinking through various values x could be (negative, 0, positive). Would any cause us to divide by 0 or perform an invalid operation? If not, then the domain is all real numbers.

      A. The domain is all real numbers (i.e., $x \in \mathbb{R}$).   B. There is a value x cannot be.

      ○ A   ○ B

   b. Solve $f(x) = mx + b$ for x in order to find the range of the function. (Replace $f(x)$ with y or some other letter before you start solving to avoid confusion.)

   c. Again, assuming there are no restraints due to the application in a specific problem, identify the correct statement about the range of all linear functions. Answer the question by looking at your answer to 1b and thinking through if there are any values y could not be.

      A. The range is all real numbers (i.e., $y \in \mathbb{R}$).   B. There is a value y cannot be.

      ○ A   ○ B

   d. Look at the equation you solved for x in 1b. Note that was really the *inverse* of the function. Is the inverse also a linear function?

      ○ Yes   ○ No

      Hint: If you're not sure, plug in any values for b and m and graph it on a calculator. Does it produce a straight line?

   e. If you needed to know what your velocity (your output) would be when the time (your input) equals 0, if you knew 2 different values of your time and your velocity (i.e., (t_1, v_1) and (t_2, v_2)) and that the general form of the relationship is $v(F) = \dfrac{F}{m}t + v_0$, which is a linear function, what formula would you use?

      Hint: Think back to what different intercepts tell you and how you can find the desired one if you know 2 points on the line.

   f. Identify if $d(t) = 5t$ is even, odd, or neither.

      ○ Even   ○ Odd   ○ Neither

   g. Identify if $d(t) = 5t + 5$ is even, odd, or neither.

      ○ Even   ○ Odd   ○ Neither

Some linear functions are odd and others are neither even nor odd. It depends on if there is a constant being added. Remember, the constants are considered to be even powers, since we could multiply them by x^0 (or whatever the input/independent variable is raised to the 0th power), a value worth 1, without changing the value.

2. **Applying Algebra – Finding the Function** – Suppose you're doing research and receive data that results in the following graph, where each dot represents the average yearly high temperature (measured in °F) for various locations in the world and at a given distance measured from the equator (the absolute distance measured in km). Notice how the data points almost form a straight line.

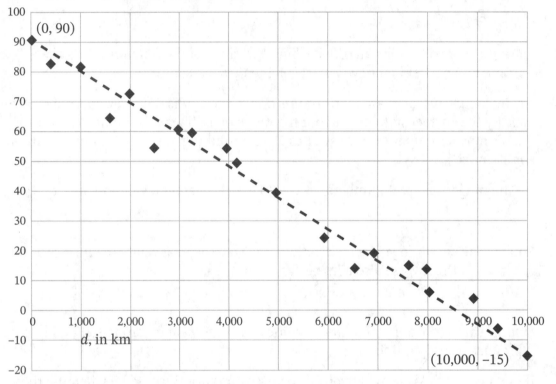

T(°F)   **Average Yearly High Temperature vs. Distance from Equator**

While the actual math behind determining the line that best describes the data (called the line of best fit) is beyond the scope of this course, let's say it was the dashed line shown. The problems below will help you find the equation that describes it, thereby writing an approximation of how the temperature varies with distance. You may ignore units.

a. Find the slope of the line. Leave your answer as a fraction.

    slope = _____

b. Find the *y*-intercept of the line. Note that the vertical coordinate there is really the average yearly high temperature at the equator (based on this hypothetical data), as it's the value when *d*, the distance from the equator, is 0.

    y-intercept = _____

c. Write a function describing the line. Use function notation (use T to represent the average yearly high temperature and d the distance from the equator). Specify the domain. Part of it is given for you, but you should include that part in your answer as well.

$T(d) = $ _____ where _____ $\leq d \leq$ _____

Hint: The notation being used to specify the domain here is hopefully one you've seen before. We're using one inequality symbol to show what d is greater than or equal to *and* one to show what it is less than or equal to.

d. Find the approximate value of d where the line intersects the x-axis (i.e., find the horizontal coordinate of the x-intercept). You'll have just found the approximate distance from the equator at which the average yearly high is 0, given the hypothetical data on the chart.

$d \approx$ _____

Hint: Use your answers to the previous 2 problems. The x-intercept happens when the vertical coordinate is 0 . . . that is, when the output is 0. So write the function of the line, set the output for 0, and solve for d to find the input that yields an output of 0.

When using a function to approximate data like this, it's important to note that we don't know if the function will hold true in the future too. We're not describing a real-life consistency God created and sustains; instead, we're just approximating data for a specific domain.

3. **Skill Sharpening**

a. Graph the function $f(x) = 2x$ on graph paper; do not use a calculator. Make sure you label your graph and have it accurately represent the function.

b. If $f(x) = 4x^{-1}x^3$ and $g(t) = 4t + \frac{1}{4}$, find $g(f(x))$.

c. If $f(x) = 4x^{-1}x^3$ and $g(x) = 4x + \frac{1}{4}$, find $g(x)f(x)$. Do not factor out any common factors.

Be sure to review the flashcards you made on Worksheet 8.1!

1. **Identifying Values** – For each function, list what the value of a, b, and c are. Remember that a in the generalized form $f(x) = ax^2 + bx + c$ stands for the coefficient of the input squared, b for the coefficient of the input, and c for the constant added.

   a. $f(t) = -3t^2 + 6t - 3$

   $a =$ _____ $b =$ _____ $c =$ _____

   b. $f(d) = 4d^2 - d + 2$

   $a =$ _____ $b =$ _____ $c =$ _____

   c. $f(x) = \dfrac{1}{2}x^2 - x$

   $a =$ _____ $b =$ _____ $c =$ _____

2. **Minimums and Maximums** – Calculate the input (i.e., horizontal coordinate) for the minimum/maximum for the functions given using the knowledge that $x_{min|max} = -\dfrac{b}{2a}$. **Show how you used the formula to find the answer.** Give your answer in decimal notation.

   a. $f(x) = -3x^2 + 3x + 18$

   b. $f(x) = x^2 + x - 4$

   c. $f(t) = -t^2 - 5t$

   d. $f(x) = x^2 - 4$

   Hint: We could rewrite this as $f(x) = x^2 + 0x - 4$.

3. **More Minimums and Maximums** – Use your answers to problems 2a–2d to calculate the output (i.e., the vertical coordinate) of the minimum/maximum point for each of the functions in problem 2. Give your answer in decimal notation.

   a.

   b.

   c.

   d.

4. **Checking Your Work** – Check your answers by graphing the functions in problems 2a–2d on a calculator. Did your answers correspond with the coordinates of the minimum or maximum point? Draw the general graphs and label the minimum or maximum point. For example, if the minimum or maximum occurs with an input of 1 and an output of 0, you'd write (1, 0) at that point on the graph.

1. **Minimums and Maximums with the Vertex Form** – Find the minimum or maximum point of these quadratic functions that are written in vertex form: $f(x) = a(x-h)^2 + k$.

   a. $f(x) = 3(x-2)^2 + 5$

   b. $f(t) = -2(x+3)^2 - 4$

   c. $f(x) = 4(x+8)^2 - 3$

2. **Writing a Quadratic from the Graph** – Given the minimum/maximum point and one other point on these parabolas, use the vertex form of the quadratic, $f(x) = a(x-h)^2 + k$, to write the function of the curve. Use $f(x)$ for the output and x for the input.

   a.
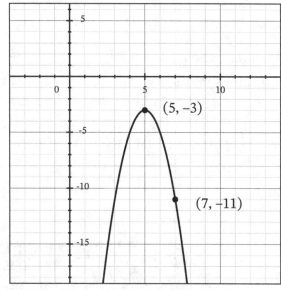

   b.
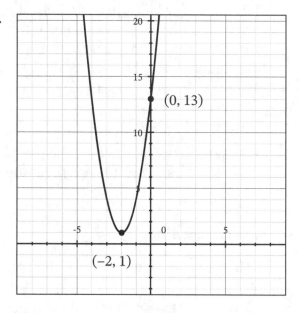

3. **Applying Algebra** – Let's say we were to throw a ball into the air starting at a height of 6 ft at a vertical velocity (think speed) of $5 \frac{m}{s}$. Because of the consistent way God causes gravity to work, that ball's vertical position (y) as a function of time (t) can be expressed by this function: $y(t) = -4.9t^2 + 5t + 6$.

   a. Graph the function and draw the general shape in your notebook.

   b. After how many seconds will the ball reach its maximum height?

   $t_{max} \approx$ _____ seconds

   c. What is the maximum height (in meters) the ball will reach?

   $\approx$ _____ meters

4. **More Applying Algebra** – Say again that we were to throw a ball into the air. Only this time, we don't know our starting velocity. We do know that we threw the ball at a vertical height of 3 meters at a time of 0 seconds. We also know the ball reached a maximum height of 8 meters after 5 seconds. Since we know that the ball's vertical position as a function of time is a quadratic relationship, write the function describing that relationship.

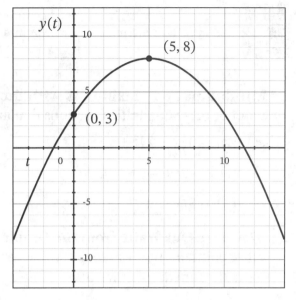

5. **Even More Applying Algebra** – Let's say a business releases a new product. Initially, the sales grow and grow, but then they slowly decline. Let's say the number of products (in thousands of products) sold as a function of time (in months) can be described by this function: $s(t) = -2t^2 + 3t + 9$.

Hint: Graph the function on a calculator to see what is being asked for.

a. After how many months will the product reach its max sales?

t_{max} =_____months

b. What will the max sales of the products be? Keep in mind that each square on the vertical axis represents one thousand products.

$s_{max} \approx$ _____ thousands of products

6. **Skill Sharpening**

a. If $x(y) = \dfrac{20}{y}$ and $g(x) = 4x^2$, find $g(x(y))$.

Example Meaning: Let's say we want to fence a garden so there will be 4 equal-sized square sections and the length of each of the sides depends on how tall we want the fence, as we want the length of the side to equal 20 divided by the height of the fence, or $\dfrac{20}{y}$ (where y represents the height of the fence), because if we make the height less than that, we've found this particular type of fence will get unstable. We also know the total area of the garden will be a function of the length of the sides of the square since the area of any square is the side squared, or x^2. Thus the area of all 4 of the square sections will be $4x^2$, where x represents the length of each side.

b. If $y(x) = \dfrac{4}{x}$ and $g(x) = 2x^3$, find $\dfrac{g(x)}{y(x)}$.

c. Is $x^6 + \dfrac{7}{x}$ a polynomial?

○ Yes   ○ No

Example Meaning: A model equation for the potential energy of an electron in a hypothetical material system when $x > 0$.

d. Looking at the graph, what are the x-intercepts?

_____

What do they tell you? _____

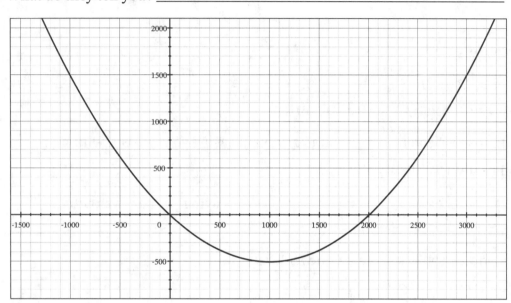

Be sure to review the flashcards you made on Worksheet 8.1!

1. **Complete the Multiplication** – Complete all of the multiplication in these problems.

   a. $(x + 3)^2$

   b. $\left(\dfrac{1}{2}y + 2\right)^2$

   c. $2(x + 3)(x + 5)$

   d. $(3x - 2)^2$

   e. $3(x + 2)(x - 3)$

   f. $5(2x + 2)(4x + 3)$

2. **More with Functions and Multiplication**

   a. If $y(x) = \dfrac{3}{x} + 2$ and $g(x) = 3x^2$, find $g(y(x))$, leaving your answer with no multiplication left to distribute.

   b. If $y(x) = \dfrac{3}{x} + 2$ and $g(x) = 3x^2$, find $g(x)y(x)$, leaving your answer with no multiplication left to distribute.

   c. The quadratic expression you wrote in 2b is:

   ○ Even   ○ Odd   ○ Neither

   d. What does your answer to 2c tell you?

3. **Identifying the Degree Review** – Name each polynomial function by the highest degree (1st, 2nd, 3rd, etc.) to which the input is raised. *Hint:* Be sure to simplify first.

   a. $y(x) = x^6 + 5a^2x^4 + 3$

   b. $f(t) = t^7 + a^9t^4 + t^3 + 5$, where a is a constant

   c. $s(t) = 3t^{10} + \dfrac{1}{2}t$

   d. $3x^2 + 2x + \dfrac{1}{2}$

   e. $\dfrac{2x^3}{x} + 3x + 2$

4. **More Applying Algebra: Working with Quadratics**

   a. Find the maximum height and the time at which the ball reaches that height of a ball that is thrown vertically if the function describing it is this: $y(t) = -4.9t^2 + 10t + 5$.

   Time at which ball reaches maximum height $\approx$ _____

   Maximum height $\approx$ _____

Suppose the starting point of a ball's vertical position (y) as a function of time (t) is a height of 5 feet at a time of 0 seconds and its maximum vertical height occurs at 10 seconds and is 20 feet. Given that this is a quadratic relationship, write a function for $y(t)$.

Hint: You've been told the maximum coordinates, along with one other point. You know the y is the vertical coordinate and the t the horizontal as you're finding y as a function of t. That is enough to write out the function using vertex form, which we discussed in the last lesson.

5. **Applying Algebra – Finding the Function** – Let's say that you are trying to buy ground beef. You've been buying it online somewhere that charges you a fixed price per pound, plus a fixed shipping charge on all orders. But you can't remember exactly what that shipping charge or price per pound was. You do remember that you bought 3 pounds for $15 (including shipping) and 5 pounds for $21 (including shipping). Figure out the function describing the total cost based on the number of pounds purchased. The questions below will help you.

a. Write down the 2 data points you've been given. Remember that we want a function where the total cost varies based on the number of pounds purchased.

   (_____) and (_____)

b. Use the formula $slope = \dfrac{y_2 - y_1}{x_2 - x_1}$ to calculate the slope based on the 2 data points in 5a.

c. Use the formula $y\text{-intercept} = \dfrac{y_1 x_2 - y_2 x_1}{x_2 - x_1}$ to calculate the y-intercept based on the 2 data points in 5a.

d. Write the function describing the relationship between the total cost and the number of pounds purchased. Part of it is given to help you, but write the entire function as your answer.

   $T(p) = \underline{\quad} p + \underline{\quad\quad}$

e. What does the slope in the function you wrote in 5d represent?

f. Thinking back to the information given you at the beginning of problem 5, what does the vertical coordinate of the y-intercept in the function you wrote in 5d represent?

g. Suppose you see that they only sell ground beef in either 1, 5, or 10 lb bags. Given that as the domain, finish filling out this table to show both the range and the domain.

Domain (i.e., inputs)	Range (i.e., outputs)
1 lb	
5 lb	
10 lb	

Be sure to review your flashcards!

1. **Term Time** – For each expression, list *all of these words* (polynomial, monomial, binomial, and/or trinomial) that describe it. **Many expressions can be described by more than one word!** For example, any binomial or trinomial is also a polynomial.

   a. $5x$

   b. $\dfrac{5}{x}$

   c. $2x + 3$

   d. $x^3 + x + 2$

2. **More Term Time** – For each expression, list *all of the words* from the words listed that describe it. **Many expressions can be described by more than one word!** For example, a first-degree polynomial and a linear function are 2 different ways of describing the same type of function.

Linear Function	First-Degree Polynomial	Fourth-Degree Polynomial
Quadratic Function	Second-Degree Polynomial	Fifth-Degree Polynomial
Cubic Function	Third-Degree Polynomial	

   a. $y = 5x$

   b. $f(x) = x^4 + 3x^2$

   c. $y(x) = x^5 + 3$

   d. $y = x^2 + 2x + 3$

   e. $f(x) = x^3 + x + 2$

   f. $f(x) = x^2 + 2$

3. **Odd and Even** – Look back at the functions in 2a–2f and identify if each one is odd or even or neither.

   a. 2a was:

      ○ Even   ○ Odd   ○ Neither

   b. 2b was:

      ○ Even   ○ Odd   ○ Neither

   c. 2c was:

      ○ Even   ○ Odd   ○ Neither

   d. 2d was:

      ○ Even   ○ Odd   ○ Neither

e. 2e was:

   ○ Even   ○ Odd   ○ Neither

f. 2f was:

   ○ Even   ○ Odd   ○ Neither

4. **Exploring Functions**

   a. Say that you know that the force on an object is a linear function of acceleration or $F(a) = ma + b$, where m is the slope and b is the vertical coordinate of the y-intercept. You've been able to measure the force and the acceleration of an object at 2 points: $(4, 20)$ and $(5, 25)$. Write the equation that would describe this function. Your equation should start "$F(a) = .$"

   b. It turns out that the slope in the equation you found in 4a is the mass of the object. What is the mass (m) of the object described in 4a?

   c. Say that the object was thrown from a height of 30 m above the ground at a vertical velocity (think speed) of $15\frac{m}{s}$. Because of the consistent way God governs all things, its vertical position (y) can be described as a function of time (t) like this: $-4.9t^2 + 15t + 30$. After how many seconds does the object reach its maximum height?

   d. What is the maximum height the object in 4c reaches?

   e. Write the function that describes the parabola shown.

   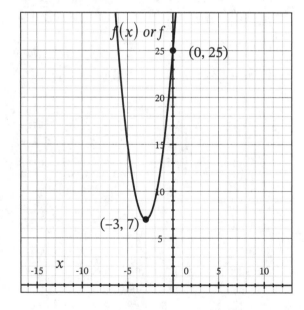

5. **Applying the Distributive Property** – Distribute the multiplication.

   a. $-2(x + 3)(x - 4)$

   b. $(x + 3)^2$

6. **Skill Sharpening**

   a. Find $p(d(x))$ if $d(x) = 2x$ and $p(x) = 4x^3 + x^2 + 2$.

      Example Meaning: The price of a product increases with the demand x according to $p(x)$, and the demand $d(x)$ doubles.

   b. Find $p(x) + s(x)$ if $s(x) = 2x$ and $p(x) = 4x^3 + x^2 + 2x$.

      Example Meaning: The price of a product increases with demand x according to $p(x)$ and the prices of another product increases with demand x according to $s(x)$. You want to know the total price of both products as a function of demand x.

Study Note: *The quiz and upcoming test will give you any formulas needed from this chapter — you do not need to memorize the various formulas covered in the chapter; however, you'll need to know how to accurately apply those formulas . . . as well as know the terms (polynomial, quadratic, odd, even, etc.) reviewed on this worksheet.*

1. **Solving More In-depth Problems** (Chapter 5)

   a. Solve for x: $\dfrac{2}{5}x - \dfrac{1}{2} = -13$

   b. Solve for x and simplify as much as possible: $\dfrac{x}{2} = \dfrac{3(2y - y)}{2} + \dfrac{1}{2}y$

   c. Simplify by factoring out common factors: $5xy^3 - 10xy - 15y$

   d. Simplify: $x(7 - 2y + 3z) - y(2 - 2x - z) + 5(3z - x)$

   e. Solve for x: $\dfrac{\frac{1}{4}x}{3 + y} = 20$

2. **Solving Systems of Equations** (Chapter 6) – At a candy store, one girl bought 2 suckers, 1 chocolate, and 3 lollypops for $2.90; another bought 1 sucker, 5 chocolates, and 2 lollypops for $4.40; and another bought 3 suckers, *returned* 2 chocolates, and bought 5 lollypops for $2.50. What was the price of a sucker, of a chocolate, and of a lollypop?

   a. Write 3 equations in 3 unknowns to describe this situation.

   b. What was the price of a sucker?

   c. What was the price of a chocolate?

   d. What was the price of a lollypop?

   e. Solve:

   $3x + y = 2$

   $\dfrac{1}{2}x + \dfrac{1}{2}y = 0$

   $x = $ _____ $y = $ _____

3. **Functions**

   a. Is the graph below of a function or not? (Lesson 7.1)

      ○ Yes   ○ No

      How do you know? _____

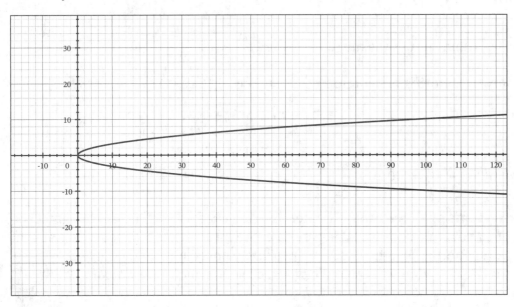

   b. In $f(t) = -4.8t^2 + 5t - 5$, what is the independent variable? (Lesson 7.1)

   c. Graph the function from 3b and draw its general shape in your notebook. (Lesson 7.3)

   d. Which does the function in 3b have: (Lesson 7.4)

      ○ a minimum point   ○ a maximum point

   e. Find $f(10)$ using the function in 3b. (Lesson 7.2)

      $f(10) =$ _____

   f. What is the inverse of the function $y(x) = 7x + 5$? (Lesson 7.7)

   g. For the function $y(x) = 2x$, finish completing the table showing the outputs for the inputs given. (Lesson 7.2)

Domain (i.e., inputs)	Range (i.e., outputs)
1	
2	
3	

   h. Given the domain and range shown below, is this a function? (Lesson 7.2)

      ○ Yes   ○ No

Domain (i.e., inputs)	Range (i.e., outputs)
2	8
5	1, 2

i. Given the domain and range shown above in 3h, is the *inverse* of the relation a function? (Lesson 7.7)

   ○ Yes   ○ No

j. If $g(x) = 2x$ and $h(x) = 5x$, find $g(x)h(x)$. (Lesson 7.5)

k. If $g(x) = 7x$ and $h(t) = 3t$, find $h(g(x))$. (Lesson 7.6)

4. **Applying Functions** (Lessons 7.5 and 7.6)

   Note: All values are completely hypothetical! In fact, as we'll explain in the box below, this scenario is included to help you see how math can give us faulty information if we use faulty assumptions.

   a. Say you've found a function to describe how many grams of sugar you intake for each meal as a function of your hourly salary in dollars. The functions are below.

   breakfast: $b_g(s) = s^2 + 4$

   lunch: $l_g(s) = 8s + 90$

   dinner: $d_g(s) = 4s + 5$

   Write a single function, $t_g(s)$, describing the total grams of sugar you intake for the day as a function of your hourly salary.

   b. Now suppose that your weight gain is dependent on the total calories you consume, and for that particular day it would be according to the function $w(x) = 4(4x - 2{,}000)$, as you burned 2,000 calories, each gram of sugar yields 4 calories, and you gain 4 ounces per calorie not burned. Use the function you wrote in 4a as the *input* to this function to find $w\big(t_g(s)\big)$, which would hypothetically be your weight gain for that day as a function of your hourly salary.

   Now, it's rather unlikely that the grams of sugar you intake is really connected with your salary! This is an example of how valid math can yield faulty results if we start with faulty assumptions. When you hear people say they've mathematically "proven" things that don't sound right, always stop and check the assumptions.

5. **Polynomial Functions**

   a. Is $5x + \dfrac{8}{x}$ a polynomial expression? (Lesson 8.1)

      ○ Yes ○ No

   b. Use the formula $x_{\text{min|max}} = -\dfrac{b}{2a}$ to find the value of x at the minimum or maximum in the function $f(x) = 3x^2 + 18x + 24$. (Lesson 8.3)

      $x_{\text{min|max}} =$ _____

   c. Use your result from 5b to find the output at the minimum or maximum in the function $f(x) = 3x^2 + 18x + 24$. (Lesson 8.3)

      $f(x_{\text{min|max}}) =$ _____

   d. Find the value of x at the minimum/maximum in the function $f(x) = -2(x+6)^2 - 4$. (Lesson 8.3)

      $x_{\text{min|max}} =$ _____

   e. Find the value of $f(x)$ at the minimum/maximum in the function $f(x) = -2(x+6)^2 - 4$. (Lesson 8.3)

      $f(x_{\text{min|max}}) =$ _____

   f. Distribute the multiplication: $a(b+c)(b+d)$ (Lesson 8.4)

   g. Distribute the multiplication: $(t-3)^2$

   h. The following is a _____ -degree polynomial:
      $f(x) = a^7x^6 + x^4$ (Lesson 8.1)

   i. The function in 5h was (Lesson 8.1)

      ○ Even ○ Odd ○ Neither

6. **Applying Polynomial Functions** – Say you know that after 5 seconds, a deer running away from the road at a constant speed is 21 meters away from the side of the road. 5 seconds later, so 10 total seconds since starting to track the distance of the deer, the deer was 36 meters away from the side of the road. View distance as a function of time, $d(s) = st + d_{\text{start}}$. Find the distance from the road that the deer started running, given that the deer started running at 0 seconds. (Lesson 8.2)

1. **Recognizing Quadratic Functions** – Are these functions quadratic?
   Hint: Complete the multiplication if needed to see if the highest power of x is 2.

   a. $f(x) = 2(x + 3)(x - 1)$

      ○ Yes   ○ No

   b. $f(x) = 2x(x + 3)(x - 1)$

      ○ Yes   ○ No

   c. $f(x) = (x + 2)(x - 2)$

      ○ Yes   ○ No

   d. $f(x) = 3(x + 5)^2 - 6$

      ○ Yes   ○ No

2. **Identifying the Roots** – Identify the roots of these functions. Remember, the roots are the input value(s) that will yield an output of 0. Check yourself by graphing on a graphing calculator.

   > *Example:* $y(t) = 2(t + 6)(t - 3)$

   > *Answer:* $t = -6$ and $t = 3$

   a. $y(t) = 3(t + 5)(t - 3)$

   b. $g(x) = -2(x - 2)(x + 3)$

3. **Expressing Quadratics from a Graph** – Finish writing the functions that are graphed. Note that even though there are no points labeled, you should be able to tell the x-intercepts and at least one other point by looking at the graph.

   a.

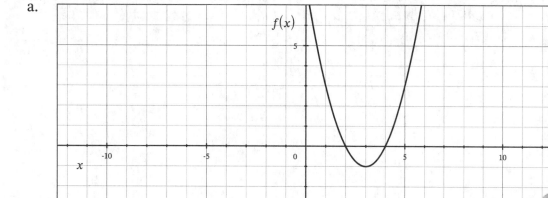

b.

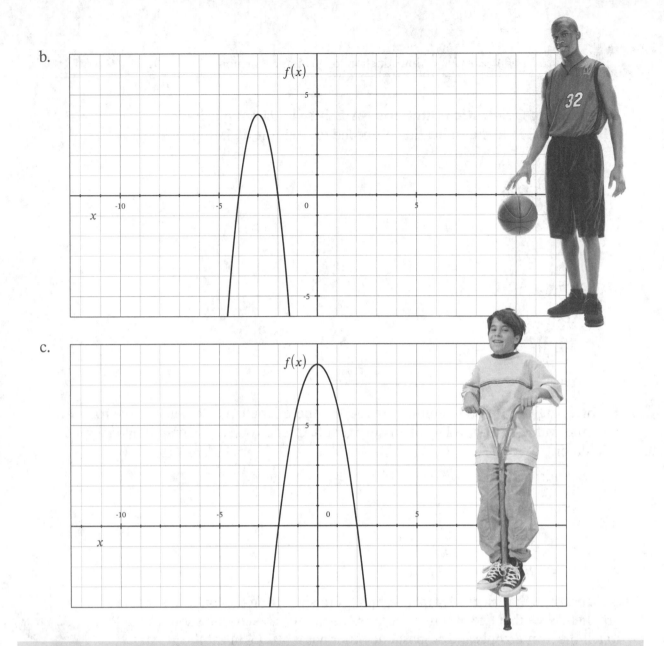

c.

Notice that the pictures give you an idea of what the functions could be representing (a. the path of a yo-yo, b. a basketball being in the air, c. the path of a kid on a pogo stick). Quadratics help us describe real-life situations!

1. **Exploring Quadratic Functions** – Let's explore the key attributes of quadratic functions using some of the terms we discussed in the last chapter. Once again, you'll get to discover these attributes yourself. *Suggestion:* Walk through these problems with your parent/teacher/classmate.

   a. Look carefully at $f(x) = ax^2 + bx + c$. Assuming there are no constraints due to the application, is the domain all real numbers or is there a value x cannot equal? Answer this question by thinking through various values x could be (negative, 0, positive). Would any cause us to divide by 0 or perform an invalid operation? If not, then the domain is all real numbers.

      A. All real numbers, or $x \in \mathbb{R}$ B. There is a value x cannot equal.

      ○ A   ○ B

   b. Write the range (i.e., the possible vertical coordinates) of $f(x) = 8x^2 + 2x + 3$. Your answer should be in the form of $f(x)$ _____ $\cap f(x) \in \mathbb{R}$, except with the blank part filled in.
      Hint: Graph the function and look at what the minimum or maximum is. The range will be all real numbers *greater than or equal to* ($\geq$) the vertical coordinate at the minimum or, if there's a maximum instead, less than or equal to ($\leq$) the vertical coordinate at the maximum.

   c. Was the function in 1b concave up or concave down?

      ○ Concave up   ○ Concave down

   d. Graph $f(x) = -8x^2 + 2x + 3$ on a calculator. Write the range (i.e., the possible vertical coordinates). Your answer should be in the form of $f(x)$ _____ $\cap f(x) \in \mathbb{R}$, except with the blank part filled in.
      Hint: See the hint for 1b.

   e. Was the function in 1d concave up or concave down?

      ○ Concave up   ○ Concave down

   f. Compare $f(x) = 8x^2 + 2x + 3$ (the function from 1b) and $f(x) = -8x^2 + 2x + 3$ (the function from 1d). What is different about the two functions?

      _____

   g. What does that one difference you found in 1f make to the graph of the functions $f(x) = 8x^2 + 2x + 3$ (the function from 1b) and $f(x) = -8x^2 + 2x + 3$ (the function from 1d) (i.e., what is the one thing different about the graph of the two functions)?

      _____

   h. If you needed to figure out what input values would make the output of a quadratic function 0, what would you find?

      _____

i. Graph $f(x) = 4x^2 + 2x + 3$ on a calculator and list the y-intercept.

j. Graph $f(x) = 4x^2 + 2x + 6$ on a calculator and list the y-intercept.

k. Graph $f(x) = 4x^2 + 2x + 10$ on a calculator and list the y-intercept.

l. Looking at your answers to 1i–1k, what value in the general form $f(x) = ax^2 + bx + c$ does the vertical coordinate of the y-intercept seem to match?

_____

Why do you think that is? _____

m. Is $f(t) = t^2 + 25$ even, odd, or neither?

   O Even   O Odd   O Neither

n. Is $f(t) = t^2 + 5t + 25$ even, odd, or neither?

   O Even   O Odd   O Neither

o. Find an inverse relationship of the simple quadratic $f(x) = x^2$.
   Hint: Replace $f(x)$ with y and then solve for x to find the inverse.

p. Is this inverse relationship you found in 1o a function?

   O Yes   O No

2. **Exploring and Manually Graphing Quadratics** – Use the function $h(x) = (x - 2)(x - 4)$ for these problems.

a. Find the roots.
   Hint: Think through what value for x would make each expression in parentheses equal 0.

b. Write the x-intercepts of the function.
   Hint: Use the roots you found in 2a as the horizontal coordinates, and remember that the vertical coordinate will be 0, since the x-intercept is on the x-axis.

c. Use the distributive property to distribute the multiplication to get the equation in the form of $f(x) = ax^2 + bx + c$ to find the value of a and b.

   $a =$ _____ $b =$ _____

d. Calculate the horizontal coordinate (i.e., the input) at the minimum or maximum.

   $x_{min|max} =$ _____

e. Using the input you calculated in 5c, calculate the vertical coordinate (i.e., the output) at the minimum or maximum (i.e., find $h(x_{min|max})$).

   $h(x_{min|max}) =$ _____

f. Graph the x-intercepts and the minimum or maximum point you've found on graph paper and connect them into a parabola. Watch that you accurately show the function and not just the general shape.

3. **Exploring and Manually Graphing Quadratics** – Use the function $f(t) = (t+3)(t-4)$ for these problems.

   a. Find the roots.
   Hint: Think through what value for t would make each expression in parentheses equal 0.

   b. Write the x-intercepts of the function.
   Hint: Use the roots you found in 3a as the horizontal coordinates, and remember that the vertical coordinate will be 0, since the x-intercept is on the x-axis.

   c. Use the distributive property to distribute the multiplication to get the equation in the form of $f(x) = ax^2 + bx + c$ (though in this case the input variable is t) so you know the value of a and b.

   $a =$ _____ $b =$ _____

   d. Calculate the horizontal coordinate (i.e., the input) at the minimum or maximum.

   $t_{\text{min|max}} =$ _____

   e. Using the input you calculated in 3c, calculate the vertical coordinate (i.e., the output) at the minimum or maximum.

   $f\left(t_{\text{min|max}}\right) =$ _____

   f. Use graphing paper to graph the x-intercepts and the minimum or maximum point you've found and connect them into a parabola. Watch that you accurately show the function and not just the general shape.

4. **Applying Algebra – A Pendulum Swinging**

   Notice that a pendulum swings with a path that looks parabolic (it is technically semi-circular, but for small angle swings we can approximate it as a parabola). We can thus use a quadratic function to approximately describe the vertical position of the pendulum as a function of its horizontal position.

   Let's say we had a pendulum swinging in front of a wall. On that wall, we drew a straight vertical line and a horizontal line, viewing the intersection as point 0 and counting off distances in both directions.

   a. If the pendulum followed the formula $y(x) = \dfrac{1}{16}(x+2)(x-6)$, at what two points does it cross the horizontal line?

b. List the function that describes the path of the pendulum shown below. Do not use a graphing calculator.

Hint: Look at which function has roots that match the horizontal coordinates of the *x*-intercepts on the graph.

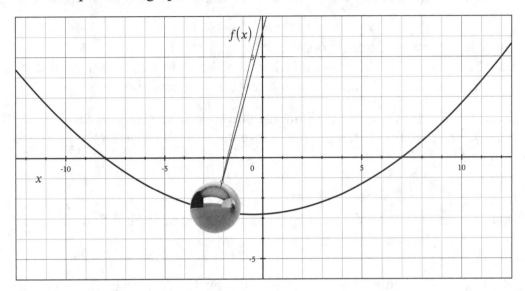

A. $y(x) = \dfrac{1}{16}(x+7)(x-7)$

B. $y(x) = \dfrac{1}{20}(x+8)(x-7)$

C. $y(x) = \dfrac{1}{20}(x-2.5)(x+11)$

○ A   ○ B   ○ C

Take some time to look back over the Chapter Synopses from Chapters 7 and 8. We'll be continuing to build on those concepts in the upcoming lessons.

1. **Factoring Quadratic Functions** – Factor the right side of these quadratic functions by hand. **Do not use a graphing calculator.**

   Example: $f(x) = x^2 - 2x - 8$

   Answer: $f(x) = (x + 2)(x - 4)$

   a. $f(x) = x^2 - x - 6$

   b. $g(x) = x^2 + 2x - 8$

   c. $y(t) = t^2 + 7t + 10$

   d. $f(a) = a^2 + 17a + 16$

2. **Finding the Roots** – Looking at the factored equations from problems 1a–1d, identify the roots of each. Remember, the roots are the values of x that yield an output of 0.

   Example: $f(x) = (x + 2)(x - 4)$

   Answer: $x = -2$ and $x = 4$

   (If x were either -2 or 4, the output would be 0, as $(-2 + 2) = 0$ and $(4 - 4) = 0$ . . . and if either expression in parentheses is 0, the entire expression on the right is 0, giving an output of 0.)

   a.

   b.

   c.

   d.

1. **Factoring Quadratic Functions** – Factor the right side of these quadratic functions by hand. **Do not use a graphing calculator.**

    Example: $f(x) = x^2 - 2x - 8$

    Answer: $f(x) = (x + 2)(x - 4)$

    a. $f(x) = x^2 + 4x - 12$

    b. $f(x) = x^2 - 4x - 12$

    c. $f(x) = x^2 + 8x + 15$

2. **Finding the Roots** – Looking at the factored functions from problems 1a–1c, identify the x-intercepts/roots of each.

    Example: $f(x) = (x + 2)(x - 4)$

    Answer: $x = -2$ and $x = 4$

    (If x were either -2 or 4, the output would be 0, as $(-2 + 2) = 0$ and $(4 - 4) = 0$ ... and if either expression in parentheses is 0, the entire expression on the right is 0, giving an output of 0.)

    a.

    b.

    c.

3. **Finding the x-intercepts** – Using the roots you found in 2a–2c as the horizontal coordinates, write the x-intercepts of each function.

    Example: $f(x) = (x + 2)(x - 4)$

    Answer: $(-2, 0)$ and $(4, 0)$

    (-2 and 4 were the roots found, and we know the vertical coordinate is 0 at the x-intercept, as it has to be for the point to be on the x-axis.)

    a.

    b.

    c.

4. **Finding the Minimum or Maximum Input** – Find the value of the input at the minimum or maximum for each of the functions in 1a–1c.

    Example: $f(x) = x^2 - 2x - 8$

    Answer: $x_{\text{max}|\text{min}} = -\dfrac{b}{2a} = -\dfrac{-2}{2(1)} = -(-1) = 1$

    a.

    b.

    c.

5. **Finding the Minimum or Maximum Output** – Find the output of the functions in problems 1a–1c for the inputs you calculated at the maximum or minimum value you calculated in problems 4a–4c.

> *Example* (based on example from problem 1, $f(x) = x^2 - 2x - 8$, where we got an $x_{max|min}$ value of 1): $f(1) = 1^2 - 2(1) - 8 = 1 - 2 - 8 = -9$

   a.

   b.

   c.

6. **Graphing the Functions** – Use the x-intercepts you found in problem 3 and the maximum or minimum input (horizontal coordinate) and output (vertical coordinate) you found in problems 4 and 5 to graph each of the functions from problems 1a–1c on graphing paper. Do not use a calculator! **While your curve does not have to be exact, make sure that it goes through the correct x-intercepts and has the correct minimum/maximum.**

> *Example* (based on the example function of $f(x) = x^2 - 2x - 8$):

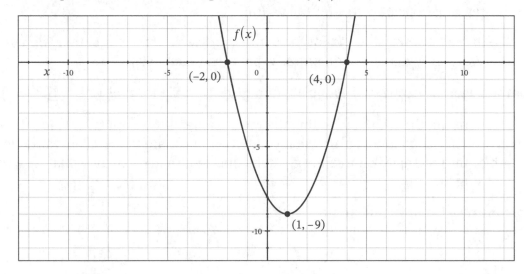

   a. $f(x) = x^2 + 4x - 12$

   b. $f(x) = x^2 - 4x - 12$

   c. $f(x) = x^2 + 8x + 15$

I know you could have used a graphing calculator to graph these equations much easier. The point of doing it yourself a few times, though, is to make sure you really understand how to interpret the graph! Otherwise, you won't be able to use the graph to really help you solve real-life problems. You're also learning some problem-solving skills along the way.

7.  **Applying Algebra** – The perimeter of a
rectangular field is 14 km and its area is 10 km².
Find its length and its width (i.e., the dimensions
of its sides — list the longer dimension as the
length and the shorter as the width). Know that the
perimeter of a rectangle equals 2 times its length
plus 2 times its width, or $P = 2l + 2w$, while the area
equals its length times its width, or $A = lw$.

    width = _____

    length = _____

If you need help breaking this problem down, the following steps can help you.

- Write out two equations — one for the perimeter and one for the area. You will have two
unknowns, the length (l) and the width (w).
Hint: Since both dimensions are given to you in km and km², you can safely ignore units
to make the problem easier to solve. Make sure to put the correct unit back in your final
answer.

    Perimeter equation: _____

    Area equation: _____

- Solve the area equation you wrote for the width.

- Substitute the value you just found for the width into the perimeter equation you wrote
and rearrange it until you have a quadratic expression equal to 0.

- Factor the quadratic expression you just found to get it in the form of $(x - r_1)(x - r_2)$.

- Find the length and the width by finding the roots — that is, the inputs at which the
output is 0 — for the quadratic expression you wrote. These are the possible values for
the length of the rectangle. Choose the greater value, and then calculate what the width
would be using that.

8. **Skill Sharpening** – Complete the multiplication.

    a. $(2x + 2)^2$

    b. $2(x + 6)(x - 2)$

1. **Working with Perfect Squares** – Rewrite these in the form of $x^2 + bx + c$.

    Example: $(x + 1)^2$

    Answer: $(x + 1)^2 = (x + 1)(x + 1) = x^2 + 2x + 1$

    a. $(x + 2)^2$

    b. $(x + 4)^2$

    c. $(x - 2)^2$

    d. $(x - 4)^2$

> *Look carefully at the answers you got to problems 1a–1d, all of which were perfect squares. Viewing a as the coefficient of x^2 in your answers, notice that in every case, $a = 1$ — that is, there was no written coefficient in front of x^2. Viewing b as the coefficient of x in your answers and c as the constant added in the general form of $f(x) = ax^2 + bx + c$, notice that $\left(\frac{1}{2}b\right)^2 = c$. Notice also that you could have gone from the form of $f(x) = ax^2 + bx + c$ to the factored version by writing $\left(x + \frac{1}{2}b\right)^2$.*

2. **Identifying Perfect Squares** – Are these quadratic expressions perfect squares? To tell, see if $a = 1$ and $\left(\frac{1}{2}b\right)^2 = c$.

    Example: Is $x^2 + 4x + 4$ a perfect square?

    Yes, as $a = 1$ and $\left(\left(\frac{1}{2}\right)4\right)^2 = 2^2 = 4$, which is the value of c in $x^2 + 4x + 4$.

    a. Is $x^2 + 12x + 36$ a perfect square?

    ○ Yes   ○ No

    b. Is $x^2 + 2x + 6$ a perfect square?

    ○ Yes   ○ No

    c. Is $x^2 + 5x + 6.25$ a perfect square?

    ○ Yes   ○ No

    d. Is $x^2 - 2x + 1$ a perfect square?

    ○ Yes   ○ No

    e. Is $x^2 - 1x + 0.25$ a perfect square?

    ○ Yes   ○ No

3. **Factoring** – Rewrite each of the perfect squares that were in problems 2a–2e in a factored form. If a problem was not a perfect square, write "not a perfect square" and do not factor.

   Example: $x^2 + 4x + 4$

   Answer: $(x + 2)^2$

   a.

   b.

   c.

   d.

   e.

1. **Working with Perfect Squares** – Rewrite these in the form of $x^2 + bx + c$.

    Example: $(x + 1)^2$

    Answer: $(x + 1)^2 = (x + 1)(x + 1) = x^2 + 2x + 1$

    a. $(x + 5)^2$

    b. $(x - 10)^2$

    c. $(x - 1)^2$

    d. ◎ **Challenge Problem:** Are perfect squares odd functions, even functions, or neither?

       ○ Even   ○ Odd   ○ Neither

    e. Graph the perfect squares above from 1a, 1b, and 1c on a calculator and answer the question: how many times do the curves touch the x-axis (i.e., how many real distinct roots do these perfect squares have)?

    _____

2. **Identifying Perfect Squares** – Are these problems perfect squares? To tell, see if $a = 1$ and $\left(\dfrac{1}{2}b\right)^2 = c$.

    a. Is $x^2 + 3x + 2.25$ a perfect square?

       ○ Yes   ○ No

    b. Is $x^2 + 8x + 16$ a perfect square?

       ○ Yes   ○ No

    c. Is $x^2 + 9x + 81$ a perfect square?

       ○ Yes   ○ No

    d. Is $x^2 - 4x + 4$ a perfect square?

       ○ Yes   ○ No

    e. Is $x^2 - 6x + 9$ a perfect square?

       ○ Yes   ○ No

3. **Factoring** – Factor each of the expressions in problems 2a–2e that was a perfect square. If a problem was not a perfect square, write "not a perfect square."

    a.

    b.

    c.

    d.

    e.

4. **Applying Algebra** – Let's say we know that the average price of a certain stock grows with time with the following relationship, where t is measured in months and the output is in dollars: $P(t) = t^2 + 12t + 36$.

   a. Rewrite the function in a factored form.

   b. At what time(s) was/will the price (the output) be 0?

5. **Recognizing the Function** – Identify the function that describes the quadratic shown. Do not use a graphing calculator.

   Hint: Find the x-intercepts as well as at what value the minimum/maximum occurs at on the graph. Then see which function produces those same x-intercepts and minimum/maximum. (Look at the roots of the function to find the horizontal coordinate of the x-intercepts — that is, the input that yields an output of 0.)

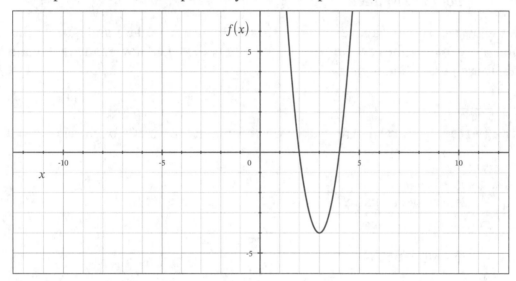

   ○ $f(x) = x^2 - 6x + 8$

   ○ $f(x) = 4(x^2 - 6x + 8)$

6. **Skill Sharpening** – If $f(x) = 2x$ and $g(x) = (x + 2)(x - 3)$, find the following and simplify.

   a. $f(x)g(x)$

   Example Meaning: You're building a storage bin to hold water, and the height of the bin needs to be two times the distance x, where x needs to be 2 units longer for the length of the bin and 3 units shorter for the width of the bin, and you need to calculate the volume contained in the bin.

   b. $g(f(x))$

   Example Meaning: The amount of money you pay or get paid is the number of hours you work minus 3 times the number of hours you work plus 2, and you want to see how that amount is in terms of half hours (so you convert your input of hours to half hours, knowing 1 hour = 2 half hours).

1. **Working with Perfect Squares** – Solve for x by taking the square root of both sides. Notice that the right-hand sides are perfect squares. **Remember to list all possible values for x.**

   a. $y = (x + 2)^2$, when $y = 16$.

   b. $f(x) = (x - 4)^2$, when $f(x) = 25$.

   c. $v^2 = (x + 3)^2$, where v^2 equals 49.

   Example Meaning: If the velocity of a car equals $49 \dfrac{\text{mi}}{\text{hr}}$, and that amount equals some unknown plus 3, all squared, what is that unknown?

2. **Using the Quadratic Formula** – Use the quadratic formula, $x = \dfrac{-b \pm \sqrt{b^2 - 4ac}}{2a}$, to find the approximate roots (i.e., the x values that will make the expression equal 0) of these quadratic expressions rounded to the third decimal place.

   a. $4x^2 + 3x - 6$

   b. $-5x^2 + 8x + 10$

   c. $-2x^2 + 4x + 6$

If you have not already memorized the quadratic formula, you need to! Make a flashcard or use whatever memorization method works for you. You will be required to know it on future quizzes and tests. You may want to look online for quadratic formula songs to help you.

1. **Working with Perfect Squares** – Solve for x. **Remember to list all potential values for x.**

    a. Solve for x when $y = 100$: $y = (x + 2)^2$

    b. Solve for x when $f(x)$ is 4: $f(x) = (x - 3)^2$

2. **Completing the Square** – The following problems will walk you through completing the square to find the roots and rewrite the function $f(x) = 2x^2 + 2x - 12$ in the form $f(x) = a(x - r_1)(x - r_2)$.

    a. Replace $f(x)$ in $f(x) = 2x^2 + 2x - 12$ with a 0. That way, you can solve for the values x has to be to yield an output of 0.

    b. Add or subtract as needed to both sides of the equation to get the terms with x on a side by themselves.

    c. Divide both sides by the same amount to get the coefficient of x^2 to be 1.

    d. Add the same amount to both sides to make the right side a perfect square.

    Hint: Figure out how to do this by calculating $\left(\frac{1}{2}b\right)^2$. Your result is the amount you need to add to both sides.

    e. Factor the right side; it should now be in the form of $\left(x + \frac{1}{2}b\right)^2$.

    f. Take the square root of both sides, making sure to put a $\pm$ where appropriate.

    g. Solve for both the roots by solving for when the $\pm$ sign is a + sign and when it is a – sign.

    h. Rewrite the function in the form of $f(x) = a(x - r_1)(x - r_2)$. You know what a is by looking at the original function. Find r_1 and r_2 by inserting the roots you found in 2g for r_1 and r_2.

    i. Check that the function you found equals the original function by multiplying and distributing out the three terms in your final expression. Show your work.

3. **Finding the Roots Using the Quadratic Formula** – Use the quadratic formula to find the approximate solutions to these equations, rounded to the third decimal point.

    a. $0 = -4.9t^2 + 10t + 50$

    b. $0 = -4.9t^2 + 80t + 100$

    c. $0 = -8t^2 + 40t + 200$

All of these equations could be finding at what points in time an airborne object touches the ground (or whatever height is being considered 0). Quadratic functions are very useful in describing parabolic motion. Notice also that the coefficient of t is consistently −4.9; this is because it's based on the acceleration of gravity on the earth. The last example is based on a hypothetical different planet with different gravity.

4. **Applying the Roots: Rewriting the Expressions** – Use your answers to 3a–3c to help you rewrite these functions in the form $f(x) = a(x - r_1)(x - r_2)$. Note that the right side of these functions are the same as the right side of the equations in 3a–3c. Remember, a is the coefficient of the input squared, and r_1 and r_2 are the roots you found in problems 3a–3c. The input is t instead of x.

a. $f(t) = -4.9t^2 + 10t + 50$

b. $f(t) = -4.9t^2 + 80t + 100$

c. $f(t) = -8t^2 + 40t + 200$

5. 📖 **Applying Algebra** – A man proposes to cut 3-in squares out of the four corners of a piece of tin. When the sides are turned up, he wants the resulting box to have a volume of 72 in³. He wants the bottom on the box to have a length 2 inches longer than the width. How long should he cut the piece of tin (i.e., what should the bottom length of the box be)? *Hint:* To keep this problem simple, go ahead and leave off the units of measure. **Just make sure you give any dimensions in inches.**

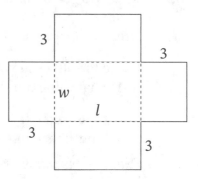

   a. Picture the sides folded up into a box. What will the height of the box be?

   b. Remembering that the volume of a rectangular prism like this equals the length times the width times the height, write an equation expressing what the volume of the finished rectangular prism will be. Insert any values you know. (Your only unknowns should be l for length and w for width).

   c. Using the information given in the description of the problem, write another equation that has l and w as the two unknowns.

   d. Using your answers to 5b and 5c, along with substitution and what you know of quadratics, find the length (l) of the box.

6. **More Applying Algebra** – Because of the consistent way God governs creation, the magnitude of the force on "a satellite in a circular orbit"[1] can be described using this function: $F = \left(\dfrac{m}{r}\right)v^2$.

a. If the mass (m) of the satellite is 4,000 kg, the radius (r) of its orbit is 4,000,000 m (where the radius is measured from the center of the earth), and the force (F) is 900 N, find the value of velocity (v) in $\dfrac{m}{s}$.

Hint: A newton (N) equals kg $\bullet \dfrac{m}{s^2}$.

b. Write a formula for finding the velocity (v) of a satellite based on the force, mass, and radius of its orbit. In other words, solve $F(v) = \left(\dfrac{m}{r}\right)v^2$ for v. Notice that we can use letters to help us generalize about problems, giving us a formula to use instead of having to solve the same problem every time. This is the same idea as what we did in the lesson when we generalized about completing a square in order to find an easier way to find the roots.

Hint: Before you start solving for v, replace $F(v)$ with just F in order to avoid errors.

c. In the formula you wrote in 6b, if we were to look at velocity (v) as a function of mass (m), what value could the domain not include? Your answer should start "$m \neq$."

7. **Skill Sharpening** – If $f(t) = (2t + 3)(t - 2)$ and $g(t) = 4t$, find $g\big(f(t)\big)$. Give your answer where all multiplication has been distributed.

Example Meaning: The area of a field equals its length and width multiplied where the length must be 2 times the height of the posts used plus 3 and the width of the field must be the height of the posts minus 2, and there will be 4 such fields made giving the total area (g).

1   David Halliday, Robert Resnick, and Jearl Walker, *Fundamentals of Physics*, 7th ed. (USA: John Wiley & Sons, 2005), p. 345.

When finding complex roots, list the real portion and then the imaginary portion and leave square roots as simplified as you can, as shown in the example.

1. **Quadratics with Complex Roots** – Use the quadratic equation to find the roots. Your answer may be complex!

   Example: $f(x) = -2x^2 - 4x - 5$

   $$x = \frac{-b \pm \sqrt{b^2 - 4ac}}{2a} = \frac{-(-4) \pm \sqrt{(-4)^2 - 4(-2)(-5)}}{2(-2)} = \frac{4 \pm \sqrt{16 - 40}}{-4}$$

   $$\frac{4 \pm \sqrt{-24}}{-4} = \frac{4 \pm \sqrt{24}\,i}{-4} = \frac{4 \pm \sqrt{4}\sqrt{6}\,i}{-4} = \frac{4 \pm 2\sqrt{6}\,i}{-4} = \frac{2(2 \pm \sqrt{6}\,i)}{-4}$$

   $$\frac{2 \pm \sqrt{6}\,i}{-2} = \frac{2}{-2} \pm \frac{\sqrt{6}\,i}{-2} = -1 \pm \frac{\sqrt{6}\,i}{2}$$

   (Notice that we left the − sign off before the 2 in the final answer; that's because it's redundant due to the ± sign.)

   a. $5x^2 + 3x + 5$

   b. $2x^2 + 5x + 6$

   c. $y(t) = t^2 + 3t + 10$

2. **Working with Complex Roots Reminder** – Simplify as much as possible without a calculator. Look back at Chapter 3 for a reminder if needed.

   Example: $\sqrt{-60} = \sqrt{60}\,i = \sqrt{6}\sqrt{10}\,i = \sqrt{3}\sqrt{2}\sqrt{5}\sqrt{2}\,i = 2\sqrt{15}\,i$

   a. $\sqrt{-40}$

   b. $\sqrt{-48}$

   c. $\sqrt{-90}$

3. ☙ **Applying Algebra** – A builder is looking to make a building with a length such that if you subtract 10 from the length and multiply the remaining amount by the length itself, the product is –27. Is this possible? The following steps will help you answer this question.

   a. Using x to represent the length, start by writing an equation showing the desired relationship.

   b. Distribute the multiplication and rearrange the equation from 3a until you have a quadratic expression on one side and a 0 on the other.

   c. Find the roots of the quadratic equation you wrote in 3b.

d. If the roots you found in 3c are real numbers, then it is possible to have that length. If you got complex roots, it's not possible! Was it possible to make a building with a length such that if you subtract 10 from the length and multiply the remaining amount by the length itself, the product is –27?

○ Yes   ○ No

Complex numbers sometimes show up while we're trying to solve a problem when that problem has no real solution. As Practical Algebra *points out while sharing the problem you just solved, if we're looking for a real-number solution and the only ones we find are complex, it means that there isn't a real-number solution![1]*

4. 📖 **More Applying Algebra** – You want to make a rectangular field where the perimeter is 18 ft and its area is 180 ft². Find its length and its width or if such a rectangle is possible to make. Know that the perimeter of a rectangle equals 2 times its length plus 2 times its width ($P = 2l + 2w$), while the area equals its length times its width ($A = lw$).

a. Start by writing out two equations — one for the perimeter and one for the area. You will have two unknowns, the length and the width.
    Hint: Ignore the units when solving . . . but be sure to add them back at the end.

    Perimeter equation: _____

    Area equation: _____

b. Solve the area equation for the width in terms of the length and plug it into the perimeter equation to solve for the length. As you do, you'll wind up with a quadratic expression equal to 0. Use the quadratic formula to find the roots, which will be the values for the length.

c. Based on the roots (i.e., length values) you found in 4b, can such a rectangle exist?

    ○ Yes   ○ No

5. **Skill Sharpening** – Find $f(x)g(x)$ if $f(x) = 4x$ and $g(x) = (x + 3)(x - 2)$

    Example Meaning: You've found the area of box g equals the length $x + 3$ and width $x - 2$ multiplied together, where x is $\frac{1}{4}$ the height of the box f, and you want to then calculate the total volume of the box.

1   Jos. V. Collins, *Practical Algebra: First Year Course* (New York: American Book Co., 1910), p. 289

When factoring, always keep your answer exact (i.e., don't round any square roots), but simplified. For example, write $\sqrt{20}$ as $2\sqrt{5}$ ($\sqrt{20} = \sqrt{4}\sqrt{5} = 2\sqrt{5}$), but simplify $\sqrt{100}$ to 10. When finding a root, assume an exact answer is wanted unless an approximate answer is asked for. So only simplify as much as you can without rounding (i.e., leave $\sqrt{20}$ as $2\sqrt{5}$) unless you're asked for an approximate answer (in which case, you'd use your calculator to approximate $\sqrt{20}$ as ≈ 4.472). Following this will make your answers easier to grade, as they'll match those in the Solutions Manual.

1. **Working with the Sum & Difference of Two Squares** – Factor these expressions without using the quadratic formula.

    Example: $x^2 - 49$

    Answer: $x^2 - 49 = x^2 - 7^2 = (x + 7)(x - 7)$

    Example: $x^2 + 49$

    Answer: $x^2 + 49 = x^2 + 7^2 = (x + 7i)(x - 7i)$

   a. $x^2 - 36$

   b. $x^2 - 25$

   c. $x^2 - 16$

   d. $x^2 - 1$ *Hint:* Note that the $\sqrt{1}$ is 1, as $1 \cdot 1 = 1$! Thus, this really is a difference of two squares.

   e. ◎ **Challenge Problem:** Are the difference of two squares odd functions, even functions, or neither?

      ○ Odd   ○ Even   ○ Neither

      What does this tell you about what their graphs will look like?

      _____

   f. $x^2 + 36$

   g. $x^2 + 25$

   h. $x^2 + 16$

   i. $x^2 + 1$

   j. ◎ **Challenge Problem:** Are the sum of two squares odd functions, even functions, or neither?

      ○ Odd   ○ Even   ○ Neither

      What does this tell you about what their graphs will look like?

      _____

k. $x^2 - 50$

l. $x^2 - 20$

m. $x^2 - 2$

n. $x^2 + 50$

o. $x^2 + 10$

p. $x^2 + 40$

2. **Factoring Out Values** – Factor out a constant in order to get the coefficient of x^2 to be an unwritten 1. Then factor without using the quadratic equation.

a. $2x^2 - 32$

b. $\frac{1}{3}x^2 - 3$

3. **When Only One Term Has the Input** – Find the value of x by solving for x^2 and then simply taking the square root of both sides. Remember, sometimes problems can be solved using simple methods!

a. $120 = 2x^2$

b. $0 = 3x^2 + 60$

4. **Recognizing the Function** – Use what you have learned about factoring to choose the correct function to describe the arc shown. Do not use a graphing calculator.
Hint: Note that on B, you can save yourself some time in finding the roots if you first factor out $\frac{1}{30}$.

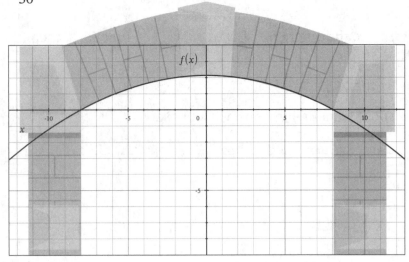

A. $y(x) = x^2 - 64$

B. $y(x) = -\frac{1}{30}x^2 + \frac{64}{30}$

C. $y(x) = x^2 - 16$

D. $y(x) = x^2 + 64$

○ A   ○ B   ○ C   ○ D

5. **Skill Sharpening: Quadratics with Complex Roots** – Use the quadratic equation to find the roots. Your answer may be complex!

   Hint: Be sure to simplify as much as possible without calculating square roots on a calculator; notice how we simplified the square root and factored in the *Student Textbook*. Review Lesson 3.5 if needed.

   a. $f(x) = 10x^2 + x + 2$

   b. $f(x) = -3x^2 - 2x - 4$

   c. $f(m) = -6m^2 - 2m - 5$

Suggestion: *Make flashcards to help you remember how to simplify different quadratic equations.*

Note: You will need to have the quadratic formula memorized on the quiz, and you need to know how to find $x_{max|min}$.

1. **Factoring Quadratic Expressions** – Factor these functions without using the quadratic formula. If you can, solve orally with your parent/teacher.

   a. $g(x) = x^2 + 14x + 49$

   b. $f(x) = x^2 + 5x - 50$

   c. $f(x) = x^2 + 18$

   d. $f(x) = x^2 - 6$

   e. $f(x) = \dfrac{1}{2}x^2 - 50$

   f. $f(x) = 2x^2 + 20x + 50$

2. **Recognizing Specific Quadratic Expressions**

   a. Which of the expressions you factored was a perfect square?

   ○ 1a ○ 1b ○ 1c ○ 1d ○ 1e ○ 1f

   b. Which of the expressions you factored was a sum of two squares?

   ○ 1a ○ 1b ○ 1c ○ 1d ○ 1e ○ 1f

3. **Identifying Roots** – Look at the factored expressions on problems 1a–1f and identify what the roots are.

   a.

   b.

   c.

   d.

   e.

   f.

4. **Complex Quadratics** – Find the root(s) of this expression: $\dfrac{1}{2}x^2 + 5$.

   Hint: You could rewrite this as $\dfrac{1}{3}x^2 + 0x + 5$, as $0x$ equals 0 if you want to use the quadratic formula . . . or you can just set the expression equal to 0 and solve for x.

5. **Simplify** – Simplify $\left(\dfrac{3}{4} - 3\right)^2$. Give your answer as a decimal to 4 places instead of the normal 3.

6. **Recognizing Quadratics** – Choose the correct function to describe the graph. Do not use a graphing calculator.

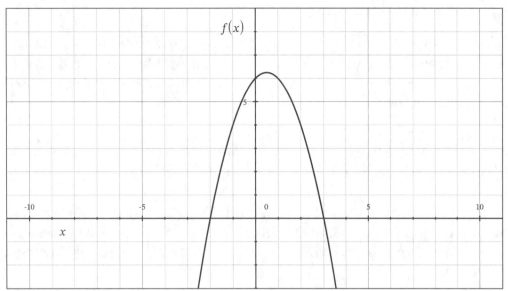

A. $f(x) = -x^2 + x + 6$ B. $f(x) = x^2 - x - 6$

○ A   ○ B

7. **Applying Algebra** – Let's say we want to find the rotational inertia based on the height of an object if the rotational inertia "of the body about a parallel axis that extends through the body's center of mass"[1] is 4. Because of the consistent way God governs creation, we'd have this function: $I(h) = h^2 + 4$.

a. Factor $I(h) = h^2 + 4$.

b. Is there a real number value at which the output will be 0?

○ Yes   ○ No

8. 📚 **More Applying Algebra** – Jack and Ed distribute $1,200 worth of food each among some poor people, giving the same amount for each person; Jack gives to 40 more people than Ed does, but Ed gives $5 more worth of food to each person than Jack does, again giving the same amount per person.

a. Write an equation showing the relationship between the total number of dollars Ed spent ($1,200), the number of people helped (n_E), and the amount spent on each person (a_E). Your equation should start 1,200 =. (You can leave units off your equations for simplicity, only be sure to add them back at the end in your answers.)

---

1   David Halliday, Robert Resnick, and Jearl Walker, *Fundamentals of Physics*, 7th ed. (USA: John Wiley & Sons, 2005), p. 252-253

b. Write an equation showing the relationship between the total number of dollars Jack spent ($1,200), the number of people helped (n_J), and the amount spent on each person (a_J). Your equation should start $1,200 =$.

c. Personalize the equation you wrote in 8b for Jack in terms of Ed — that is, use a_E and n_E as your only unknowns. For example, the number of people Jack helps is the number Ed helps plus 40, or $n_E + 40$. Substitute this value in for n_J in equation 8b. Do a similar thing for a_J. Your equation should start $1,200 =$.

> *When we speak of finding something in terms of something else, we're finding a formula rather than working with exact values. We're trying to see what the relationship is between unknowns.*

d. Solve the equation you wrote in 8a for n_E and substitute that into the equation from 8c; solve the new equation for a_E to find the dollars' worth of food Ed gave per person. Note that it doesn't make sense to give a negative dollar amount, so you're only interested in the positive root.

$a_E =$ _____

e. Use the value you found in 8d to find n_E.

$n_E =$ _____

f. Given your answers to the earlier questions, find n_J and a_J.

$n_J =$ _____ $a_J =$ _____

9. ◎ **Challenge Problem: Quadratics Where You Don't Expect Them** – Solve this system of equations by solving the second equation for y and substituting that value into the first equation to find x. As you do, you will wind up with an equation you can rearrange to be a quadratic expression. Use the quadratic formula to find the two values for x. You do not need to plug the values of x back into the equations to find the two possible values of y even though that would be fully solving the system (just report the two possible values of x).

$$\frac{2}{x} + \frac{3}{y} = -2$$

$$-4x - y = -5$$

1. **Using the Fundamental Theorem of Algebra** – Identify the number of total roots each of these functions or expressions has (the roots can be repeated or complex).

   a. $f(x) = -2x^4 + 3x^2 + 5$

   b. $f(x) = -3x^4 + 2x^3 + x^2$

   c. $g(x) = 8x^3 - 216x$

   d. $t(x) = x^4 - 1$

2. **Exploring Roots** – Graph each function given in problems 1a–1d and list all the roots shown on the graph. For example, if the curve intersects the x-axis when $x = 9$, list $x = 9$. Note that those are the *real roots only*. On non-integer roots, give approximate answers rounded to the third decimal place.

   a.

   b.

   c.

   d.

3. **Exploring Roots** – Find *all* of the roots for the functions in problems 1a–1d by solving for when the output equals 0 and calculating the approximate values of the roots on the calculator so you can compare with your answers to 2a–2d. When all of the roots are real, your answers will be the same as what you found on the graph, but show how you found the answer algebraically. Note that you may need to break the problem down as needed to help you, using the strategies discussed in the lesson. In fact, the function in 1b is the exact same function as was partially solved in the lesson.

   a.

   b.

   c.

   d.   *Hint:* Since $1 \cdot 1 = 1$, simply use m to stand for x^2 and view as the difference of two squares, with x^2 being a square and 1 being a square (of $1 \cdot 1$). Then solve for the roots of the remaining two quadratics.

4. **Skill Sharpening**

   a. Without graphing it, can you tell if the function in 1a will yield the same results for positive and for negative inputs (i.e., is it symmetrical around the y-axis)? Another way of asking this is if you can tell whether the function in 1a is even.

      ○ Yes   ○ No

   b. Is the function in 1c even, odd, or neither?

      ○ Even   ○ Odd   ○ Neither

   c. Find the roots of $2x^2 + 10x + 12$ without using the quadratic formula.
      Hint: Factor so that the coefficient of x^2 is 1, and it will be easy to find the roots!

1. **Using the Fundamental Theorem of Algebra** – Identify the total number of roots each of these functions or expressions has (the roots can be repeated or complex).

    a. $x^2 + 2x + 3$

    b. $f(x) = 5x + 3$

    c. $y(t) = t^4 - 2$

    d. $y(x) = x^5 + 5x + 3$

2. **Applying Algebra** – The dimensions of a rectangular garden are $3y$ by $4y$. Running along three sides of it (bottom, right, and left), as in the picture, is a walkway of uniform width throughout, whose total area is y^2. What is the width of the walkway, marked as x in the picture? The questions below will help you break this problem down.

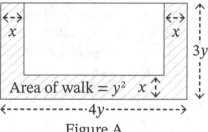

Figure A

   a. The area of a rectangle equals length times width. Write an equation showing how to find the area of each vertical portion of the walk (i.e., the section shaded gray in Figure B) in terms of x and y. Use A_v to stand for the area (the subscript v is to remind us we're finding the area of a vertical portion).

   b. Since there are two vertical portions, write an equation showing the total area of the vertical portions of the walk in terms of x and y. Use A_{Tv} to stand for the total area of the vertical portions.

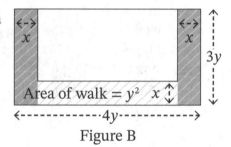

Figure B

   c. Write an equation showing the area of the remaining portion of the walk in terms of x and y. Use A_h for this area to remind you you're finding the area of the horizontal part of the walk.

   d. Write an equation showing the total area of the walk, which we were told equals y^2.

   e. Solve the equation you wrote in 2d for x in terms of y, calculating the approximate answers on a calculator.

   f. You should have gotten two answers in 2e. Which of these answers makes sense given that $2x \leq 4y$ (we know that the walk is running along both sides of it, so 2 times the walk's width (x) can't be more than the width of the whole garden, or $4y$)?

The above problem illustrates how important it is to break down real-life problems. At first, it seemed like we didn't have enough information to solve. But we did! We just needed to break it down step by step. Note also that since we were solving in terms of y, we couldn't have used a graph. We needed to know how to solve algebraically!

3. 📖 **More Applying Algebra** – The area of a circle is πr^2, or $A = \pi r^2$. What is the radius (r) of a circle (to 3 decimal places) whose area is 30.1 ft²? Note that you really have a quadratic equation . . . but one you can solve a lot more simply than with the quadratic formula.

4. **Even More Applying Algebra** – Let's say that you decided to run a marathon, which is about 26 miles long, and that you run at an average speed of $5\frac{\text{mi}}{\text{hr}}$. You take a break after 3 hours and then run another 2.2 hours to finish the marathon. You want to write a function showing your distance as a function of time where $t = 0$ is at the end of your break rather than at the start of the race (you're also ignoring the time you spent on the break and only counting time that was spent running). Since distance is speed multiplied by time, you know that the function will have the form $d(t) = st + b$.

Finish writing the equation by finding the missing value.

$$d(t) = \left(5\frac{\text{mi}}{\text{hr}}\right)t + \underline{\qquad}$$

Hint: Substitute 0 for $d(t)$ in $d(t) = \left(5\frac{\text{mi}}{\text{hr}}\right)t + b$ (since your distance was 0 at the start of the race) and −3 for t (this would have been your time at the start of the race when the distance, or $d(t)$, was 0, since the break happened 3 hours into the race); then solve for b.

1. **Using Graphing to Find Solutions** – Find the real values that satisfy both of the functions given. Your answer should be one or more coordinate pairs, such as (1, –2). If you cannot find a real value that satisfies both functions, write "no real solution."

   Hint: Remember back to Lesson 7.3 and how you can adjust the scale on your graphs. You may need to do so on some of these!

   a. $g(t) = -4.9t^2 + 2t + 5$ and $g(t) = \dfrac{50}{t}$

   b. $f(x) = x^3 + 46$ and $f(x) = x^2 + 2x - 5$

   c. $f(d) = 3d^2 + 20$ and $f(d) = \dfrac{d}{15}$

1. **Using Graphing to Find Solutions** – Find the real values that satisfy both of the functions given. Your answer should be one or more coordinate pairs, such as (1, –2). If you cannot find a real value that satisfies both functions, write "no real solution."

    a. $y(t) = -8t^2 + 2t + \dfrac{11}{2}$ and $g(t) = 5$

    b. $y(t) = -9t^2 + 3t - 50$ and $g(t) = t^2 + 2t - 40$

    c. $y(t) = -t^2 + 2t + 25$ and $g(t) = t^2 + 2t + 3$

2. ✆ **Algebra Applied** – A tank is supplied by 2 pumps. One day the tank was 80% filled by working the small pump 2 hours and the large pump 3 hours. The next day, the tank was again 80% filled, this time by working the small pump for 4 hours and the large pump for 2 hours. What percent of the tank does each pump fill every hour? The subproblems below will help you solve this problem using graphing.

    a. Write two equations using two unknowns (one representing the percent of the tank the small pump fills each hour; the other the percent of the tank the large fills each hour).

    _____

    _____

    b. Solve both equations for the percent of the tank the large pump fills each hour.

    _____

    _____

    c. Graph both of the equations you solved in 2b; where they intersect is the solution! List your answer as a percent (i.e., write 30% instead of 0.3).

    Percent of the tank the small pump fills each hour: _____

    Percent of the tank the large pump fills each hour: _____

3. ⌨ **Applying Algebra** – The hypotenuse of a certain right-angled triangle is 2.6 ft greater than the triangle's height and 1.6 ft greater than the triangle's base. What are the lengths of the height (a), the base (b), and the hypotenuse (c), given that these dimensions are all positive?
    Hint: Use the knowledge that $a^2 + b^2 = c^2$ (the Pythagorean theorem) and substitution to get that equation to have only one unknown, and then solve for that unknown!

    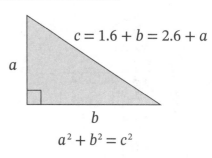

    $a \approx$_____ $b \approx$_____ $c \approx$_____

Don't get confused between the a and b in the Pythagorean theorem and the a and b in the quadratic formula. They are representing different quantities. Remember, the a and b in the quadratic formula (which you'll use while solving for a side of the triangle) describe the coefficients of the input . . . and the a and b in the Pythagorean theorem the sides of the triangle. Feel free to use different letters to stand for the sides of the triangle to avoid confusion if needed.

4. **Skill Sharpening**

   a. Look back at the functions in 1a. How many roots does each have?

      $y(t)$:＿＿＿＿＿＿ $g(t)$:＿＿＿＿＿＿

   b. How many total roots does $x^7 + x^5 + x^3$ have?

   c. Is the function $f(x) = x^7 + x^5 + x^3$ even, odd, or neither?

      ○ Even   ○ Odd   ○ Neither

   d. What does your answer to 4c tell you about the function?

   e. How many total roots does this expression have? $x^4 + 2x^2 - 15$

   f. Find the roots of the expression given in 4e.

   g. Find the roots of $0.5x^2 + 3x + 4.5$ without using the quadratic formula. *Hint:* Factor so that the coefficient of x^2 is 1, and it will be easy!

1. **Graphing Inequalities, Part 1 –** Graph these inequalities by graphing the corresponding equalities on your calculator and then drawing the general shape and shading the appropriate region in your notebook. Be sure to use a dashed line when needed to show that the values on the line are not included.

   a. $y > \dfrac{1}{30}x^2 + 5x$

   b. $y < 3x + 5$

   c. $y \geq x^3$

2. **Graphing Inequalities, Part 2 –** Finish graphing these inequalities by copying the graphs into your notebook (they don't have to be exact — just the correct general shape) and then shading the appropriate region in your notebook.

   a. $y > 5x$ and $y < 2x + 10$

   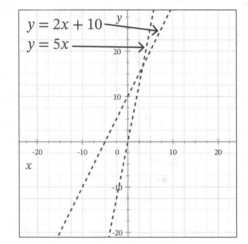

   b. $y < 5x$ and $y < 2x + 10$

   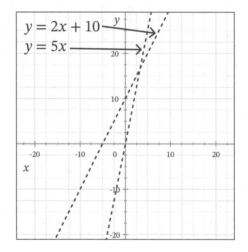

   c. $y < 5x$ and $y > 2x + 10$

   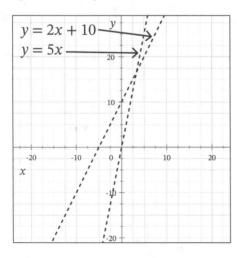

   d. $y > 5x$ and $y > 2x + 10$

   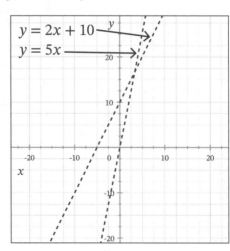

e. $y \leq -x^2 + 5x$ and $y > 2x^2 - 10x$

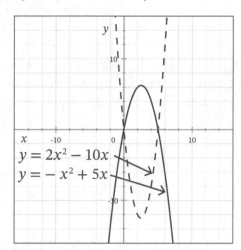

f. $y \geq -x^2 + 5x$ and $y > 2x^2 - 10x$

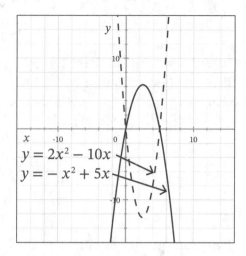

g. $y \leq -x^2 + 5x$ and $y < 2x^2 - 10x$

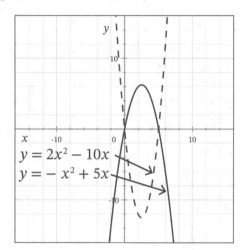

h. $y \geq -x^2 + 5x$ and $y < 2x^2 - 10x$

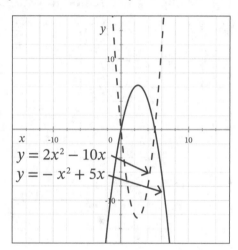

1. **Graphing Inequalities, Part 1** – Finish graphing these inequalities by copying the graphs into your notebook (they don't have to be exact — just the correct general shape) and then shading the appropriate region in your notebook.

   a. $y \leq x^2 - 5x$ and $y < 2x + 10$

   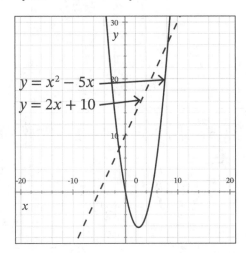

   b. $y \leq x^2 - 5x$ and $y > 2x + 10$

   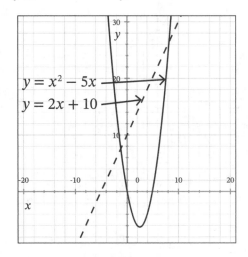

   c. $y \geq x^2 - 5x$ and $y < 2x + 10$

   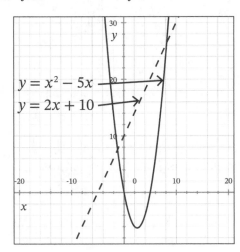

   d. $y \geq x^2 - 5x$ and $y > 2x + 10$

   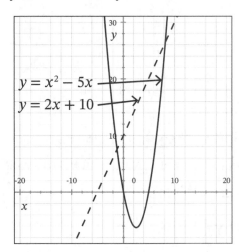

Continued on the back.

e. $y \le 5x^3$ and $y > x^2$

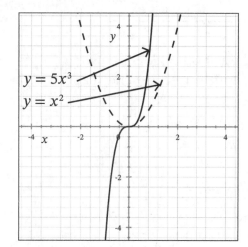

f. $y \le 5x^3$ and $y < x^2$

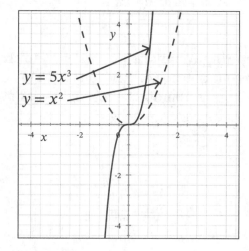

g. $y \ge 5x^3$ and $y < x^2$

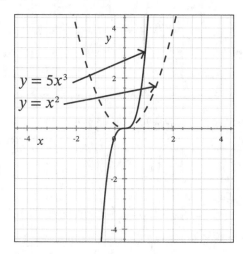

h. $y \ge 5x^3$ and $y > x^2$

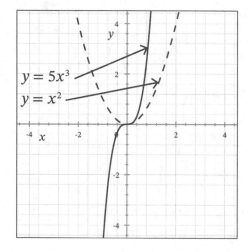

2. **Graphing Inequalities, Part 2**

   a. Is there a set of values that satisfy both of these inequalities: $f(x) > x^2 + 5x$ and
      $f(x) < \dfrac{1}{100}x^2$?

      O Yes   O No

   b. Draw the general shape showing the graph of the functions given in 2a in your notebook.

3. **Applying Algebra** – Suppose Jane has been offered two different jobs. At Job A, she would make $10 an hour, plus a set stipend of $100 a week. At Job B, she'd make $15 an hour, but would have no set stipend.

    Hint: Think through this problem, thinking about the information you know and how you could go from that to the information you need to find — you have all the skills you need!

    a. How many hours would she have to work in a week for the total she makes to be the same, and after that point, which job will give her more money?

    Hours worked at which totals are the same: _____

    Job that makes more after that point:

    ○ Job A   ○ Job B

    b. Jane is also considering other jobs. Use graph paper to draw a graph showing the solutions for which she'd make *more than* both of these jobs.

    c. Use graph paper to draw a graph showing all the possible combinations at which she'd make more than Job A but less than or equal to Job B.

4. **More Applying Algebra** – In economics, there's something known as supply and demand. Suppose the supply for a product can be approximated by the function $y = -x + 30$, where y is the price of each product and x is the quantity of that product purchased. The demand for a product (that is, how much people will want to buy the product) can be approximated by $y = x + 3$, where again the y is the price of each product and x is the quantity of that product available to purchase (i.e., quantity). We have omitted units for simplicity.

    a. At what quantity do the supply and demand curves intersect, and what is the price at that quantity?
    Hint: Remember when listing your answers that y represents the price and x the quantity.

    Quantity = _____   *Price* = _____

    Note: This is known as the equilibrium point — at this quantity, the supply matches the demand, meaning the quantity available of the product is the same as the quantity desired of a product.

    b. Use graph paper to draw a graph with a shaded region showing the quantities that would result in a price that is greater than the demand quantity (i.e., where $y > x + 3$) but less than or equal to the supply quantity (i.e., where $y \leq -x + 30$).

5. 🎯 **Challenge Problem: Even More Applying Algebra** – The following is adapted from an ancient problem from India: One fourth a herd of camels was seen in the forest; twice the square root of the herd had gone on mountain slopes; and the remaining 15 were on the banks of the river. How many camels were in the herd? Only list the whole number solution.

6. **Skill Sharpening**

    a. Find the roots of $x^4 + 5x^2$.

    b. Find the roots of $5x^3 + 10x^2$.

1. **Fundamental Theorem of Algebra** – Identify the number of total roots the following expressions have.

   a. $x^5 - 9x^3$

   b. $x^4 - x^2 - 6$

   c. $x^2 + 5$

2. **Finding Roots** – Find all of the roots (real and complex) for each expression in problems 1a–1c.

   a.

   b.

   c.

3. **Even and Odd** – Identify if the expressions in problems 1a–1c are even, odd, or neither.

   a.

        O Even   O Odd   O Neither

   b.

        O Even   O Odd   O Neither

   c.

        O Even   O Odd   O Neither

4. **Graphing Equalities** – List the input(s) and output(s) these equations share. Your answer should be one or more pairs of coordinates in the form of (x, y).

   a. $f(x) = 5x + 6$ and $f(x) = x^2 - 3$

   b. $g(t) = t^3 - 5$ and $f(t) = t^2 + 2t - 3$

5. **Graphing Inequalities** – Choose the set of inequalities that accurately describes the graph. Note that you might need to use your knowledge of linear and quadratic equations (such as recognizing the y-intercept or finding x-intercepts or the minimum/maximum point) to help you figure out which inequality is the right one! **Be sure to do this without using a graphing calculator — you will not be allowed to use a graphing calculator on a portion of the quiz.**

a.

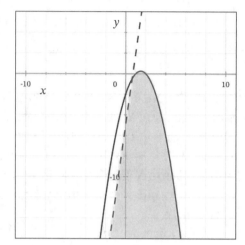

A. $y \geq -x^2 + 3x - 2$ and $y < 7x - 5$

B. $y \leq -x^2 + 3x - 2$ and $y < 7x + 0.9$

C. $y \leq -x^2 + 3x - 2$ and $y < 7x - 5$

D. $y \leq (x - 2)(x - 1)$ and $y < 7x - 5$

○ A   ○ B   ○ C   ○ D

b.

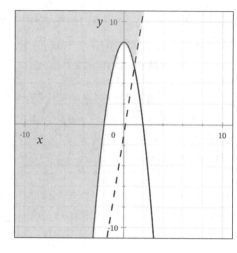

A. $y \geq -2(x^2 - 4)$ and $y < 6x - 1$

B. $y \geq -2(x^2 - 4)$ and $y > 6x - 1$

C. $y \leq -2(x^2 - 4)$ and $y < 6x - 1$

D. $y \leq -2(x^2 - 4)$ and $y > 6x - 1$

○ A   ○ B   ○ C   ○ D

6. 📖 **Applying Algebra** – The distance from New York to Chicago over the New York Central and Lake Shore lines is 960 mi. The 20th Century Limited covers this distance in 5.75 hr less time than the Fast Mail Limited going at a speed 12.9 $\frac{\text{mi}}{\text{hr}}$ faster. Know that *distance = speed • time*.

And note that there won't be anything this involved on the quiz . . . but we hope it gives you a glimpse into how what you're learning could apply.

Note: You may omit units while solving for simplicity, but make sure to give your final answers in the correct units.

a. Find what the speed to traverse the 960 mi is for the Fast Mail Limited.
    Hint: Based on what we've been told here, we can write this: $960 = st$ (We know that the Fast Mail Limited's speed times time equals the total distance, which is 960 mi.)

    Since we know how the trains' speeds and time relate, we can also write an equation for the 20th Century Limited's time in terms of the Fast Mail Limited's:

    $$960 = (s + 12.9)(t - 5.75)$$

    (We know the 20th Century Limited takes 5.75 hours less and goes at a speed that's 12.9 $\frac{\text{mi}}{\text{hr}}$ faster.)

Solve $960 = st$ for t, and then substitute that value into $960 = (s + 12.9)(t - 5.75)$ and solve for s. You will end up needing to use the quadratic formula! Find the approximate negative root only (i.e., the root from the quadratic equation that uses the negative sign), as that will give you a positive speed.

b. Use your answer to 6a to find the Fast Mail Limited's time.

c. If 20th Century Limited is traveling at $53.304\ \dfrac{\text{mi}}{\text{hr}}$, write a function in function notation for 20th Century Limited that shows distance as a function of time. Remember that *distance = speed • time* (i.e., $d = st$).

d. Say that the Fast Mail Limited train has already gone a distance of 40 mi out from New York when the 20th Century Limited leaves the station in New York. The functions describing the distance as a function of time for the trains would then be the 20th Century Limited function you wrote in 6c and $d(t) = 40.404t + 40$ (function for Fast Mail Limited). At what distance and time will the 20th Century Limited catch up to the Fast Mail Limited? Assume that there are two sets of tracks side-by-side the trains can travel on and they traverse at the speeds you already found.
    Hint: Use a calculator to graph and find the intersection point.

    Distance at which they are at the same place $\approx$ _____

    Time at which they are at the same place $\approx$ _____

e. Use graphing paper to draw a graph showing the range of times that would result in distances greater than or equal to that of a train traveling at $d(t) = 15t$ but less than a train traveling at $d(t) = 100t$.

1. **Exploring Rational Functions**

    a. Knowing that $F = ma$, if the F (the force) equals 20 N, graph on a calculator how the acceleration depends on the mass. Draw the general shape in your notebook.
    Hint: You will need to solve the formula for acceleration first.

    b. In the situation described in 1a, do negative values for mass make sense?

    ○ Yes   ○ No

    Note: The mass of an object is similar to its weight, except that mass doesn't depend on the gravitational force like weight does. Your mass, unlike your weight, is the same on the earth and the moon.

    c. Is $m(a) = 6a^{-1}$ a rational function?

    ○ Yes   ○ No

    d. Is $m(a) = 6a^{-1}$ a polynomial function?

    ○ Yes   ○ No

    e. Rewrite $m(a) = 6a^{-1}$ as a fraction with a in the denominator.

    f. If the total money you make in a week needs to equal $400 to pay your bills, write a rational function describing the number of hours you work in a week as a function of the amount you make per hour.
    Hint: First write an equation describing the relationship between the total you make in a week, the number of hours you work in a week, and the amount you make per hour. If you're not sure what the relationship is, try starting with an actual example. Suppose you make $\frac{\$10}{\text{hr}}$ and work 20 hours; how much will you make in a week? Once you've written that problem out, use letters to stand for the hourly rate, hours worked, and total earned. You now have a problem that can describe the relationship, regardless of your hourly rate and hours worked! Then solve that algebraic problem for the number of hours you work in a week and write that as a function.

    g. Use a calculator to graph the function you wrote in 1f, and draw its general shape in your notebook.

    h. Is the function you wrote in 1f a rational function?

    ○ Yes   ○ No

    i. Is the function you wrote in 1f a polynomial function?

    ○ Yes   ○ No

    j. Given the meaning of the function you wrote in 1f, do negative values make sense in this scenario?

    ○ Yes   ○ No

2. **Simplifying Units**

   a. Say you have the equation $x = ma + F$, where m represents mass in kg, a represents acceleration in $\dfrac{\text{m}}{\text{s}^2}$, and F represents force in $\text{kg} \cdot \dfrac{\text{m}}{\text{s}^2}$. What unit of measure will x be?

   b. Say you have the formula $3x = \dfrac{y}{\pi r^2}$; find the units for x if r is in meters and y is in kg.

   c. Given the formula $F = ma$, suppose you're trying to find the force of an object that has a mass of 7 kg and an acceleration of $5\,\dfrac{\text{ft}}{\text{min}^2}$. If you don't convert any of the units, what unit would the resulting force (F) be in, given that force equals mass times acceleration? *Hint:* Only plug in the units of measure — you don't need to find the actual value of the force, only the units.

   d. In the past, we've looked at the gravity formula: $F = G\dfrac{m_1 m_2}{r^2}$. Find the units of G if F is $2.2 \times 10^{-8}\ \text{kg} \cdot \dfrac{\text{m}}{\text{s}^2}$, m_1 is 5,000 kg, m_2 is 6,000 kg, and r is 300 m. *Hint:* Solve the formula for G and *then* plug in the correct units — you don't have to worry about the values!

3. **Exploring a Polynomial Function** – Let's explore the polynomial function we looked at in Lesson 11.1 regarding the fuel efficiency of a hypothetical drag race car. By dividing the function describing the car's position based on its time by the function describing its fuel use based on its time, we came up with this: $f(t) = \dfrac{x(t)}{b(t)} = \dfrac{0.011\,t^2}{\dfrac{1}{1{,}000}t^5 + \dfrac{1}{40}t^4 + \dfrac{1}{200}t^2 + t}$.

   a. Look at just the numerator of the function. It is a _____ degree.

      ○ monomial   ○ polynomial

   b. Look at just the denominator of the function. It is a _____ degree.

      ○ monomial   ○ polynomial

   c. To find out the fuel efficiency when the car crosses the finish line, we need to first find the time when the car crosses that line. To do that, we'll use $x(t)$, the formula describing the car's position over time. Let's say the drag race is 805 m long, or roughly 0.5 mi. Solve $x(t) = \dfrac{0.011t^2\ \text{mi}}{\text{s}^2}$ for t's approximate value when the output $x(t)$, which represents the distance, is 0.5 mi. Notice that we added back in the units — go ahead and do the calculation with the units to prove that you do, indeed, end up with an answer in seconds (s).

   d. Use the positive time you found in 3c — the time when the car finishes the race — as the t in the formula $f(t)$ to calculate the fuel efficiency. You can leave off units for simplicity — your answer will be in miles per gallon.

e. Fuel efficiencies are found by taking the miles traveled divided by the gallons used. Say your car goes 300 miles and uses 9 gallons to do it. What is it's fuel efficiency? Your answer will be in $\frac{\text{mi}}{\text{gal}}$.

f. Ask your parents how many miles per gallon their car gets, or look online to see how many miles per gallon any specific car you like gets. Most cars have a *much* higher fuel efficiency than this hypothetical drag race car (drag race cars are all about speed and not fuel efficiency)!

car make: _____

miles per gallon car gets: _____

1. **Applying Algebra** – Let's say that a group wants to rent out a room at a theater to have an independent Christian movie shown. Because it's a public event, they have to get a license from the studio that produced the movie in order to show it. The license costs $100 no matter how many people actually show up to the showing, plus $0.05 times the number of people who come squared, plus another $0.05 times the number of people who come, plus $50 for renting out the theater. (The license is charged this way so that the studio incentivizes groups to have multiple showings rather than just a single large showing.) At the same time, they decide to sell tickets for $12 and receive sponsorships from 4 individuals for $75 each. Their revenue will equal $12 per person who comes to the movie, plus the sponsorships.

   a. Write a function $f(p)$ describing the expense of showing the movie as a function of the number of people who come.

   b. Write a function $y(p)$ describing the revenue made as a function of the number of people who come.

   c. Write function $r(p)$ describing the ratio of the revenue $(y(p))$ over expenses $(f(p))$ as a function of the number of people who come.

   $$r(p) = \frac{y(p)}{f(p)} = \underline{\hspace{3cm}}$$

   d. What happens to the $r(p)$ ratio as the number of people (p) increases?
   Hint: Graph the ratio to see this! You might need to play with your zoom functions to see different aspects of it. We suggest setting your axes from 0 to 1,000 for the horizontal axis and 0 to 4 for the vertical axis.

   _____

   e. What does the change in the $r(p)$ ratio as the number of people increases indicate in this scenario?

   _____

2. **Units of Measure & Sound Waves**[1] – Notice in the sound wave pictured that the wave goes up and down consistently. We call the time between one up and down cycle the period of the wave (T). Some waves move faster than others; we can measure how fast they move by measuring how many periods pass in a certain amount of time. We call this the frequency of the wave (f). The relationship between frequency and period is a rational function and can be described like this: $f(T) = \dfrac{1}{T}$. By looking at the frequency of various sounds, we can discover some neat things about the order God placed within sounds.

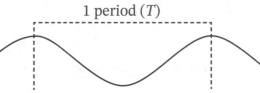

1 period (T)

a. Let's say you read that middle C has a frequency of about 261.6 Hertz, or $\dfrac{1}{s}$ (the $\dfrac{1}{s}$ stands for once per second). What is its period (T)? You can ignore units for now.

b. Figure out the units for the problem in 2a, using a unit of $\dfrac{1}{s}$ (once per second) for frequency (f). Note that you will need this answer for problems 2c and 2d.
Hint: Use the equation you'd solved for T in 2a to help you.

c. The "speed [of a wave] is equal to one wavelength (the distance traveled between pulses) divided by one period (the time between pulses) for a single cycle, or $v = \dfrac{\lambda}{T}$." If the wavelength (λ) is measured in cm, what is the speed (v) measured in?

d. The C above middle C has twice the frequency of middle C, which has a frequency of $261.6\dfrac{1}{s}$. What is its period (T)?

Did you know that notes that sound harmonious together actually relate together mathematically? Each note not only has a primary frequency, but they also have subtler sounds with other frequencies . . . and those frequencies turn out to be the primary frequencies of other notes that sound good with them! Entire books could be written exploring the mathematics of music. Suffice it to say that God put incredible order within sounds (and gave us ears to appreciate that order!) . . . and that math helps us discover this order.

1   Equation and frequency of middle C from W. Thomas Griffith and Juliet Brosing, *The Physics of Everyday Phenomena: A Conceptual Introduction to Physics*, 6th ed. (New York: McGraw-Hill, 2009), p. 310 and 324.

3. **Skill Sharpening**

   a. Find the roots of $f(x) = x^2 - 121$.

   b. How many total roots does $f(x) = x^4 + 2x^3$ have?

   c. Find the approximate roots of $x^4 + 2x^3 - 2x^2$.

   d. Find $f(x) = \dfrac{g(x)}{h(x)}$ if $g(x) = 5x$ and $h(x) = 2x^2 + 3$.

   e. Is your answer to 3d a rational function with the input appearing in the denominator?

   ○ Yes   ○ No

   f. Graph the function from 3b and the final function you wrote in 3d on a calculator. What input values are solutions to both functions? You should find four; list them as coordinates (i.e., in the form of (x, y)).

   g. Choose the inequality that is shown in the graph. Do not use a graphing calculator.

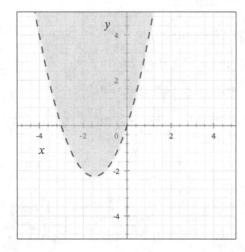

   A. $y > x^2 + 3x$
   B. $y \geq x^2 + 3x$
   C. $y > x^2 - 3x$
   D. $y < x^2 + 3x$
       ○ A   ○ B   ○ C   ○ D

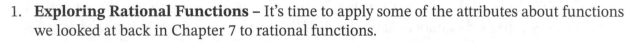
1. **Exploring Rational Functions** – It's time to apply some of the attributes about functions we looked at back in Chapter 7 to rational functions.

   a. In a rational function with an input that could be written *in the denominator* such as

      $$y(x) = \frac{x^2 + 1}{5x + 3} \text{ or } F(d) = \frac{50}{d} \text{ or } F(d) = 20\,d^{-1},$$ can the domain ever be all real numbers?

      Hint: Think about if there's any value the *input* cannot be.

      ○ Yes   ○ No

   b. Graph $y(x) = \frac{x^2 + 1}{5x + 3}$ and $F(d) = \frac{50}{d}$ on a calculator. Do both of the graphs have asymptotes (lines we could draw on the graph that the graph's curve doesn't touch)? Note that the question is not whether the calculator shows the asymptote line, but whether one *could* be drawn.

      ○ Yes   ○ No

   c. Explain your answer to 1b, commenting on why the graphs do or don't have asymptotes.

      _____

2. **Identifying the Value the Input Cannot Equal**

   a. In $f(x) = \frac{x^2 + 2x - 8}{2x - 4}$, what value can x not equal? Your answer should start "$x \neq$."

   b. In $f(x) = (x^4 + 5)x^{-1}$, what value can x not equal? Your answer should start "$x \neq$."
      Hint: Rewrite the negative exponent in the denominator and the answer will be obvious.

3. **Simplifying Rational Functions** – In simplifying these, **be sure to write out what $x \neq$ as part in your answer — that is, include the domain.**

   a. Simplify: $\dfrac{x^2 + 2x - 8}{2x - 4}$

   b. Simplify: $f(x) = \dfrac{x^2 + 7x + 12}{x + 3}$

   c. Simplify: $f(x) = \dfrac{x^2 + 7x + 12}{x^2 + 6x + 9}$

4. **Asymptotes and Discontinuities** – Graph each function you simplified in 3a–3c on a calculator and choose whether the graph shows an asymptote or a discontinuity or both at the value(s) the input cannot equal. Remember, an asymptote shows as two curves approaching an invisible line, while a discontinuity shows as an undefined value at a single point.

   a. ○ Asymptote   ○ Discontinuity   ○ Both

   b. ○ Asymptote   ○ Discontinuity   ○ Both

   c. ○ Asymptote   ○ Discontinuity   ○ Both

1. **Defining the Domain** – Specify the value(s) the input cannot equal in these functions (i.e., add $x \neq$ [any value(s) x cannot equal]), if any. If there are no values the input cannot equal, say "There are no values that the input cannot equal." Note that there may be more than one value the input cannot equal.

   a. $f(x) = \dfrac{x^2 + 4x - 12}{x^2 - 36}$, where _____

   b. $f(x) = \dfrac{x^2 + 4x - 12}{x^2 - 25}$, where _____

   c. $f(x) = \dfrac{x - 5}{x^2 - 4x - 5}$, where _____

   d. $f(x) = \dfrac{-6x^3 + 3x^2 - x}{2}$, where _____

   e. $y(v) = \dfrac{16v^3 + 2v^2 + 10v}{v - 2}$, where _____

   f. $f(x) = \dfrac{x^5 - x}{x^2 + x}$, where _____

2. **Simplifying Rational Functions** – Use factoring to help you simplify the functions specified. Be sure to check that any values the input cannot be are still noted for the domain and if not, add "where $x \neq$ [any value(s) x cannot equal]" to your simplified function.

   a. $f(x) = \dfrac{x - 5}{x^2 - 4x - 5}$

   Note: This is the function from 1c.

   b. $f(x) = \dfrac{x^3 - x}{x^2 + x}$

3. **Recognizing Asymptotes**

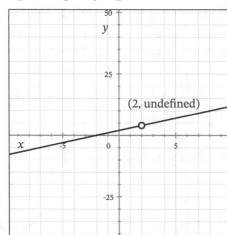

A.

B.

a. Which graph has a visible asymptote?

   ○ A   ○ B

b. Which graph has a visible discontinuity?

   ○ A   ○ B

4. **Applying Algebra: Shattering Glass** – You've probably heard about or seen videos of a wine glass shattering from sound alone. Using the skills you've learned, you can actually figure out at what frequency the sound coming at the glass has to be to get it to shatter.

   The amplitude or intensity of the oscillation in the glass $I(\omega)$ is a function of the frequency of the sound coming at the glass (ω). The formula is approximately

   $$I(\omega) = \frac{1}{(\omega - \Omega)^2 + \Gamma}.$$

   Notice that this is a rational function! Ω is called the resonance frequency (it varies based on each individual glass), and Γ is a damping factor; we'll view them both as constants right now, using various values for Ω and Γ.

   a. Given the function $I(\omega) = \dfrac{1}{(\omega - 400)^2 + 10}$, at what value of ω does the function spike (i.e., reach a maximum value)?
   Hint: Graph the function on a calculator, setting your minimum and maximum horizontal values to 350 and 450, and your vertical values to 0 and 0.15.

   b. Given the function $I(\omega) = \dfrac{1}{(\omega - 300)^2 + 20}$, at what value of ω does the function spike?

   c. Look carefully at the denominator: $\dfrac{1}{(\omega - \Omega)^2 + \Gamma}$. What does the denominator equal when ω and Ω are the same value?
   Hint: Pick any value for Ω and make ω equal the same value. What does the denominator then equal? Your answer will be an unknown.

d. It turns out when the denominator equals Γ, the glass will invariably shatter! After all, the denominator is the smallest then, meaning the output is the maximum, meaning the glass is vibrating at the highest possible intensity. Knowing this and given your answer to 4c, what value would the frequency coming at a glass (ω) need to be to shatter a glass if its resonance frequency (Ω) is 350 Hz?

Always remember that the skills you're learning are helpful ways of exploring God's creation . . . and pause long enough to praise God that He is so faithful in how He upholds creation that we can predict how glass will respond to sounds ahead of time. He is a God we can trust.

5. **Skill Sharpening**

   a. Graph the solution to $y > -x$ and $y \geq x^2 - 6$ by copying the general graph given into your notebook and shading the appropriate region.

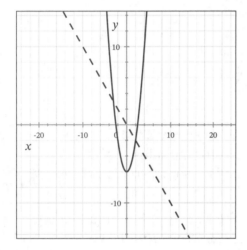

   b. Given $B = \dfrac{\mu_0 I}{2\pi r} + H$, find the units of μ_0 if r has units of meters (m), I has units of amps (A), and B and H have units of $\dfrac{\text{N}}{\text{A} \bullet \text{m}}$ (newton per amp-meter). Your final answer should be only in terms of newtons, amps, and/or meters.

See the footnote for more information on the relationship you explored in 5b, which represents the magnetic field produced from a current flowing through a metal wire;[1] God sustains consistency even in details such as magnetic fields . . . and math helps us describe it.

---

[1]   *B* represents the magnetic field, *r* the distance between the wire and that magnetic field, *I* the current in the wire, *H* is the ambient background magnetic field (which will vary with direction), and μ_0 a constant value known as the magnetic permeability constant. See Randall D. Knight, *Physics for Scientists and Engineers with Modern Physics: A Strategic Approach* (Pearson, Addison Wesley, NY: 2004), p. 1,006; note that the reference equation does not account for the ambient background (*H*).

1. **Finding the Roots** – Let's say that we needed to find the input value that would cause the right-hand side of the equations below to equal 0 (these are the same as the right-hand side of the functions you looked at in Worksheet 11.2B, problems 1a–1f). You can find this by finding the roots of the numerator, being careful to check to make sure those roots are not the values you found on Worksheet 11.2B, problems 1a–1f, that the input cannot equal. It is possible for there to be no solution, in which case, you should write "no solution."

   a. $0 = \dfrac{x^2 + 4x - 12}{x^2 - 36}$

   b. $0 = \dfrac{x^2 + 4x - 12}{x^2 - 25}$

   c. $0 = \dfrac{x - 5}{x^2 - 4x - 5}$

   d. $0 = \dfrac{-6x^3 + 3x^2 - x}{2}$

   e. $0 = \dfrac{16v^3 + 2v^2 + 10v}{v - 2}$

   f. ◎ **Challenge Problem:** $0 = \dfrac{x^5 - x}{x^2 + x}$

2. **Connecting with a Graph** – Graph the functions below (which are the right side of the functions in section 1), drawing the general shape in your notebook and **labeling the coordinates of the x-intercept**. Use the graph to help you check your work on problems 1a–1f; any real numbers (some were complex) you wrote in problems 1a–1f as input values that would make the equation 0 should show as roots on the graph.

   a. $f(x) = \dfrac{x^2 + 4x - 12}{x^2 - 36}$

   b. $f(x) = \dfrac{x^2 + 4x - 12}{x^2 - 25}$

   c. $f(x) = \dfrac{x - 5}{x^2 - 4x - 5}$

   d. $f(x) = \dfrac{-6x^3 + 3x^2 - x}{2}$

   e. $y(v) = \dfrac{16v^3 + 2v^2 + 10v}{v - 2}$

   f. $f(x) = \dfrac{x^5 - x}{x^2 + x}$

3. **Applying Algebra: Building** – Suppose you are trying to figure out what length to make a device based on a variety of different criteria. You've solved the problem and gotten this equation, where x is the length: $\dfrac{x^3 + 7x^2 + 3}{x^4 + 6x^3 - 2} = 0$. Are there any *real*-number *positive* solutions?

   Hint: You might need to use a graphing calculator to help you with this problem.

   ○ Yes ○ No

   If so, what are they?

   _____

   Note: If there aren't any, you'll know you can't make a device to meet all the criteria you've used, as a length needs to be positive . . . and a real number.

4. **Skill Sharpening**

   a. In $f(t) = \dfrac{-4.9t^2 + 5t - 3}{3t - 1}$, can t equal $\dfrac{1}{3}$?

   ○ Yes ○ No

   Why or why not?

   _____

   b. What are the roots of $\dfrac{-4.9t^2 + 5t - 3}{3t - 1}$?

   c. Simplify: $\dfrac{d^2 - 2d - 3}{3d + 3}$

   Hint: Remember to include a domain if someone looking at the simplified form wouldn't know what d can't equal!

   d. The radius of a black hole (an object in space with so much mass that the gravitational force it exerts won't even allow light to escape) is given as follows:

   $$r = \frac{2GM}{c^2}$$

   Here r is the radius in meters (m), G is the gravitational constant, M is the mass of the black hole in kilograms (kg), and c is the speed of light in meters per second $\left(\dfrac{m}{s}\right)$.

   2 is just a unitless constant. Find the units of the gravitational constant (G).

e. Copy the general shape of this graph into your notebook and shade in the region that shows the solution to $y > -8x + 5$ and $y \geq x^2 - 3x + 2$.

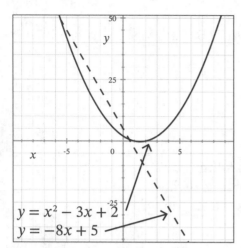

$y = x^2 - 3x + 2$
$y = -8x + 5$

f. Find the two solutions to $f(x) = -8x + 5$ and $f(x) = x^2 - 3x + 2$. List your answers in the format of (x, y).

Hint: If you graph these functions on your calculator and zoom in, you'll be able to see what the intersection points are.

1. **Rewrite These Partial Fractions as One Fraction** – Be sure to simplify as much as possible!

   a. $\dfrac{5}{7} + \dfrac{1}{5}$

   b. $\dfrac{-4.9\,t^2 + 4t - 12}{5t} - 1$

      Example Meaning: The tangent of an angle of a falling object (found by dividing the vertical change based on time divided by the horizontal change based on time) minus the tangent of a 45-degree angle (which equals 1).

   c. $\dfrac{17}{125F} + \dfrac{3}{4}$

      Example Meaning: The ratio of accelerations of two objects (found by dividing one acceleration by another, while viewing acceleration as a function of the force on the object in the denominator) plus an acceleration ratio of $\dfrac{3}{4}$.

   d. $\dfrac{40t + 5}{30t + 7} + \dfrac{2}{3}$

      Example Meaning: The ratio of two distances as a function of time (found by dividing one distance by another, with each distance written as a function of time) plus another $\dfrac{2}{3}$ ratio.

   e. $\dfrac{x^2 + 6x}{x + 4} - \dfrac{3x + 4}{x + 4}$

      (Do not try to simplify by factoring after combining into one fraction, although you should combine like terms.)

2. **Digging Deeper 1** – Use the rational expression you wrote in 1b to answer these questions.

   a. What value can t not be? Your answer should start "$t \neq$."

   b. If we needed the entire expression to equal 0, what real or complex value(s) of t would make that true?

   c. Set the expression equal to $f(t)$ and graph it (you do not need to draw the graph). Does it form an asymptote?

      ○ Yes   ○ No

3. **Digging Deeper 2** – Use the rational expression you wrote in 1c to answer these questions.

   a. What value can F not be? Your answer should start "$F \neq$."

   b. If we needed the entire expression to equal 0, what real or complex value(s) of F would make that true?

   c. Set the expression equal to $g(F)$ and graph it (you do not need to draw the graph). Does it form an asymptote?

      ○ Yes   ○ No

4. **Digging Deeper 3** – Use the rational expression you wrote in 1d to answer these questions.

   a. What value can t not be? Your answer should start "$t \neq$."

   b. If we needed the entire expression to equal 0, what real or complex value(s) of t would make that true?

   c. Set the expression equal to $f(t)$ and graph it (you do not need to draw the graph). Does it form an asymptote?

      ○ Yes   ○ No

5. **Digging Deeper 4** – Use the rational expression you wrote in 1e to answer these questions.

   a. What value can x not be? Your answer should start "$x \neq$."

   b. If we needed the entire expression to equal 0, what real or complex value(s) of x would make that true?

   c. Simplify the rational function you wrote in 1d. **Be sure to specify any values x cannot equal.**

   d. At what point is there a discontinuity in the rational function you wrote in 1d? *Hint:* You can graph the function to see.

1. **Rewrite These Partial Fractions as One Fraction**

   a. $\dfrac{5}{x+7} + \dfrac{1}{2}$

   b. $\dfrac{3x+2}{2x^2+3} - 4x$

   c. $\dfrac{3t+6}{9t-3} + 2$

   d. $\dfrac{4+t}{2t} - \dfrac{5+t}{6t}$

2. **Applying Algebra –** Let's say that you can crochet 3 rows of a blanket every 5 minutes. The price for which you sell a blanket depends on the time it takes you to crochet the blanket — you charge $0.00005 per minute times the number of minutes squared plus $0.0005 per minute times the number of minutes plus a flat $5.

   a. Write function $b(t)$ describing the rows on the blanket sewed as a function of time. Specify a domain of greater than or equal to 0 minutes. **List the entire function (including the part given to you) in your answer.**
   Note: Even though this isn't a rational function, we're still specifying a domain, as it doesn't make sense to crochet negative minutes!

   $b(t) = $_____, where t _____

   b. Write function $p(t)$ describing the blanket price as a function of time. Be sure to specify the same domain you used in 2a.

   $p(t) = $_____, where t _____

   c. Write function $r(t)$ describing the ratio of the blanket price and the rows sewed as a function of time. Again, include the same domain you used in 2a. You do not need to simplify.

   $r(t) = $_____, where t _____

   d. Is there a number of minutes at which you cannot compute a value for $r(t)$?

   ○ Yes   ○ No

   If so, what is that value?

   _____ minutes

e. Is there a real-number value for the number of minutes that will make the ratio between the blanket price and the number of rows crocheted be 0?

○ Yes ○ No

If so, what is that value?

_____ minutes

f. Let's say a blanket contains 60 rows. How many minutes will it take you to make such a blanket, and what would the ratio of the price of that blanket per row be?

minutes: _____

price per row: _____

3. **More Applying Algebra** – For each lever, $\dfrac{F_1}{F_2} = \dfrac{d_2}{d_1}$, as shown in the picture, where F_1 and F_2 represent the force on one side of the lever required to balance the lever and d_1 and d_2 the distance between the end of the lever and the pivot point on that side. We have an 80 lb rock that we are trying to balance (F_2).

a. Write a function showing F_1 as a function of d_2 if F_2 is 80 lb and if $d_1 = 4$ ft. Simplify your answer. The left side is given to you (but be sure to rewrite it as part of your answer).

$F_1(d_2) = $ _____,
(function is for a 4-ft lever)

b. Write a function showing F_1 as a function of d_2 if the F_2 is 80 lb and if $d_1 = 2$ ft. Simplify your answer. Again, be sure to include the left side of the equation in your answer.

$F_1(d_2) = $ _____, (function is for a 2-ft lever)

c. Assuming that d_2 is the same for both levers, write a ratio of the 4-ft lever from 3a to the 2-ft lever from 3b. Simplify the ratio to find the percentage less force the 4-ft lever requires than the 2-ft lever.

Percentage less force the 4-ft lever requires: _____

4. **Skill Sharpening**

   a. Copy the general shape of this graph to your notebook and shade the appropriate region that shows the solution to $y \leq x^2 + 3x$ and $y \geq x^3 - 3$.

   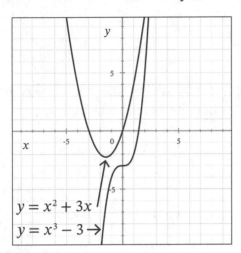

   b. The potential energy of a spring with a weight hanging from it is given as $U = \frac{1}{2}kx^2 + mgh$, where x is in meters (m), U is in kg $\cdot \frac{m^2}{s^2}$, m is in kg, g is in $\frac{m}{s^2}$, and h is in meters (m). Find the units of k in terms of the other units given.

   Hint: Remember, values such as $\frac{1}{2}$ or 2 that don't have units can be ignored when you insert the units.

1. **Reviewing Negative Numbers** – Simplify the following expressions. Remember that the opposite of a negative number equals a positive! Remember too that the negative sign outside of the parentheses applies to everything inside the parentheses. You'll need to remember this when performing long division of polynomials.

   a. $5x^2 - (-2x^2)$

   b. $5x^2 - 2x - (3x^2 - x)$

   c. $-10t^2 + 3t - (-3t^2 + 4t)$

2. **Reviewing Multiplication and Division of Terms with Exponents** – Remember, to multiply like terms with exponents, we add the coefficients. To divide them, we subtract. **From now on, in the division problems, be sure to note whatever value the x cannot be, unless it is still obvious in the final expression.**

   Example: $\dfrac{x(x^5)}{x} = \dfrac{x^6}{x} = x^5$, where $x \neq 0$

   a. $x(x^7)(x^6)$

   b. $\dfrac{x^5}{x}$

   c. $\dfrac{x^4 x^3}{x^2}$

   d. $\left(\dfrac{3x^3}{x^2}\right)\left(\dfrac{5x^3}{x-1}\right)$

   e. $\left(\dfrac{7x^4}{2x+1}\right)\left(\dfrac{3x}{3x^2}\right)$

   f. $(f(x))(g(x))$, where $f(x) = \dfrac{4x}{x-1}$ and $g(x) = \dfrac{x+2}{3x}$

3. **Performing Polynomial Division** – Complete the requested divisions to simplify. Be sure to watch your negative signs!

   a. $x^2 - 3x + 4$ divided by $-x$

   b. $10x^2 + 4x - 2$ divided by $5x + 2$

   c. $\dfrac{x^2 - 7x + 12}{x - 4}$

   d. $\dfrac{-x^3 + 2x}{x + 1}$

4. **Partial Fractions and Checking Your Work** – Notice that your answers to 3a–3d were partial fractions! Go back and check your work by multiplying the quotient you got by the original divisor.

   a.

   b.

   c.

   d.

1. **Polynomial Division** – Complete the requested divisions to simplify.

   a. $\dfrac{2x^2 - 3}{x + 2}$

   b. $\dfrac{16v^3 + 2v^2 + 10v}{v - 2}$

   c. $f(x) = \dfrac{x^3 - 2x + 1}{x + 1}$ (Divide the right side of this function.)
   Hint: Remember to add a $0x^2$ term to the dividend to avoid mistakes!

   d. $\dfrac{x^3 - 2x^2 + x + 8}{x - 4}$

   e. $\dfrac{x^2 + 8x - 20}{x + 10}$

2. **Partial Fractions and Checking Your Work** – Notice that your answers to 1a–1e were partial fractions! Go back and check your work by multiplying the quotient you got by the original divisor.

   a.

   b.

   c.

   d.

   e.

3. **Thinking Through Your Answer**

   a. Look back at the fraction in 1e; based on your answer, what factor do both the numerator and denominator share?
   Hint: Notice that $x + 10$ was the denominator. If the fraction divided evenly (i.e., there was no fraction with $x + 10$ as the denominator in the answer), then that means that it was a factor of the numerator — that is, a value it can divide evenly by.

   b. Look back at the fraction in 1e; based on your answer, what root do both the numerator and denominator share?
   Hint: Remember, the root is the value of x that will make the expression equal 0. If they share a factor, then look at what value of x will make that factor equal 0.

4. **Skill Sharpening**

   a. Solve for x, giving your answers as approximate values: $\dfrac{25x^4 - 3x^2 - 5}{5x} = 0$

   b. Solve for x: $\dfrac{x^3 - 9x}{x + 3} = 0$

5. **Simplifying Rational Expressions**

   a. Simplify: $\dfrac{x^2 + 2x - 15}{x^2 + 3x - 10}$

   b. Graph the original function in 5a to help you answer this question (you do not need to draw the graph). At what value of x is there a discontinuity?

6. **Applying Algebra** – The net acceleration on an object equals the net force applied divided by the mass of the object, or $a = \dfrac{F}{m}$. Suppose the force being applied on a rocket changes based on time according to the function $6t^2 + 40$ for the domain $45 \geq t \geq 0$, and the mass of the rocket changes based on time according to the function $100 - 2t$ for the same domain.

   a. Write a rational function showing the acceleration (a) as a function of time (t) for the domain given.

   b. Complete the division in the rational function you wrote in 6a using polynomial division. Be sure to include the domain again!

7. **More Applying Algebra** – Let's say that you can chop 5 pieces of wood every minute. While doing this, the total calories you burn equal 2 times the square of the number of minutes plus 29.

   a. Write function $w(t)$ describing the pieces of wood chopped as a function of time.

   b. Write function $c(t)$ describing the calories burned as a function of time.

   c. Write function $r(t)$ describing the ratio of the wood chopped and the calories burned as a function of time.

   d. Is there a number of minutes at which you cannot compute a value for $r(t)$?

   $\bigcirc$ Yes $\bigcirc$ No

   If yes, what is that value?

   _____ minutes

   e. At what number of minutes will the ratio between the wood chopped and the calories burned be 0?

8. **Skill Sharpening**

   a. What value(s) for t satisfies both of these functions?
      $d(t) = -50t + 30$ and $d(t) = 40t - 20$

   b. In a fluid being sheared, the shear stress τ is related to the shear rate $\dot{\gamma}$ times the viscosity η, or in equation form:

      $$\tau = \eta\dot{\gamma}$$

      If τ has units of Pa (Pascals) and $\dot{\gamma}$ has units $\frac{1}{s}$, what are the units of η in terms of Pa and s?

   c. Copy the general curves shown in your notebook and shade the region that shows the solution to the inequalities $d \leq 4t + 3$ and $d < t^2 + 6$.
      Hint: Even though the curves are not labeled, you can easily figure out which is which by looking at the inequalities.[1]

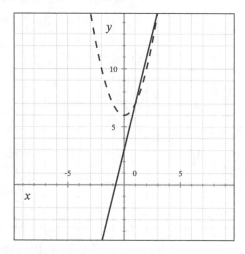

---

1 *Note:* Distance can be a quadratic equation like the one shown here when there is a constant acceleration.

Worksheet 11.5B ▪▪ 227

Today's worksheet helps you review the chapter while focusing on rational functions in business settings. Remember, the skills you're learning are useful tools that help us in completing real-life tasks!

1. **Break-even Point**[1] – Let's say these graphs show the actual values of the fixed costs and the sales price per unit for the past 6 years:

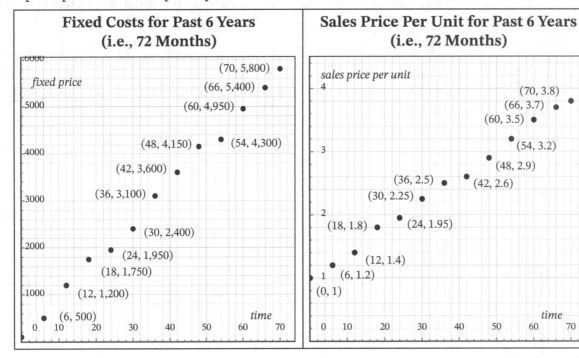

Fixed Costs for Past 6 Years (i.e., 72 Months)

fixed price

(70, 5,800)
(66, 5,400)
(60, 4,950)
(48, 4,150)   (54, 4,300)
(42, 3,600)
(36, 3,100)
(30, 2,400)
(24, 1,950)
(18, 1,750)
(12, 1,200)
(6, 500)

time

Sales Price Per Unit for Past 6 Years (i.e., 72 Months)

sales price per unit

(70, 3.8)
(66, 3.7)
(60, 3.5)
(54, 3.2)
(48, 2.9)
(36, 2.5)   (42, 2.6)
(30, 2.25)
(18, 1.8)   (24, 1.95)
(12, 1.4)
(6, 1.2)
(0, 1)

time

Notice that the fixed costs can be approximated as a function of time (in months) like this: $F = \dfrac{\$80}{\text{month}}t + \$100$. The sales price per unit over the past 6 years (i.e., 72 months) can also be approximated as a function of time (in months) as $P = \dfrac{\$0.04}{\text{month}}t + \$1$, as this item costs \$1 at first and increased by \$0.04 in cost each month.

---

[1] This relationship can be found in numerous sources online, although note that the letters and wording used varies. Examples include My Accounting Course: Accounting Education for the Rest of Us, "Break-Even Point," https://www.myaccountingcourse.com/financial-ratios/break-even-point, and QuickBooks Asia, "7 Accounting Formulas Every Business Should Know" (January 8, 2020), https://quickbooks.intuit.com/sg/r/finance-funding/7-accounting-formulas-every-business-should-know.

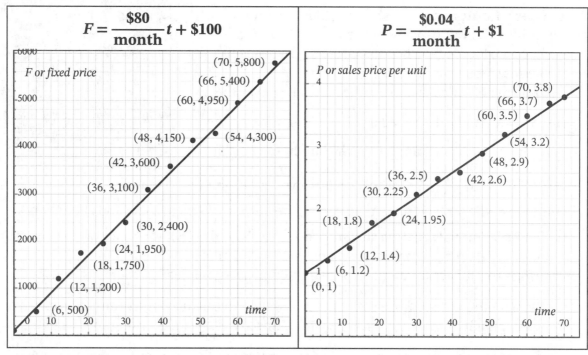

$$F = \frac{\$80}{month}t + \$100$$

F or fixed price

(70, 5,800)
(66, 5,400)
(60, 4,950)
(48, 4,150)
(54, 4,300)
(42, 3,600)
(36, 3,100)
(30, 2,400)
(24, 1,950)
(18, 1,750)
(12, 1,200)
(6, 500)

time

$$P = \frac{\$0.04}{month}t + \$1$$

P or sales price per unit

(70, 3.8)
(66, 3.7)
(60, 3.5)
(54, 3.2)
(48, 2.9)
(42, 2.6)
(36, 2.5)
(30, 2.25)
(18, 1.8)
(24, 1.95)
(12, 1.4)
(6, 1.2)
(0, 1)

time

Business owners need to know at what point they will actually make back their costs; this point is known as the break-even point. The formula for finding this is $B = \dfrac{F}{P - C}$, where B is the number of items sold to reach the break-even point, F is the fixed costs of producing those items (which we just found a function to approximate), P is the price each item sells for (which we again found a function to approximate), and C is the cost per unit in addition to the general fixed costs. Suppose that the variable cost per unit (C) has been a steady $0.50 for all 6 years.

a. Using the functions that were used to approximate F and P and the formula $B = \dfrac{F}{P - C}$, write a rational function describing the break-even point (B) as a function of time (t). Be sure to include the domain for which this function has held true; you should give it in months, since that is the unit of t.

b. Use long division to complete the division in the function you wrote in 1a. You may ignore units.

c. Show that the expression you found in 1b is indeed the quotient by multiplying it by the divisor (i.e., undoing the division you did in 1b).

We know the break-even point will always equal the fixed costs divided by the price each item sells for minus the cost per unit because that's how we're defining it. However, **we don't know if the formulas for the fixed cost and price per unit will stay true in the future.** Unlike with consistencies of creation that stay true year after year because of God's faithfulness, equations like $F(t) = \dfrac{\$80}{month}t + \$100$ are simply modeling what happened for the past 6 years (i.e., 72 months) . . . if situations change, they could change too.

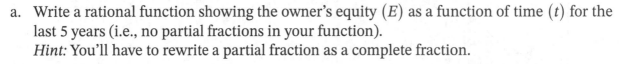

2. **Owner's Equity** – Owner's equity (E) is a way of describing the value the owners have in a business. It's found by taking the business' assets (A) minus its liabilities (L), or $E = A - L$.

   For one hypothetical business, the assets (A) over the last 5 years can be described by $\dfrac{t^2 + 5t + 2}{2t}$, where time (t) is in years. At the same time, the liabilities (L) can be described by $\dfrac{3t}{10} + 3$. For this problem you may ignore units (just know if you plug in t in years, the output will be in thousands of dollars).

   a. Write a rational function showing the owner's equity (E) as a function of time (t) for the last 5 years (i.e., no partial fractions in your function).
   Hint: You'll have to rewrite a partial fraction as a complete fraction.

   b. Look at the function you wrote in 2a. What, if any, is the value t cannot be based on that value making the denominator equal 0? Specify this domain using the $\neq$ sign.

   c. Based on the information given in this setting and the form of the function, what is the domain for which this function describes the owner's equity if we consider the current t value to be 5? Use an inequality symbol on either side of t to show this.

   _____ t _____

   d. Graph the function you wrote in 2a on a calculator. If the owner's equity continues to follow this same function for the next year (set the horizontal scale on your graph from 0 to 6), will the ending equity be about the same or greater than the starting equity?

   O about the same   O greater than

   e. Given the function you wrote in 2a, can we assume the owner's equity will continue to follow the same function for the next year?

   O Yes   O No

   f. What, if any, are the roots of the function you wrote in 2a *that are within the domain you found in 2c*?

   g. Is there an asymptote on the graph?

   O Yes   O No

   If there is one, at what value of t is it at?

3. **Skill Sharpening**

   a. Rewrite the expression on the right side of this function as a single fraction:
   $$f(x) = \frac{7x^2 - 2x + 3}{3x + 1} + 5x$$

   b. Is there a value that x in the expression you wrote in 3a cannot be?

   ○ Yes ○ No

   If yes, what is it? Your answer should start "$x \neq$."

   _____

   c. Complete the division in this rational expression: $\dfrac{-8x^3 + 5x}{x - 2}$.

   d. Is there a value that x in $\dfrac{-8x^4 + 5x^2}{x - 2}$ cannot be?

   ○ Yes ○ No

   If yes, what is it? Your answer should start "$x \neq$."

   _____

   e. What approximate value(s) of x make $\dfrac{-8x^4 + 5x^2}{x - 2}$ equal 0 (i.e., what are the approximate roots of the function)?

   f. If the denominator in the expression in 3e changed to $x(x - 2)$, what would the approximate roots of the function be?

   g. Complete the division in this rational expression: $\dfrac{5x^2 - 23x - 10}{x - 5}$

   h. ⊙ **Challenge Problem:** Simplify: $(t^2 - 1)(t^2 + t - 2)^{-1}$
   Hint: Start by rewriting the negative exponent as a positive exponent in the denominator. **Be sure to specify any values t cannot equal that are not still obvious in the final expression.**

   i. The capacitance of an electrical circuit component is defined as follows:
   $$K = \frac{Q}{V}$$

   Here Q is the charge in coulombs (C) and V is the voltage across the component in joules per coulomb $\left(\dfrac{J}{C}\right)$. Find the units of K in terms of C and J.

Intentionally left blank

1. **Identifying Exponential Functions**
   Hint: Some functions may not be exponential at all. If the input/independent variable is in the exponent, then the function is an exponential function. Remember that decay occurs when the exponent is negative *or* the g in the form of $P(t) = P_i g^{ct}$ is less than 1 but greater than 0.

   Example: $f(x) = 2^{\frac{x}{3}}$ is an exponential function as the x is in the exponent; $f(x) = 2x^3$ is not as the x is *not* in the exponent.

   A. $f(x) = 8^x$ B. $f(t) = 8^{\frac{t}{2}}$ C. $f(x) = 0.5^{4x}$ D. $f(t) = 8t^4$ E. $f(t) = 8^{-2t}$

   a. Which of the above functions show exponential growth?

   b. Which of the above functions show exponential decay?

2. **Exploring Exponential Functions** – Consider the function $f(x) = 8^{\frac{1}{3}x}$. What is its value when x equals 1?
   Hint: If you use a calculator to simplify, make sure you put parentheses around the exponent $\frac{1}{3}$ when you input it into the calculator so the calculator knows you don't mean $\frac{8^1}{3}$.

   $f(1) =$ _____

3. **Applying Exponential Growth and Decay** – Use $P(t) = P_i g^{ct}$ to solve.

   Remember, when a partial quantity doesn't make sense in an answer (i.e., you can't have a portion of a turtle, person, etc.), leave off the fractional part of the answer (i.e., round down to the nearest whole).

   a. A population of a town has been doubling every 4 years (which means $g = 2$, as we're doubling or multiplying by 2 each time the growth occurs), and $c = \frac{1}{4}$ yr, as the growth occurs 1 time every 4 years). What will the population be in 10 years if this growth continues and the current population is 30,000?

   b. In the scenario in 3a, what was the population 2 years ago (i.e., when $t = -2$)?

   c. If a lake starts with 50 catfish and then has 4 times that amount 3 years later, how many catfish will be in the lake after 10 years, assuming the growth continues at the same rate?
   Hint: When figuring out the time cycle (c), note that the growth here of 4 times is occurring 1 time per 3 years.

d. If a lake starts with 50 catfish and then has 4 times that amount 15 months later, how many catfish will be in the lake after 10 years, assuming the growth continues at the same rate?
Hint: You will need to convert the years to months so all of the units cancel out in the exponent.

e. If a baby weighs 9 lb one week and 10 lb the next, can you use an exponential function to find its weight for future weeks?

○ Yes   ○ No

Why or why not? _____

Reminder: Be sure to round to the nearest whole number on problems where a partial answer doesn't make sense (for example, we can't have a partial student).

1. **Applying Exponential Growth and Decay** – Remember that $P(t) = P_i g^{ct}$. Also remember that you can find g for a period of time by dividing the population at the end of that time period by the population at the beginning of it. And if you're given a fractional rate of decay, find g like this: $g = 1 - r$.

   a. If a lake starts with 50 catfish and then has 60 catfish after 1 year, how many catfish will it have in 10 years assuming the growth continues at the same rate?

   b. Suppose a college had 10,000 students 5 years ago and now has 30,000 students. If the current growth continues, how many students will it have 6 years from now?

   c. The number of students at a college has been decreasing by $\frac{1}{10}$ every year. If this continues, how many students would you expect to be there 5 years from now if there are currently 20,000 students enrolled?

   d. If a vitamin's presence in your body decreases by $\frac{1}{4}$ every 4 hours, how much will be left after 1 day if it starts at 500 mg?

   e. Suppose a certain bacteria colony doubles in size every 10 minutes. How many bacteria will the 100 starting bacteria grow to in 60 minutes?

   f. Given the information in 1e, how many bacteria with there be after 1 day at the same growth rate?
   Note: The number you get here will be very large. Most population growth can't sustain itself for very long at the same rate because of things dying off or other external factors; therefore, we'd never have as many bacteria around as you calculate here in real life, as the exponential growth model would break down at some point!

   g. The amount of water in a pot that is boiling is measured to be 4 gallons. An hour later, it only has 3 gallons left. If it continues to evaporate at the same rate, how many gallons will be left after 3 hours from the initial time it was measured as 4 gallons?

We used exponential decay to describe the situation in 1g as opposed to a linear formula because we were told the evaporation continued at the same rate, which would be exponential decay since that rate would be calculated based on the water left after each hour, not the initial water.

h. Based on observations and a sample size, the population of squirrels in an area is estimated to be around 200. A year later, the same process yielded an estimate of 250. If the growth continues at the same rate (and if these estimates are accurate), how many squirrels will there be in the area in 5 years since the initial 200 measurement?

i. Can we safely assume that the growth of a population of foxes will be exponential?

    ○ Yes   ○ No

    Why or why not? _____

2. **More Applying Algebra: Vitamin Concentration**

    a. If a certain vitamin concentration decreases in your body by 4% each hour, how much will be left after 1 entire day if you start with a concentration of 700 mg?
        Hint: Remember to use the same units of measure! Also, note that you're really being given a fractional rate of decay here (4% means $\frac{4}{100}$), so remember that $g = 1 - r$.

    b. The problem in 2a *assumes* that the vitamin concentration decreases at 4% each hour. Would your answer still be accurate if that rate was different due to, say, some condition present in your blood?

    c. Write a function to describe how the concentration changes based on time for the situation described in 2a.
        Hint: Insert the values given into the general exponential form just like you did in 2a, except leave *t* as a variable, as you're being asked for the general formula for this vitamin concentration rather than for the value after a specific amount of time.

    d. Graph the function you wrote in 2c and draw the general shape in your notebook. Does it show exponential growth or decay?

        ○ growth   ○ decay

    e. If a certain bacteria concentration *decreases* in your body by 5% each hour, write a function showing how much you will have after a certain number of hours if you start with 100.

    f. Graph the function you wrote in 2e and draw the general shape in your notebook. Does it show exponential growth or decay?

        ○ growth   ○ decay

3. **Skill Sharpening**

   a. Complete the division in this rational expression: $\dfrac{5x^3 - 2x^2 + 8}{-x + 3}$. Be sure to check your work!

   b. In 3a, is $-x + 3$ a factor of the numerator?
      Hint: Notice that $-x + 3$ was the denominator. If the fraction divided evenly (i.e., there was no fraction with $-x + 3$ as the denominator in the answer), then that means that it was a factor of the numerator — that is, a value it can divide evenly by.

      O Yes O No

   c. What value is an invalid input to $f(t) = \dfrac{t^3 - t^2 + 3t}{2t + 3}$? Use a $\neq$ to specify.

   d. Graph $f(t) = \dfrac{t^3 - t^2 + 3t}{2t + 3}$ on a calculator, drawing the general shape in your notebook and drawing a dashed line where there's an asymptote at the value you identified as an invalid input in 3c.

   e. If we want $f(t)$ to equal 0 in $f(t) = \dfrac{t^3 - t^2 + 3t}{2t + 3}$, what input values would let that occur?

1. **Calculating Interest** – On all problems, assume there are exactly 365 days in a year (i.e., ignore leap years). **Round answers that are in dollars to the nearest cent.** While you can use different formulas to solve, the *Solutions Manual* will show the solution using $P(t) = P_i \left(1 + \dfrac{r}{n}\right)^{nt}$, as that is typically the one to use when dealing with rates. The key is to make sure that whatever you end up with as the base of the exponent is the amount you need to multiply by each time the growth occurs to find the new ending balance, and the exponent is the number of times the growth occurs.

   a. If you deposit $25,000 in an account earning 2% annual interest that is compounded *daily*, how much will the $25,000 grow to in 4 years?

   b. If you deposit that same $25,000 in an account earning 2% annual interest that is compounded *monthly*, how much will the $25,000 grow to in 4 years?

   c. Which account would yield you a higher ending balance in 4 years?

      ○ the account in 1a   ○ the account in 1b

      Why do you think that is? _____

   d. If your investments are earning an average of 5% annual interest compounded monthly and you invest $30,000 when you are 30 years old, how much will you have when you retire at age 65? Notice that interest can add up over the years!

1. **Applying Algebra: Interest** – On all problems, assume there are exactly 365 days in a year (i.e., ignore leap years). While you can use different formulas to solve, the *Solutions Manual* will show the solution using $P(t) = P_i\left(1 + \dfrac{r}{n}\right)^{nt}$ whenever finding compound interest, as that is typically the one to use when dealing with rates.

   a. If you invest \$1,000 at an annual interest rate of 3% compounded monthly, how much money will you have at the end of 5 years? Round to the nearest cent.

   b. If you invest \$1,000 at a *simple* interest rate (i.e., where only the investment earns interest) of 3% each year, how much will you have at the end of 5 years? Note that simple interest is calculated by $P(t) = P_i(1 + rt)$.

Notice that 1a and 1b had the same amount being invested for the same number of years, yet your answer to 1b was less than in 1a. The ending balance was less when earning simple interest, since in simple interest you don't earn interest on the interest.

   c. Express your ending money as a function of the time (in years) if you invest \$10 at an annual interest rate of 3% compounded monthly. Do not round (that is, just write the function but don't calculate the value).

   _____, where *t* is in years

   d. Express the ending money as a function of the time in years if you invest \$500 at an annual interest rate of 4.25% compounded daily. Do not round (that is, just write the function but don't calculate the value).

   _____, where *t* is in years

2. **Exponential Growth Given a Rate of Growth**

   a. What is the growth multiplication factor (g) if the rate of growth is 3%?
   Hint: When exponential growth is given as a rate, $g = 1 + r$.

   b. If you expect the revenue of a company to increase by 3% every 6 months, and the current revenue is \$200,000 a year, what will the revenue be in 4 years, assuming the growth rate you calculated in 2a? Round to the nearest cent.

   c. What is the growth multiplication factor (g) if the rate of decay is 3%?
   Hint: We saw in Lesson 12.1 that when exponential decay is given as a rate, $g = 1 - r$.

3. **Mixed Exponential Growth & Decay Problems** – These problems may need any of the skills you have learned!

   a. Suppose you're told that a medication leaves your system at a rate of 14% each hour. How much will be left after 10 hours if you start with 300 mg?

   b. Let's say there are 14 people left in the church choir. One year ago, there were 30 people. At what rate (r) per year did people leave the choir?
   Hint: $g = 1 - r$. Find g by dividing the ending amount for the time period by the beginning, and then solve for r.

   c. If the situation in 3b continues as exponential decay, how many people will be left in the choir in 2 more years?

   d. If the rate in 3b was a constant rate for all the years since the choir had formed and thus the choir size had been decreasing exponentially for many years, how many were in the choir 4 years before the current amount of 14 members?

   e. Let's say that people leaving the choir could be described as a linear function, not an exponential one. And let's say that instead of an exponential decay, where the decay is based on the amount left, people have been leaving at a steady rate of 40% of the original choir each year instead. How many people would there be in the choir after 2 more years (so 3 years from the beginning), given that the choir started at 30? Use $P(t) = P_i - P_i rt$.

4. **Skill Sharpening**

   a. Complete the division in this rational expression: $\dfrac{-3x^3 + 12x}{x - 2}$. Be sure to check your work!

   b. Factor the numerator in 4a. Is $x - 2$ a factor of the numerator?
   Hint: Start by factoring out a $-3x$.

   ○ Yes   ○ No

   c. In 4a, is $x = 2$ a root of the numerator?

   ○ Yes   ○ No

   d. What value(s) can x not equal in $f(x) = \dfrac{x^2 + 9}{x^2 - 9}$? Use a $\neq$ to specify.

   e. What value(s) of x would yield an output of 0 in $f(x) = \dfrac{x^2 + 9}{x^2 - 9}$? Use a $\neq$ to specify.

   f. Rewrite as a single fraction: $\dfrac{7}{2x + 3} - \dfrac{3x - 5}{x}$

1. **Understanding Check**

   a. Which of these formulas approximates the value for e in terms of a number (n) when n approaches infinity?

   $$\bigcirc \left(1 + \frac{1}{n}\right)^n \qquad \bigcirc \left(1 + \frac{1}{n}\right)^{cn} \qquad \bigcirc \ (1 + r)^n$$

   b. When should the formula $P(t) = P_i e^{rt}$ be used instead of the other formulas we've looked at for exponential growth and decay?

2. **Continuous Growth** – Notice that these problems all deal with *continuous growth* and give a *continuous growth rate*. Thus, you need to use the formula $P(t) = P_i e^{rt}$.

   a. If a population of elephants grows continuously at a rate of 5% each year, what will the population be in 15 years if it is currently 100?

   b. If a population of elephants grows continuously at a rate of 5% each year, what will the population be in 30 days if it is currently 30? Use 365 days per year.

   c. If a population of elephants grows continuously at a rate of 3% per year, what was the population 5 years in the past if it is currently 30?

1. **Applying Algebra: Continuous Growth and Decay** – Notice that these problems all deal with *continuous growth and give a continuous growth rate*. Thus, you need to use the formula $P(t) = P_i e^{rt}$.

   a. A population of bacteria grows continuously at a rate of $\dfrac{1.2}{\text{wk}}$. If the initial population was just 10, what will its value be after 10 weeks if left unchecked?

   b. Suppose that we're a banker and we want to offer continuously compounded interest. We want to see how an investor's total will vary based on the rate r over 8 years if $1,000 is invested. Write a function expressing this in terms of the rate (r).

   c. Using the function in 1b, compare the investor's total after 8 years when the continuous rate is $\dfrac{0.056}{\text{yr}}$ versus when it is $\dfrac{0.00023}{\text{day}}$. Which rate is better for the *banker* and which is better for the *investor*? Use 1 yr = 365 days, ignoring leap years.

   Rate better for banker: ○ $\dfrac{0.056}{\text{yr}}$ ○ $\dfrac{0.00023}{\text{day}}$

   Rate better for investor: ○ $\dfrac{0.056}{\text{yr}}$ ○ $\dfrac{0.00023}{\text{day}}$

   d. If a bacteria population dies off at a continuous rate of $-\dfrac{0.36}{\text{day}}$ due to treatment, and there were 50,000 bacteria to start, write function $P(t)$ to show the number of bacteria left over time.

   e. Graph the function you wrote in 1d on a calculator and draw the general shape in your notebook.

2. **Miscellaneous Exponential Growth and Decay** – You might need any of the skills we've covered so far to answer these questions! **Round any answers in dollars to the nearest cent.**

   a. Suppose an aquarium advertises that their fish population that was 120 in 2016 grew to 500 in 2019. If this growth continues the same way, what will the fish population be in 2021?

b. Suppose a plant that wasn't native to the area gets introduced and starts to take over. Initially, the plant was present on 5 acres. After 1 year, the plant was present on 100 acres. If this growth remains unchecked and continues at the current rate, how many acres will have the plant in another 1.5 years from the present time that is at 100 acres?

c. If a rich uncle places $20,000 in a savings account for college for their nephew at birth, how much will be in the account when the child turns 18, assuming it earns 7% annual interest compounded daily? Assume 365 days in a year (i.e., ignore leap years).

d. If that same rich uncle places $20,000 in a savings account for college for his nephew at birth, how much will be in the account when the child turns 18, assuming it earns 7% *simple* interest each year (i.e., only the initial investment earns interest)? The simple interest formula is $P(t) = P_i(1 + rt)$.

e. Compare your answers to 2c and 2d. How much more was the $20,000 worth when the nephew turned 18 when invested at compound interest?

_____

Why do you think that is?

_____

_____

3. **Skill Sharpening**

a. Complete the division in this rational expression: $\dfrac{3x^4 - 2x^2 + 2}{x - 1}$. Be sure to check your work!

b. Simplify: $f(x) = (2x^4 + 3x^2)(2x)^{-1}$ (Be sure to include what x cannot equal.) *Hint:* Remember that negative exponents can be rewritten in the denominator as a positive exponent.

c. On a calculator, graph $f(x) = (2x^4 + 3x^2)(2x)^{-1}$. Draw the general shape in your notebook, drawing and labeling an empty circle at the value x cannot equal (i.e., where there's a discontinuity).

d. Rewrite as a single fraction: $\dfrac{5}{x - 3} - \dfrac{3 + x}{2}$

1. **Multiplying and Dividing Exponential Expressions** – Simplify as much as possible. Notice how the same principles apply in more complicated expressions.

    a. $a^2 a^3$

    b. $v^{2x} v^{3x}$

    c. $e^{2x}(e^{3x})$

    d. $(2)(e^{2t})(3)(e^{3t})$

    e. $\dfrac{a^2}{a^3}$

    f. $\dfrac{d^{2t}}{d^{3t}}$

    g. $\dfrac{5^{2x}}{5^{3x}}$

2. **Adding and Subtracting Exponential Expressions** – Simplify as much as possible.

    a. $5a^2 + 7a^2$

    b. $(15)a^{2x} + (3)a^{2x}$

    c. $x^2 + x^2$

    d. $y^{2x} + y^{2x}$

3. **Simplifying with Factoring** – Factor any amount you can.

    a. $14e^{5r} + 13e^{6r}$

    a. $2e^{2r} + 4e^r$

    b. $3v^{3t} + 6v^{4t}$

4. **Rules Expressed with Algebra**

    a. Take a look at this rule expressed as an algebraic equation: $ma^x(na^y) = mna^{x+y}$. Write an example using actual values of this in action by making $m = 2$, $x = 3$, $n = 4$, and $y = 5$ and simplifying. Leave a as an unknown in your example.

    b. Simplify: $4x^3 3x^7$

    c. Did the simplification in 4b apply the principle being described by $ma^x(na^y) = mna^{x+y}$, which you looked at in 4a?

    ○ Yes   ○ No

1. **Simplifying Exponential Functions**

   Example: Find $f(x)g(x)$ if $f(x) = 2e^{2x}$ and $g(x) = 3e^{-x}$

   $$f(x)g(x) = (2e^{2x})(3e^{-x}) = 6e^{2x+-x} = 6e^{x}$$

   Notice that we just plugged in what the functions equaled and then simplified using what we learned about simplifying exponential expressions in Lesson 12.4. This is the same thing you did on Worksheet 12.4A, except now there's the extra step of substituting the values to find the expression you need to simplify.

   a. Find $f(x)g(x)$ if $f(x) = 3e^{4x}$ and $g(x) = 5e^{-2x}$.

   b. Find $\dfrac{f(x)}{g(x)}$ if $f(x) = 20b^{4x}$ and $g(x) = 5b^{3x}$.

   c. Find $f(x) - g(x)$ if $f(x) = 5g^{5x}$ and $g(x) = 7g^{5x}$.

   d. Find $f(t) - g(t)$ if $f(t) = (10)e^{-2t}$ and $g(t) = (5)e^{-2t}$.

   e. Find $f(t)g(x)$ if $f(t) = 3e^{4t}$ and $g(x) = e^{2x}$.

   f. Find $f(t) + g(x)$ if $f(t) = 3e^{4t}$ and $g(x) = e^{2x}$.

   g. Find $f(t) + g(t)$ if $f(t) = 4e^{3t} + 2e^{2t}$.

   h. Find $f(t) - g(t)$ if $f(t) = 3a^{10t}$ and $g(t) = -9a^{7t}$.

2. **Rules Expressed with Algebra**

   a. Take a look at this rule expressed as an algebraic equation:
   $b^{x}(mb^{y} + n) = mb^{x+y} + nb^{x}$. Write an example using actual values of this in action by making $m = 2$, $n = 3$, $x = 4$, $y = 5$, and leaving b as an unknown and simplifying.

   b. Apply the principle in 2a to distribute the multiplication in this expression: $x^{2}(3x + 2)$

3. **Applying Algebra: Total of Two Accounts** – Let's say you have a checking account that has an initial deposit of $1,000 and grows continuously according to the function: $C(t) = \$1,000\,e^{0.01t}$. You also have a savings account with an initial deposit of $5,000 and grows continually according to the function $S(t) = \$5,000\,e^{0.01t}$. We could write a function that shows the total balance you have in both accounts based on time like this:

   $$T(t) = C(t) + S(t)$$

   a. Substitute the values for $C(t)$ and $S(t)$ into $T(t)$ and simplify, if possible.

   b. Calculate the total you'll have in both accounts when $t = 5$. Round your answer to the nearest cent.

   $$T(5) = \underline{\hspace{3cm}}$$

4. **Applying Algebra: Bank Account Transfer** – Suppose you have a checking account that grows continuously according to the function $P(t) = \$2{,}000e^{0.02t}$, where t is in months. After a certain number of months, which we'll call t_1, you withdraw all your money and put it into a savings account that grows at a rate of $S(t) = De^{0.10t}$, where D is the initial deposit. What is the function that shows how your savings account will grow with time? The questions below will help you think this through.

a. Rewrite $P(t) = \$2{,}000e^{0.02t}$ to calculate the ending balance for the checking account after t_1.

    Hint: Just replace t with t_1. Your answer should start "$P(t_1) =$."

b. The savings account will have an initial deposit of all the money from our checking account when we take it out at t_1. Substitute the value of $P(t_1)$ (see your answer to 4a) for the D in $S(t) = De^{0.10t}$ and simplify, if possible.

c. Use the function you wrote for $S(t)$ in 4b to calculate the value of your savings account when $t = 4$ if $t_1 = 3$ (i.e., 4 months into the savings account deposit after making the deposit after an initial 3 months). Round to the nearest cent.

    $S(4) = $_____

> *Continuously compounded interest is not common. But it's important to understand what is meant by it if you do encounter it!*

5. **Skill Sharpening**

a. Simplify as much as possible: $3e^{2x}(4e^{-4x})$

b. Simplify as much as possible: $e^{2x} + e^{2x}$

c. If a certain population grows continually at a rate of 0.56 per day, how much will 10 grow to over a period of 30 days?

d. Complete the division in this rational expression: $\dfrac{25x^4 - 10x^2 - 5}{5x}$. Be sure to check your work!

1. **Reviewing the Concept** – Simplify.

   a. $\left(x^6\right)^2$

   b. $\left(a^3\right)^{\frac{1}{2}}$

   c. $\left(4e^2\right)^3$ (Leave e as a symbol; do not calculate it.)

2. **Applying the Concept: Rewriting Exponential Expressions with a Different Base and Numerically Simplifying** – Simplify, rewriting bases as another number raised to a power as needed.

   Example: $9^{3x} + 3^{6x} = 3^{2(3x)} + 3^{6x} = 3^{6x} + 3^{6x} = 2\left(3^{6x}\right) = 2\left(3^6\right)^x = 2\left(729^x\right)$

   a. $8^{4x} + 2^{12x}$

   b. $4^x + 2^{2x}$

   c. $9^{2t} + 81^t$

   d. $4^{6t} + 16^{3t}$

3. **Applying the Concept: Simplifying Multiplications and Divisions with Exponents** – Simplify the following as much as possible.

   a. $(2a)^2$

   b. $(4e)^3$ (Leave e as a symbol in your answer.)

   c. $\dfrac{7^y}{3^y}$

   d. $\sqrt{\dfrac{a^{2c}}{b^{2c}}}$

   e. $\left(\dfrac{a^{3x}}{b^{3x}}\right)^{\frac{1}{3}}$

1. **Algebraic Explanations**

   a. Take a look at this algebraic relationship: $(m^x)^y = m^{xy}$. Write an example using actual values of this in action by making $m = 2$, $x = 3$, $y = 4$ and simplifying.

   b. Simplify: $(3x^{3y})^y$

   c. Did the simplification in 1b apply the principle being described by $(m^x)^y = m^{xy}$?

      ○ Yes   ○ No

2. **Rewriting Exponential Expressions with a Different Base** – Simplify, rewriting bases as another number raised to a power as needed.

   Example: $9^{3x} + 3^{6x} = 3^{2(3x)} + 3^{6x} = 3^{6x} + 3^{6x} = 2(3^{6x}) = 2(3^6)^x = 2(729^x)$

   a. $5^{2x} + 25^x$

   b. $16^{2x} + (4^{2x})^2$ (Simplify so there is as little left as an exponent as possible.)

3. **Simplifying Exponential Expressions** – Simplify the following as much as possible. Use factoring as you're able.

   a. Find $f(x)g(x)$ if $f(x) = (3x)^2$ and $g(x) = \left(\dfrac{x}{3}\right)^2$.

   b. Find $\dfrac{f(x)}{g(x)}$ if $f(x) = 8^x$ and $g(x) = 7^x$.

   c. Find $f(x) - g(x)$ if $f(x) = 8^{2x}$ and $g(x) = 4^{4x}$.

   d. Find $f(x) - g(x)$ if $f(x) = 8^{2x}$ and $g(x) = 8^{5x}$.

   e. Find $f(x) + g(x)$ if $f(x) = 8^{2x}$ and $g(x) = 8^{5x}$.

4. **Applying Algebra: Adding Probabilities** – In advanced physics, scientists use something known as a partition function to tell how likely it is for a system of particles (i.e., gas molecules, liquid molecules, etc.) to be in a given thermodynamic (related to energy) state. It turns out that these partition functions are just the sums of exponential functions with various exponents.

   Let's say that we have a gas system that can have its molecules exist in three different energy states E_1, E_2, and E_3. Its partition function would look like the following:

   $$Z = e^{-\beta E_1} + e^{-\beta E_2} + e^{-\beta E_3}$$

   Here β is a constant related to the temperature.

   a. If $E_1 = 2$, $E_2 = 4$, and $E_3 = 8$, simplify the expression for the partition function. Notice that you'll end up applying factoring!

   b. If E_1, E_2, and E_3 all equal 3, simplify the expression for the partition function.

5. 🎯 **Challenge Problem: More Applying Algebra: Adding Probabilities 2** – It turns out the probability of a given gas molecule in a system having energy E is $p(E) = \dfrac{n(E)e^{-\beta E}}{Z}$, where $n(E)$ is known as the density of states.
   Hint: Here, $n(E)$ is written in function notation. Treat it as a single unknown.

   a. Calculate and simplify the probability a gas molecule has an energy (E) of 8 if $n(E) = 1$; use the value for Z you calculated in 4a.

   $p(8) = $_____

   b. Calculate and simplify the probability a gas molecule has an energy (E) of 3 if Z is the value you found in 4b and $n(E) = 3$.

   $p(3) = $_____

6. **Applying Algebra: Rabbit Growth** – Suppose that Rabbit Population A increases by a multiple of 4 every 10 days (while this value is hypothetical, rabbits can have babies very frequently . . . and they have a lot at a time) and that another rabbit population, which we'll call Rabbit Population B, multiplies by 2 every 5 days. If Population A starts at 10 rabbits and Population B starts at 20 rabbits, what will the ending population of both rabbits be after 30 days? The questions below will help you answer this.

   a. Using the general form $P(t) = P_i g^{ct}$, write function $P_A(t)$ describing the ending population of Rabbit Population A (P_A) as a function of the time (t) in days.

   b. Using the general form $P(t) = P_i g^{ct}$, write function $P_B(t)$ describing the ending population of Rabbit Population B (P_B) as a function of the time (t) in days.

   c. Add the functions you wrote in 6a and 6b together, simplifying as much as possible so as to end up with a single term.
   Hint: Rewrite all your exponential terms such that the base is 2.

   d. What will be the total combined populations after 30 days? Use your answer from 6c to calculate, substituting 30 for t.

   $P_A(30 \text{ days}) + P_B(30 \text{ days}) = $_____

7. **Skill Sharpening**

   a. Simplify: $2e^{\frac{1}{2}t} 3e^{\frac{1}{4}t}$
   Hint: Don't let the fractions throw you! Use what you already know about fractions to solve.

   b. Simplify by factoring out common factors: $4e^x - 2e^{2x}$

c. Combine into a single fraction and then simplify: $\dfrac{x^3}{x} + \dfrac{x}{x+2}$ (Be sure to specify what x cannot equal if it's not still obvious in the final expression.)

d. Graph on a calculator and then draw the general shape of $y = \dfrac{x^3}{x} + \dfrac{x}{x+2}$, adding a dashed line to represent the asymptote and an empty circle to represent the discontinuity.

e. Look at your graph in 7d to identify the requested values:

The asymptote is when $x =$_____.

The discontinuity is when $x =$_____.

f. Complete the division: $\dfrac{x^2 + x - 20}{x + 5}$

g. Factor the numerator in 7f; what common factor do both the numerator and denominator in 7f share?

1. **Skill Checking**

   a. Find $\dfrac{f(x)}{g(x)}$ if $f(x) = 8^{2x}$ and $g(x) = 8^{6x}$.

   b. Find $f(x)g(x)$ if $f(x) = 8^{2x}$ and $g(x) = 8^{5x}$.

   c. Find $f(x) + g(x)$ if $f(x) = 4e^{2x}$ and $g(x) = 2e^{4x}$.

   d. Simplify: $4^x + 2^{2x}$

   e. Simplify: $3a^7 - 9a^5$

   f. Simplify: $3^{3x} + 27^x$

   g. Simplify: $(2a)^3 \left(\dfrac{a}{b}\right)^2$

   h. Simplify: $\left(\dfrac{a^3}{b^3}\right)^{\frac{1}{3}}$

2. **Applying Algebra: Debt**

   a. Let's say that a certain stock has consistently lost an average of 1.2% each year. If you invested $500 dollars in the stock 20 years ago, how much money do you now have left in the stock? Round to the nearest cent.
   Hint: Your rate will be negative since you've lost money.

   b. Suppose a credit card offers 18% APR — this is the annual rate. If you carry a balance of $5,000 on that card and don't make payments, how much interest will get added to pay off after just half a year if the interest is compounded daily? Assume 365 days in the year. Round to the nearest cent.
   Hint: First figure out the total amount you'll owe after half a year, and then calculate how much more that is than the $5,000.

   c. A small online college has been told by their board that they need to grow from their current 1,000 students to 3,000 students in 5 years. To meet this goal, what should their 2-year goal be as far as the number of students they should have assuming exponential growth of students?

   d. Suppose the college in 2c assumes a simple percentage growth instead (i.e., one based only on the initial student population). What should their 2-year goal be as far as the number of students they should have if they again start at 1,000 students and want to grow to 3,000 students in 5 years? Use the formula $P(t) = P_i(1 + rt)$.
   Hint: You can find the rate (r) needed by first solving for r using the fact that we know that at $t = 5$, we want to have 3,000 students. Then solve for $t = 2$, using the value for r you found.

   Interest works both ways! The Bible warns that "the borrower is the slave of the lender" (Proverbs 22:7; ESV). Borrowing money can literally lead to slavery, as it adds up fast, since the amount owed grows exponentially!

3. **Applying Algebra: Radioactive Dating**

   Note: Ask your parent/teacher about doing 3b and 3c orally.

   Besides carbon-14 dating, another radiometric dating technique used is called potassium-argon dating. The equation for the radioactive decay has the following form:

   $$A = \alpha K\left(1 - 2^{\frac{-t}{\tau}}\right)$$

   Let's explore this equation further, along with some of the information about the misguided assumptions in the dating method from an Answers in Genesis article.[1] In the formula, A is the amount of argon-40 in the sample. We call argon-40 the "daughter element," since potassium-40 (called the "parent element") decays into it. K stands for the amount of potassium-40 in the sample (the parent element), α a correction factor to differentiate how much potassium decayed into calcium-40 (another "daughter element" potassium-40 decays into), t how much time has passed, and τ the half-life (the time it takes for half of the potassium-40 to decay into argon-40).

   a. The article explains that a team of scientists found some samples of rocks that formed from volcanic lava flow that were formed less than 50 years prior that contain potassium-40. Given that the measured half-life (τ) of potassium is approximately 1.8×10^9 years (based on modern observations in laboratory settings), calculate what you would expect $\frac{A}{\alpha K}$ to equal after a time (t) of 50 years. *Hint:* Solve the equation for $\frac{A}{\alpha K}$ and then substitute the value you've been given on the other side.

   b. According to the information in the article, the group of scientists actually measured the actual values of $\frac{A}{\alpha K}$ to be around 0.001 (several samples were taken, with values that varied) . . . which is a *lot* larger than you would expect given the dating method's assumptions. Discuss why you think there is such a large difference in the measured value and what you calculated.

   c. One of the assumptions secular scientists use with this dating method is that all the argon-40 they find trapped in a sample must have formed from the decay of the potassium-40 in the sample. Argon is a gas while potassium is a solid, so the idea is that all the argon gas escaped into the atmosphere when the sample was molten (i.e., liquid lava), meaning that when the rock cooled and formed, there wasn't any argon-40. The thinking then is that any argon-40 gas present in the solid rock must have formed from decay of potassium-40 and that we can then solve the above equation for t and back-calculate how long ago the rock formed. Discuss what might be wrong with this thinking.

   It turns out that the measured values, taken with the dating method assumptions, yield a time of between 270,000 and 3.5 million years. In other words, rocks we know formed only 50 years ago came back with ages significantly older. The article lists many other examples of rocks of known ages being dated grossly incorrectly. There's clearly something wrong with the assumptions!

---

1   Dr. Andrew A. Snelling, "The Cause of Anomalous Potassium-Argon 'Ages' for Recent Andesite Flows at Mt. Ngauruhoe, New Zealand, and the Implications for Potassium-Argon 'Dating'" (*Answers in Depth*, December 30, 2009), https://answersingenesis.org/geology/radiometric-dating/anomalous-potassium-argon-ages-implications/

4. **Rules Expressed with Algebra** – Write an example using actual values of this rule in action by substituting actual values for each of the letters given (use 2 for m, 3 for n, 4 for x, and 5 for y) and then simplifying as much as possible: $\dfrac{ma^x}{na^y} = \dfrac{m}{n}(a^{x-y})$.

   Note: Leave a as an unknown in your example.

1. **Applying Algebra** – The following graph shows the arc of a window that is shaped like a parabola, where the measurement scale is in inches.

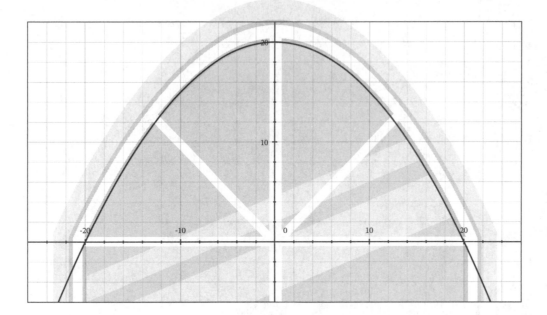

   a. At about how many inches horizontally from the center is the vertical height of the arc 0? (Lesson 9.1)

   about _____inches and _____ inches

   b. What do we call the horizontal coordinate where the vertical coordinate is 0?

2. **Find the Roots of These Quadratic Expressions *Without* Using the Quadratic Formula** (Lessons 9.2, 9.3, and 9.5)

   a. $x^2 - x - 2$

   b. $x^2 + 4x + 4$

   c. $x^2 + 1$

   d. $x^2 - 16$

3. **Solve for x Using the Quadratic Formula** (Lessons 9.4, 9.5)

   $0 = 3x^2 - 5x + 3$

4. **The Fundamental Theorem of Algebra** (Lesson 10.1) – Identify the number of roots each expression has and solve for them all. Note that some may be repeated or complex.

   a. $2x^4 - 2$

   number of roots: _____   roots: _____

   b. $7x^3 + 3x$

   number of roots: _____   roots: _____

5. **Solving Systems of Equalities and Inequalities Graphically** (Lessons 10.2 and 10.3)

   a. Use your calculator to graph both $y = -4.9t^2 + 3t + 6$ and $y = 5t$ on the same graph. List the points that satisfy both equalities.

   b. Graph $y \geq 7x^5 - 4$ and $y < 2x + 6$ on a calculator and draw the solution in your notebook.

6. **Asymptotes** – (Lessons 11.1 and 12.1)

   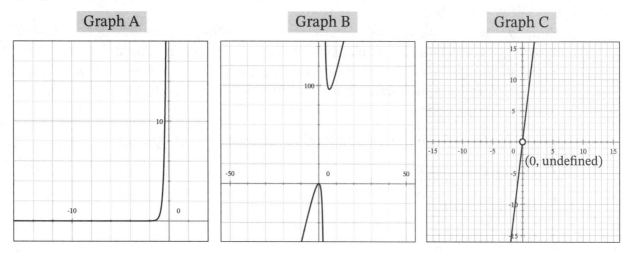

   Graph A   Graph B   Graph C

   c. Which graph(s) have an asymptote? Note that a graph has an asymptote if there's a value the curve(s) approaches but never equals; it doesn't matter if a dashed line is shown to mark the asymptote or not.

   ○ A   ○ B   ○ C

   d. Which graph(s) have a discontinuity?

   ○ A   ○ B   ○ C

7. **Applying Algebra** – Let's say that the rate b of wood used to burn a hypothetical fire is based on the mass of the wood: $b(m) = 10m$. At the same time, the heat the fire produces is also based on its mass according to this function: $h(m) = 0.2m^2 + m$, for the domain $m \geq 0$.

   a. Write a rational function showing the ratio between the rate of the burning of the wood and the heat produced as a function of mass; be sure to simplify as much as possible. Part of the function is given here, **but be sure to write the entire function in your notebook.** (Lesson 11.1)

   $f(m) =$ _____, where $m \neq$ _____ and $m \geq$ _____

   b. What are the two values the input cannot equal? Include values outside of the specified domain in the problem. (Lesson 11.2)

   c. Does this function as a whole ever have an output of 0? (Lesson 11.3)

   ○ Yes   ○ No

8. **More with Rational Functions**

   a. Rewrite the expression on the right of this function as a single fraction:

   $f(x) = \dfrac{2x^2 + 10}{x - 3} - \dfrac{2}{x}$ (Lesson 11.4)

   b. Complete the division: $\dfrac{x^3 - 2x + 3}{x + 1}$. Be sure to check your work. (Lesson 11.5)

9. **Exponential Functions** (Chapter 12)

   a. Suppose that you wanted to find out what a population that started out at 50 and is growing at a 4% continuous rate per year plus another population that started at 70 and is also growing at a 4% continuous rate per year is after some time (t) in years. Write a formula (and simplify) describing this situation using $P_F(t)$ to stand for the final combined population.

   b. Calculate the value for the situation you wrote in 9a if $t = 10$ years.

   $P_F(10 \text{ years}) = $ _____

   c. Simplify: $2^{4x} + 16^x$

   d. Simplify: $7x^{7x} + 5x^{2x}$

   We're not reviewing Chapter 12 as much, as hopefully it's still fresh in your memory! Be sure to make sure you understood all of the problems on Chapter 12's quiz as well.

   ---

10. ▦ **More Applying Algebra** – A builder is looking to make a building such that the length of a side is such that if you subtract 5 from the length and multiply the remainder by the length itself, the product is 30. (Lesson 9.5)

    Is this possible?

    ○ Yes   ○ No

    If so, what is the length?

    length = _____

11. ▦ **More Applying Algebra** (Lesson 10.2) – A tank is supplied by two pumps. One day the tank was 60% filled by working the small pump 3 hours and the large pump 1 hour. The next day, the tank was 100% filled, this time by working the small pump for 4 hours and the large pump for 2 hours. What percent of the tank does each pump fill every hour? Solve this by writing out a system of equations and solving each equation to make the large pump dependent on the small pump. Then graph to find the rate of each! The y value will be the percent per hour of the large pump, and the x value the percent per hour of the small pump.

    Percent the large pump fills each hour: _____

    Percent the small pump fills each hour: _____

12. **Function Recognition** – Choose the correct function to describe each graph.

a.

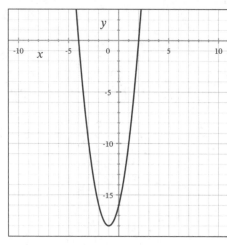

A. $f(x) = x^2 + 2x - 8$

B. $f(x) = 2x^2 + 4x - 16$

    ○ A   ○ B

b.

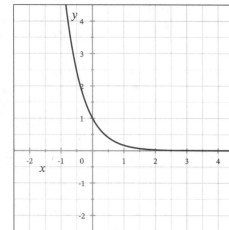

A. $f(x) = 6^x$

B. $f(x) = 6^{-x}$

C. $f(x) = x^2 + 3$

    ○ A   ○ B   ○ C

c.

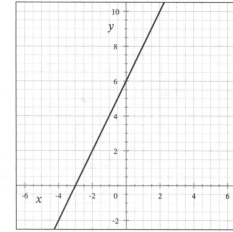

A. $f(x) = 2x + 6$

B. $f(x) = -2x + 6$

C. $f(x) = 2x - 3$

    ○ A   ○ B   ○ C

Note that other concepts may be covered on the test. Be sure to read through the Chapter Synopsis and look over the quizzes for Chapters 9–12. Pay special attention to word problems, as the test contains many of those.

Intentionally left blank

Make flashcards or work on learning these vocabulary words and concepts some other way so you'll be familiar with what is meant when we use them.

$$\log_3(9)$$
base ———⌐ └——— argument

$\log_3(9) = x$ means the same thing as $3^x = 9$.

Notice that the base (3) is indeed the base of the exponent when rewritten as $3^x = 9$.

1. **Understanding Logarithms** – Find the requested logarithms by thinking through how many times you'd have to multiply the base by itself to reach the value in parentheses (i.e., the argument).

   Hint: Just start multiplying the base by itself until you get the value in the parentheses. Keep track of how many times it took, as that's the answer! For example, to find $\log_3(81)$, we'd start by multiplying 3 • 3 and keep multiplying by 3 until we reach a product of 81. In this case, 3 • 3 • 3 • 3 = 81, so the answer would be 4, since we could rewrite 3 • 3 • 3 • 3 as 3^4.

   a. $\log_7(49)$

   b. $\log_5(125)$

   c. $\log_6(1{,}296)$

   d. $\log_2(16)$

   e. $\log_9(729)$

2. **More with Logarithms** – Calculate the following logarithms using what you learned in the "Special Logarithms" box in the *Student Textbook*. If a particular logarithm cannot be calculated, write "undefined."

   a. $\log_3(1)$

   b. $\log_2(0)$

   c. $\log_3(3)$

3. **Solving Problems with Logarithms** – Simplify as much as you can, and then take the logarithm of *both sides* of these equations to solve for the variable.

   a. $250 = 10(5^{2t})$

   b. $64 = 2^{\frac{1}{2}t}$

   c. $686 = 2(7^{4x})$

4. **More with Understanding Logarithms**

   a. If $\log_3(2) = a$, what does $3^a + 6$ equal?

   b. If $\log_{10}(4) = y$, what does 10^y equal?

   c. If $\log_e(3) = x$, what does e^x equal?

5. **Skill Sharpening** – Simplify the following, factoring where possible.

a. $4e^{7t} + 6e^{3t}$

b. $\left(\dfrac{3a}{b}\right)^3 (4a)^2$

1. **Calculate the Logarithms** – Calculate the requested logarithms on your calculator.

   Example: $\log_{10}(40) \approx 1.602$

   a. $\log_{10}(700)$

   b. $\log(0.78)$
   Hint: Remember, when no base is written, it's assumed to be 10.

   c. $\ln(800)$

   d. $\ln(5,000)$

   e. $\log_{10}(250)$

   f. $\log(0.65)$

   g. $\ln(30)$

   h. $\ln(500)$

2. **Understanding Logarithms** – Go back and rewrite the values in parentheses in problem 1a–1d (which are listed again here) as the base from problem 1 raised to the power you calculated using your calculator.

   Example: $40 \approx 10^{1.602}$

   a. 700

   b. 0.78

   c. 800

   d. 5,000

   a. 250

   b. 0.65

   c. 30

   d. 500

3. **More with Logarithms** – Calculate the following logarithms using what you learned in the "Special Logarithms" teal box of Lesson 13.1. If a particular logarithm cannot be calculated, note it as undefined. **Do not use a calculator!**

   a. $\log_a(0)$

   b. $\log_2(2)$

   c. $\log_5(1)$

4. **Solving Problems with Logarithms** – Take the logarithm of *both sides* of these equations to solve for the variable.

   a. $550 = 10^{7x}$

   b. $400 = e^{8t}$

5. **Applying Algebra** – Use your knowledge of logarithms to solve these problems. Notice that they are very similar to the types of problems we looked at in the last chapter in Lesson 12.3, only this time the unknown is in the exponent. You may plug in values for variables as you go, but wait until the last step to calculate logarithms.

   a. Suppose a zoo has noticed that a particular type of insect grew from a population of 20 to 100 in 10 days. What is its rate of growth per day if the growth is continuous?

   b. Suppose a bank charges continuously compounded interest on its loans. If you will end up paying $6,000 for a loan of $4,000 over the course of a 5-year loan, what is the continuous rate per year (i.e., the annual rate)?

   c. If a certain bacteria colony is decreasing in population continuously such that it went from 1,000 to 20 in 30 days, what is the continuous rate of decay per day?

6. **Solving Algebraically**

   a. In all the problems in section 5, you had to repeat a lot of steps in order to solve for the rate (r). Try solving the formula $P(t) = P_i e^{rt}$ for *r before plugging in any values*. Notice that you'll then have a formula into which you could plug values and simplify, without having to rearrange the equation each time!

   b. Go back and resolve problem 5a by simply plugging the values into your answer to 6a. Notice that you get the same answer but don't have to do all the rearranging, as you've already rearranged the formula.

Make a flashcard or be sure to make a note somewhere of the change of base formula,

$$\log_a(b) = \frac{\log_x(b)}{\log_x(a)},$$ *so you can work on learning it and easily access it as you continue the chapter.*

1. **Rewriting Logarithms with Different Bases** – Rewrite the following logarithms to have a base of 10 so that they can be easily calculated on a calculator using the "LOG" button. Then find the approximate value on the calculator.

   a. $\log_5(20)$

   b. $\log_{2.3}(0.1)$

   c. $\log_6(15)$

2. **Rewriting Logarithms with Different Bases** – Rewrite the following logarithms to have a base of e so that they can be easily calculated on a calculator using the "LN" button. Then find the approximate value on the calculator.

   a. $\log_{14}(40)$

   b. $\log_7(30)$

   c. $\log_{4.5}(26)$

1. **Logarithms** – Solve these problems by taking the logarithm of both sides. Rewrite with a different base as needed in order to use your calculator to calculate the logarithm.

   Example: $250 = 2^{7x}$

   Answer: $\log_2(250) = \log_2(2^{7x})$

   $\log_2(250) = 7x$ (simplified the right side by thinking through that the exponent we have to raise 2 to in order to equal 2^{7x} is $7x$)

   $\dfrac{\log(250)}{\log(2)} = 7x$ (rewrote $\log_2(250)$ in base 10 — remember, a base of 10 is assumed when none is written)

   $\dfrac{\dfrac{\log(250)}{\log(2)}}{7} = x$ (divided both sides by 7)

   $1.138 \approx x$ (calculated the logarithms and completed the division on a calculator, doing it all in a single step to avoid having to round or write down a lot of digits)

   a. $40 = 3^x$

   b. $60 = 3^{5x}$

   c. $2{,}000 = 1.05^{\frac{1}{2}x}$

   d. $1{,}000 = 4^{8x}$

2. **Applying Algebra** – Use your knowledge of logarithms to solve these problems. You will also need the formula $P(t) = P_i(1 + r)^t$. Notice again that they are very similar to the types of problems we looked at in the last chapter in Lesson 12.2, only this time the unknown is in the exponent. You may plug in values for variables as you go, but wait until the last step to calculate logarithms.

   a. If you deposit $800 in a bank at an annual interest rate of 5%, how many years will it take to grow to $1,500?

   b. If you deposit $1,200 in a bank at a monthly interest rate of 3%, how many months will it take to grow to $2,000?

   c. Based on your answer to 2b, how many *years* will it take to grow $1,200 to $2,000?

   d. ◎ **Challenge Problem:** Solve the formula $P(t) = P_i(1 + r)^t$ for t. Notice that you could have used this to solve problems 2a and 2b instead of rearranging for each problem.

While we can use math to help us work with money, remember that money itself doesn't bring satisfaction. Be sure to view it as a tool to serve the Lord.

He who loves money will not be satisfied with money, nor he who loves wealth with his income; this also is vanity. (Ecclesiastes 5:10; ESV)

3. **Skill Sharpening**

   a. Insert letters (make $a = 2$, $x = 3$, and $y = 4$) to illustrate this algebraic relationship (leave your answer with an exponent): $a^x a^y = a^{x+y}$

   b. If $\ln(50) = x$, what does e^x equal?

   c. If $\log_5(100) = x$, what does 5^x equal?

   d. If $\log(x) = 0$, what does x equal?

   e. Simplify by factoring where possible: $5a^{3t} + 2a^{4t}$

4. **Understanding Time** – In Lesson 13.1, we mentioned that the logarithm of any base where that same base was in the parentheses (i.e., the base and the argument are the same) equals 1 $\left(\text{i.e., } \log_c(c) = 1\right)$. Now that you know how to change the base, you can see that the change of base formula would show you this as well. Change the base for $\log_4(4)$ to base 10. Notice that you get a fraction with the same numerator and denominator . . . which is worth 1! **Show your work.**

Make a flashcard or be sure to make a note somewhere of the product and quotient rules.

Product Rule for Logarithms

$$\log_c(a) + \log_c(b) = \log_c(ab)$$

Quotient Rule for Logarithms

$$\log_c(a) - \log_c(b) = \log_c\left(\frac{a}{b}\right)$$

1. **Using the Product Rule** – Use the product rule to simplify these expressions to a single logarithm. **Do not actually calculate the resulting logarithms.**

   a. $\log(x) + \log(y)$

   b. $\log(5) + \log(2)$

   c. $\log_3(13) + \log_3(x) + \log_3(2)$
   Hint: Yes, the product rule applies to more than two terms! You can easily see this by applying it to the first two terms, and then applying it to the resulting term and the next term.

Remember, a "term" is simply part of an expression separated by + or – signs.[1] We explored them back in Chapter 5.

2. **More Using the Product Rule** – Use the product rule to rewrite these expressions as separate logarithms. Each logarithm's argument in your answer should only contain one value or variable. **Do not actually calculate the resulting logarithms.**

   a. $\log_6(800x)$

   b. $\ln(0.3y)$

   c. $\log_2(40xy)$

3. **Simplifying** – Go back and calculate any logs from your simplified answers to problem 2 that you can.

   Example: $\log_2(7) + \log_2(x) = \dfrac{\log(7)}{\log(2)} + \log_2(x) \approx 2.807 + \log_2(x)$

   Note: We applied the change of base formula to rewrite $\log_2(7)$ as $\dfrac{\log(7)}{\log(2)}$.

   a.

   b.

   c.

---

1   Definition adapted from Joseph Victor Collins, *Practical Algebra: First Year Course* (New York: American Book Co., 1910), http://google.com/books?id=hNdHAAAAIAAJ&pg=PP1#v=onepage&q&f=false, p. 27. See footnote 5 for Chapter 3 in the *Student Textbook* for more details.

4. **Using the Quotient Rule** – Use the quotient rule to simplify these expressions to a single logarithm. **Do not actually calculate the resulting logarithms.**

   a. $\log(x) - \log(y)$

   b. $\log(5) - \log(2)$

   c. $\log_3(13) - \log_3(x) - \log_3(y)$

   Hint: Yes, you can apply the quotient rule to more than two expressions! You can easily see this by applying it to the first two terms, and then applying it to the resulting term and the next term.

5. **More Using the Quotient Rule** – Use the quotient rule to rewrite these expressions as separate logarithms. Each logarithm's argument in your answer should only contain one value or variable. **Do not actually calculate the resulting logarithms.**

   a. $\log_3\left(\dfrac{5}{x}\right)$

   b. $\log_4\left(\dfrac{x}{8}\right)$

   c. $\log_5\left(\dfrac{7}{xz}\right)$

6. **Simplifying** – Go back and calculate any logs from your simplified answers to problem 5a–5c that you can.

   Example: $\log_2(7) - \log_2(x) = \dfrac{\log(7)}{\log(2)} - \log_2(x) \approx 2.807 - \log_2(x)$

   a.

   b.

   c.

1. **Working with Logarithms** – Use the product or quotient rule to help you simplify these expressions as much as possible, calculating the logarithms where you can (use a calculator). Note that you will need to use the change of base formula for some problems as well.

   Example: $\log_2\left(\dfrac{5}{x}\right) = \log_2(5) - \log_2(x) = \dfrac{\log(5)}{\log(2)} - \log_2(x) \approx 2.322 - \log_2(x)$

   a. $\dfrac{\log(1{,}000{,}000x)}{36}$

   b. $\log(5x)$

   c. $\log_2\left(\dfrac{8}{x}\right)$

   d. $\log_3\left(\dfrac{7}{x}\right)$

   e. $\log_2(52) + \log_2(89)$

   f. $\log_3(40) + \log_3(0.8)$

   g. $\log_5(1{,}000) - \log_5(2{,}000)$

   h. $\log_6(5{,}000) - \log_6(100)$

2. 🎯 **Challenge Problem: Understanding the Product Rule** – The following questions will help you walk through for yourself how the product rule really just summarizes what would happen if you solved problems where it applies a much longer way!

   a. Substitute $a = 10^x$, $b = 10^y$, and $c = 10$ in the expression $\log_c(a) + \log_c(b)$, which is the left-hand side of the product rule.

   b. Simplify what you wrote in 2a by thinking through what the logarithms must equal (your answer will still be variables).

   c. Finish making the equation below equal by writing the appropriate exponent of 10 that would make the sides equal. **Rewrite the whole equation in your notebook as your answer so you can refer back to it.**
   Hint: Think about what a logarithm means. If the logarithm in base 10 equals $x + y$, what does that mean 10 is raised to? For example, $\log_{10}(10^4) = 4$.

   $\log_{10}(10\underline{}) = x + y$

   d. Use what you know about exponents to rewrite the left side of the equation in 2c to be 10 raised to a power times 10 raised to another power. Your answer should be in the form of $\log_{10}(10\underline{}) = \log_{10}(10\underline{}10\underline{})$, but with the blanks filled in.

   e. You now know that the expression you wrote in 2a equals $x + y$ and that each side of the expression you wrote in 2d equals $x + y$ (you saw this in 2c and 2d); therefore, write an equation showing the expression you wrote in 2a as equal to the right side of the equation you wrote n 2d.

f. Substitute a back for 10^x, b back for 10^y and c back for 10 into the equation you wrote in 2e. If you did everything right, you should have written the product rule!

3. **Applying Algebra: Chemistry** – In chemistry, we explore the consistencies God created at the microscopic level. When chemicals are combined, they often react and form different chemicals. But at some point, they stop reacting. We characterize when this happens using something called the equilibrium constant (K). Without going into all the details (you'll need to study chemistry for that), this value is related to something called the change in Gibbs free energy (ΔG) and can be represented like this: $\Delta G = -RT(\ln(K))$, where R is the gas constant and T the temperature.

Suppose $K = \dfrac{c}{ab}$ in a particular chemical reaction, where a, b, and c represent the equilibrium concentrations of the different chemicals involved in the reaction.[1]

Hint: Treat ΔG as a single unknown — only it is one that we use two symbols, the Δ and the G, to represent.

a. Substitute the value given for K into the formula $\Delta G = -RT(\ln(K))$.

b. Use the quotient rule for logarithms to finish rewriting your answer to 3a with two separate logarithms. Your answer will be in the form of $\Delta G = -RT(\ln(\underline{\quad\quad}) - \ln(\underline{\quad\quad}))$.

c. Use the product rule to rewrite your answer to 3b so that it contains three separate logarithms; your answer should be in this form:
$\Delta G = -RT(\ln(\underline{\quad\quad}) - \ln(\underline{\quad\quad}) - \ln(\underline{\quad\quad}))$.

d. Distribute the negative sign in front of RT in your answer to 3c to make this formula even more simplified and easy to use!

e. Find ΔG using the formula you wrote in 3d if $a = 10^{-6}$, $b = 10^{-6}$, and $c = 10^6$ (these are measurements of concentrations of different chemicals, such as iron, chloride, and iron chloride), $T = 300$ Kelvin (use a K to stand for Kelvin), and $R = 8.314 \dfrac{\text{J}}{\text{mol} \cdot \text{K}}$.

4. **Skill Sharpening**

a. If $\log(1) = x$, what does x equal?

b. Insert letters (make $a = 2$, $x = 3$, and $y = 4$) to illustrate this algebraic relationship:
$\dfrac{a^x}{a^y} = a^{x-y}$

c. Simplify: $\dfrac{x^2}{4y^2}(4y^2)$

---

1 In chemistry, we'd write brackets [] around the c, a, and b to show that we're representing concentrations, like this: $\dfrac{[c]}{[a][b]}$. However, since this isn't a chemistry course, we left those off for simplicity.

Make a flashcard or be sure to make a note somewhere of the power rule.

Power Rule
$$\log_c(a^b) = b\log_c(a)$$

1. **Practicing the Power Rule** – Simplify these expressions using the power rule, bringing the exponent down from inside the log to outside of it.

    a. $\log(x^6)$

    b. $\log(x^7)$

    c. $\log(y^x)$

    d. $\log(y^{-1})$

2. **More Practicing the Power Rule** – Rewrite these expressions using the power rule — this time, you're rewriting the multiplication in front of the log as an exponent inside the log.

    a. $3\log(x)$

    b. $4\ln(y)$

    c. $z\log(x)$

    d. $-\log(3)$
    Hint: Remember that you can view a negative sign as a multiplication by –1.

3. **Using Exponents to Invert Logarithms** – Use the knowledge that you can make both sides the exponent of the *same base* without changing the value to solve for x.

    a. $4 = \log_2\left(\dfrac{x}{2}\right)$

    b. $64 = 8\log_4(5x)$
    Hint: In order to make both sides the exponent of the same base to help you simplify, you have to first make sure there's only a logarithm on the right side. So you first need to divide both sides by 8.

4. **Applying the Power Rule and Using Exponents to Reverse Logarithms** – Apply the power rule to solve these problems for x. Also make *both sides* the exponent of the *same base*. You may leave your final answer as a base raised to a power, as calculating these values on a calculator will likely result in an overflow error because of how large the exponents of the numbers are.

    a. $510 = \log_2(x^3)$

    b. $2{,}401 = \log_5(x^7)$

    c. $100 = \log_2(x^{-1})$

Note that each of these unknowns were raised to odd powers. When an unknown is raised to an even power, there are two answers: an even and an odd one. For example, both 2^2 and $(-2)^2$ equal 4. But you won't be asked to apply the power rule to logarithms of unknowns raised to even powers in this course.

Make a flashcard or be sure to make a note somewhere of the power rule.

Power Rule
$$\log_c(a^b) = b\log_c(a)$$

1. **Understanding Logarithms** – Think about the definition of a logarithm to answer these. $\log(a) = b$ means that the value 10 (the unwritten base) has to be raised to in order to equal a is b. Thus, $10^b = a$.

   a. If $\log(4) = x$, what does 10^x equal?

   b. If $\ln(5) = a$, what does e^a equal?

   c. If $\log_3(35) = d$, what does 3^d equal?

2. **Using Exponents to Reverse Logarithms** – Use the knowledge that you can make *both sides* the exponent of the *same quantity* without changing the value to solve for x. **Give your answers in scientific notation** (i.e., list 120,000 as 1.2×10^5).

   a. $18 = 3\log\left(\dfrac{3}{x}\right)$

   Hint: You'll need to first divide both sides by 3 so you just have a logarithm on one side of the equation.

   b. $34 = \log(4x)$

3. **Applying the Power Rule** – Apply the power rule and then make both sides the exponent of the same base to solve these problems for x. You may leave your final answer as a base raised to a power.

   a. $65 = \log_3(x^5)$

   b. $75 = \log_4(x^3)$

   c. $-42 = \log_3(x^7)$

4. **Finding Unknowns** – Use any of what we've looked at about logarithms to help you simplify these expressions.

   a. $\log(x) + \log(x^{-1})$

   b. $\log(x^2) - \log(x)$

5. **Applying Algebra: Magnitude of Starlight[1]** – If you look up at the stars at night, you'll notice that some are brighter than others. While some of this is due to their distance from earth, if we factor out the distance, the stars themselves still differ in brightness. To describe the magnitude of one star's light over another, we need some sort of scale or standard against which to rank them. One scale uses — you guessed it — logarithms! The formula for finding the magnitude of a star using the Pogson scale (named after the man who invented it) is $m = -2.5\log\left(\dfrac{F}{F_0}\right)$. Here,

F is the measurement of something called the flux,[2] and F_0 is a reference flux against which that is measured. In other words, it's a way of measuring the energy that reaches us from a star. The m stands for the magnitude. *Note:* To keep things simple, we'll leave units off this problem.

a. If $\dfrac{F}{F_0}$ equals 10^{-5}, what does m equal?

b. If $\dfrac{F}{F_0}$ equals 10^{-4}, what does m equal?

   Note: This was a huge change in the flux ratio — 10^{-4} is 10 times 10^{-5} — yet it only resulted in a small change in the magnitude. Logarithmic scales like this one let us express large changes concisely. We'll explore this more in a couple of lessons.

c. Rewrite $m = -2.5 \log\left(\dfrac{F}{F_0}\right)$ using the power rule.

d. Using the quotient rule, rewrite your answer to 5c as two separate logarithms.
   Hint: You'll need to remember something we looked at in the last chapter about how to rewrite $\left(\dfrac{a}{b}\right)^n$ as $\dfrac{a^n}{b^n}$.

e. Say you know that $F_0 = 10$ and $m = 10$. What does F equal? Notice that the power rule comes in handy!
   Hint: Insert values and simplify.

f. Using the original formula $m = -2.5\log\left(\dfrac{F}{F_0}\right)$, find what F would have to equal in order for the magnitude (m) to equal 8 with F_0 equal to 10?

The Bible talks about how stars differ in "glory" — that is, how their brightness varies. It then uses it to tell us that the resurrection bodies for those who know Jesus are going to differ from what they are now, yet somehow be related in a way.

> *There is one glory of the sun, and another glory of the moon, and another glory of the stars: for one star differeth from another star in glory. So also is the resurrection of the dead. It is sown in corruption; it is raised in incorruption. (1 Corinthians 15:41–42)*

And it's math that helps us explore and categorize this difference in glory between the stars — a glory God created.

> *I form light and create darkness, I make well-being and create calamity, I am the Lord, who does all these things. (Isaiah 45:7; ESV)*

6. **More Applying Algebra –** Suppose there's a population that's growing at an exponential growth factor of 3. The population started at 15.

   a. Write an exponential function showing the final population as a function of the time using the formula $P(t) = P_i g^t$. Notice we ignored the time cycle (c) (the full formula is $P(t) = P_i g^{tc}$), as we will assume a value for t that is in the same units as the time cycle and the number of times the growth is calculated.

   b. Now, let's say you want to know at what point in time the population $(P(t))$ will equal 10,935. Using the function you wrote in 6a and what you know about logarithms, find the value of t when $P(t) = 10{,}935$.

7. **Skill Sharpening**

   a. If $\log(0) = x$, what is x?

   b. Simplify by factoring out common factors: $3e^4 + 9e^2$

1. **Rewriting Exponential Functions** – Rewrite $f(t) = 20e^t$ as a linear function, following the steps below.

   a. Take the logarithm in base e of both sides.

   b. Apply the product rule to your answer to 1a and simplify any logarithms you can (do not actually calculate any logarithms on a calculator). For example, simplify $\log_4(4^x)$ to x.

   c. Rewrite the logarithm of the output (which should be one side of your answer to 1b) as y.

   d. Graph the function you wrote in 1c and draw the general shape in your notebook.

   e. In your graph in 1d, what is the value of $f(t)$ when the output on the graph is 3? Remember, the output on the graph is of $\ln(f(t))$; you want to find $f(t)$ when $\ln(f(t))$ is 3.

2. **More Rewriting Exponential Functions**

   a. Rewrite $f(t) = 10(1 + 0.06)^t$ as a linear function by simplifying within the parentheses, taking the logarithm of both sides in the base that's being raised to t, applying the product rule, changing the base to calculate any logarithms you can, and rewriting the logarithm of the output as y.

   b. Graph the function you found in 2a and draw the general shape in your notebook.

   c. When the output (y) in the function you graphed is 39.517, what is $f(t)$?

3. **Graphing Rewritten Exponential Functions**

   a. Find the log of each value for $f(t)$. **You may round your answers.**

t	$f(t)$	$\log(f(t))$
0	5	
1	11	
2	41	
3	221	
4	1,301	

   b. Pull out graphing paper and draw a coordinate plane with each box on the paper representing 0.5 in both directions and both axes covering the values 0 through 4.5. Plot the values from 3a for t and $\log(f(t))$ as points on the graph; use the value for t as the horizontal coordinate and the corresponding value for $\log(f(t))$ as the vertical one. Notice how the points fall approximately on a straight line. Use a ruler to draw a straight line that best seems to connect the points.

   c. Use what you know about straight lines and the line you drew in 3b to find the approximate formula to describe the line you drew in 3b. Based on the approximate formula you found, choose the correct formula from the choices given.

   ○ A. $y = 1.75x + 0.5356$ ○ B. $y = 0.6133x + 0.5356$ ○ C. $y = 0.6133x + 1$

4. Graphing Rewritten Exponential Functions in a Spreadsheet Program

Because a computer program like Excel, Google Sheets, or LibreOffice is necessary to complete this problem, it may be considered optional if you do not have a program like this available.

Use a computer program to find $\log(f(t))$, insert a scatter plot graph displaying t as the input and the $\log(f(t))$ as the output, and display the formula describing the resulting line, as explained in the text. Save and send your finished file to your parent/teacher for grading.

t	$f(t)$	$\log(f(t))$
0	100	
1	105	
2	110	
3	219	
4	750	

5. Scofield Scale[1]

Because a computer program like Excel, Google Sheets, or LibreOffice is necessary to complete this problem, it may be considered optional if you do not have a program like this available.

The spiciness of peppers and similar spicy foods is often quantified by something called the Scofield scale. The scale is related to the concentration of two chemicals that cause the peppers to be spicy: capsaicin and dihydrocapsaicin. Since concentrations vary greatly, the corresponding Scofield scale also varies greatly, making it hard to really tell how spicy the food is. Below is a table based on one paper[1] trying to qualitatively interpret what the Scofield values mean in terms of the spiciness.

Spiciness	Scofield Scale Value s
Non Spicy	0 to 700
Mildly Spicy	700 to 3,000
Moderately Spicy	3,000 to 25,000
Highly Spicy	25,000 to 80,000
Very Highly Spicy	> 80,000

Let's say we want to make our own custom scale called the "Pepper Scale" for spiciness that only goes from 0 to 4.

Spiciness	Scofield Scale Value s	Pepper Scale $P(s)$
Non Spicy	0 to 700	0 to 1
Mildly Spicy	700 to 3,000	1 to 2
Moderately Spicy	3,000 to 25,000	2 to 3
Highly Spicy	25,000 to 80,000	3 to 4
Very Highly Spicy	> 80,000	> 4

1   Zeid Abdullah Al Othman, Yacine Badjah Hadj Ahmed, Mohamed Abdelaty Habila, and Ayman Abdel Ghafar, "Determination of Capsaicin and Dihydrocapsaicin in Capsicum Fruit Samples using High Performance Liquid Chromatography," *Molecules* 2011, 16(10), 8,919–8,929, p. 8,920, https://doi.org/10.3390/molecules16108919 *Note:* The paper uses the term "pungent" instead of "spicy," but we changed that here to avoid using a word students might not know.

How do we convert a Scofield Scale value to a value on the Pepper Scale? Well, what we really need is a formula where the Scofield Scale value is the input, and we get an output of a Pepper Scale value. Notice, though, that the Scofield Scale values are really large compared to the Pepper Scale ones. So let's start by finding the logarithm of the lowest Scofield Scale value in each category and use those values as the input, with the corresponding Pepper Scale value as the output. Plotting those points and looking at the line of best fit for them will give us an approximate formula we can use to convert from a Scofield value to a Pepper scale one. The steps below will help walk you through this. **The answer you submit should be an equation for the Pepper Scale**.

- Enter the following points into a spreadsheet program such as Excel or Google Sheets. When you enter the values in column x, they should change to what those logarithms equal.

x	y
$= \log(700)$	1
$= \log(3{,}000)$	2
$= \log(25{,}000)$	3
$= \log(80{,}000)$	4

Note: We didn't use the 0 point as that would involve a logarithm of 0, which is undefined.

- Insert a scatter plot.

- Insert the trendline and have the computer show the equation of the line. It will have the form $y = mx + b$. Write out the equation. You've now found an equation to help you convert between those scales! You just have to remember that the x in the equation is the *logarithm* of the Scofield Scale value . . . and the y is the Pepper Scale value.

> *Nevertheless he left not himself without witness, in that he did good, and gave us rain from heaven, and fruitful seasons, filling our hearts with food and gladness. (Acts 14:17)*
>
> *As we use math to categorize foods' spiciness, we're reminded again of God's goodness in even giving us taste and such a wide variety of foods to enjoy. This is a point John UpChurch makes well in "Taste & See," pointing out that "food is an intentional God-given 'witness' to remind human beings daily about the Creator's goodness."[2]*

6. **Skill Sharpening**

   a. Combine into one term: $\log(x) + \log(5x)$

   b. Combine into one term and simplify: $\log(x^2) - \log(x^{-3})$

   c. Solve for x: $56 = 2e^x + 5$

   d. Calculate $\log_3(45)$

   e. Solve for x: $7 = 2\log_3(3x)$

2   John UpChurch, "Taste & See" *Answers Magazine* (February 2017), https://answersingenesis.org/biology/taste-see/

General Form of a Logarithmic Function
$$f(x) = a\log_b(cx - d)$$

1. **Exploring Logarithmic Functions** – These problems are designed to make you think and let you learn about logarithmic functions yourself. It is okay if you have to get help finding the answers, but try to think through them for yourself first. The point of this exercise is to better understand the different components of a logarithmic function so you can better look at one and know the general relationship. It also builds reasoning skills! Use the graph to help you.

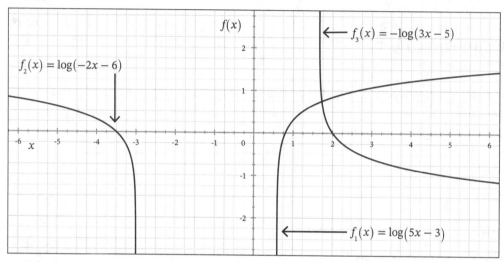

a. Solve $cx - d = 0$ for x. (Note that $cx - d$ is really the argument to the logarithm in the general form of a logarithmic function, so you're really finding a formula for seeing when the argument will equal 0.)

b. Looking at each equation graphed and comparing it to the general form, identify the value in the equation that is in the same place as c and d in the general form. Note that there's a negative sign in front of d in the general form, so the negative sign is *not* part of the value of d you should use in your formula. Any negative sign in front of c, though, would be.

c in $f_1(x)$: _____ d in $f_1(x)$: _____

c in $f_2(x)$: _____ d in $f_2(x)$: _____

c in $f_3(x)$: _____ d in $f_3(x)$: _____

c. Using the formula you found in 1a and the values for c and d you found in 1b, calculate the x values where the asymptotes of the functions shown on the graph occur.

Asymptote of $f_1(x)$: _____

Asymptote of $f_2(x)$: _____

Asymptote of $f_3(x)$: _____

d. Copy the general shape of the graph given at the start of the problem onto graph paper and draw a dashed line where the asymptotes are. Label the dashed lines with their x value. For example, if an asymptote occurs when $x = 2$, label the dashed line you draw there $x = 2$.

In the case of logarithms, we can't take logarithms of negative values, so there are no values beyond the asymptotes (i.e., if $c > 0$, there are no values to the left of the asymptote, and if $c < 0$, there are no values to the right of the asymptote). Also notice that, because of this, the domain (i.e., the potential input values) of each function could be described as real values such that $x > \dfrac{d}{c}$.

e. Solve $cx - d = 1$ for x. (Note that $cx - d$ is really the argument to the logarithm in the general form of a logarithmic function, so you're really finding a formula for seeing when the argument will equal 1.)

f. Use the formula you wrote in 1e and the values for c and d you found in 1b to find the root for each of the functions graphed at the start of problem 1. Look at the graphs — if you did the math right, the roots should be the x-intercepts!

Root of $f_1(x)$: _____

Root of $f_2(x)$: _____

Root of $f_3(x)$: _____

2. **Applying Algebra: Richter Scale** – The Richter scale relationship for earthquakes is given in logarithmic form such that $M_L(A) = \log\left(\dfrac{A}{A_0(\delta)}\right)$ where the magnitude is M_L, A is the maximum amplitude of a seismograph signal, and A_0 is normalization factor as a function of the distance δ from the earthquake epicenter (i.e., $A_0(\delta)$ altogether is the normalization factor — it's written in function notation and represents the output of another function). We've left units of measure off for simplicity.

a. What value would $A_0(\delta)$ have to be if $A = 5{,}000$ and the magnitude is 5.5?

$A_0(\delta) \approx$ _____ when $A = 5{,}000$ and the magnitude is 5.5.

b. Insert 4×10^{-3} for $A_0(\delta)$ in $M_L = \log\left(\dfrac{A}{A_0(\delta)}\right)$ to find a function for when $A_0(\delta)$ equals 4×10^{-3}.

c. Graph the function you wrote in 2b, making the vertical scale 0 to 10 and the horizontal scale 0 to 20,000; draw the general shape in your notebook. Notice how it takes a huge change horizontally (the maximum amplitude, A) to create just a small change vertically (the magnitude, M_L). Logarithmic functions, like log scales, help us express big changes concisely.

d. In the function from 2b, when the maximum amplitude (A) is 4,000, what do we say the magnitude of the earthquake is?

3. **Rewriting Logarithmic Functions**

a. Rewrite $f(t) = 45e^t$ as a linear function by taking the logarithm of both sides, and then applying the product rule to rewrite as two separate logarithms. Simplify and calculate any logarithms you can.

b. Graph the function you found in 3a and draw the general shape in your notebook. When you graph it, input $\ln(f(t))$ as y, as it is your output.

c. Looking at the problem in 3a and your graph of it in 3b, what is the value of $f(t)$ when the output on the graph is -11.193? Give your answer as a value in scientific notation. *Hint:* Each output on the graph represents $\ln(f(t))$.

4. **Connecting the Dots** – Back in Lesson 7.8, we looked at inverse functions and how they are the function rearranged to make the output the input — in other words, to solve the problem for x. For example, $y = 5x$ can be rearranged to $\frac{y}{5} = x$, or $x = \frac{y}{5}$. Thus, $x = \frac{y}{5}$ is the inverse function of $y = 5x$. Keeping this in mind and what you know about logarithms, answer the following questions.

a. What is the inverse function of $y = 8^x$?

b. What is the inverse function of $y = 5e^x$? Calculate all logarithms you can in your answer.

Logarithmic functions are the inverse of exponential functions.

5. **Skill Sharpening**

a. Rewrite as a single logarithm: $\ln(8) + \ln(x) + \ln(y)$

b. Rewrite as two separate logarithms; do not calculate the values: $\ln\left(\dfrac{5}{x}\right)$

1. **Understanding and Working with Logarithms**

    a. If $\log(y) = 3$, what is y?

    b. If $\log(x) = 2$, simplify $\dfrac{x^2}{4}$.

    c. A certain population doubles every year. If it starts at 10, after how many years will it be at 810? Use the formula $P(f) = P_i g^t$ to solve.
    Note: We left the number of growth cycles per unit time c out of the formula, since the growth is every year and the time we're looking for is also in years.

    d. What is $\log_3(3)$?

    e. What is $\log_3(0)$?

    f. Calculate: $\log_3(55)$

    g. Calculate: $\log_2(3) - \log_2(6)$

    h. Simplify to a single logarithm: $\log_x(a) + \log_x(b) + \log_x(c)$

    i. Solve for t: $10 = \log_2(4t)$

    j. Rewrite using the power rule so that there is no exponent inside the logarithm's argument: $\log(3^{2t})$

    k. Rewrite $f(t) = 40e^{2t}$ as a linear function where the output y is the log of the original output by taking the logarithm of both sides, applying the product rule, simplifying any logarithms you can, replacing the logarithm of $f(t)$ with y, and calculating any logarithms you can.

2. **Applying Algebra: The Gaussian Curve** – In statistics, we often use something known as the Gaussian curve. Let's explore one together: $f(x) = 10e^{-\frac{x^2}{25}}$. Notice that there's an x^2 in the exponent — we haven't encountered functions like this before, but you have all the skills you need to explore it!

    a. Graph the function on your calculator and draw the general shape in your notebook. Notice from the graph that in this curve, there is a highpoint, with mirror image curves on both sides. This is characteristic of the Gaussian curve.

    b. Take the logarithm in base e of both sides of the function and use the product rule to rewrite the right side of the function as two terms. Do not simplify anything yet (including terms like $\ln(e^z)$).

c. Simplify the right-hand side of the function you wrote in 2b. Calculate any logarithms you can.

d. Graph the function you simplified in 2c on your calculator and draw the basic shape in your notebook, treating $\log(f(x))$ as your new output (which means you'd input it as y on your calculator). Notice that you get a simple parabola rather than a straight line due to the x^2. A parabola is still easier to manipulate than the original curve (we'll learn more about manipulating, or transforming, functions in the next chapter).

3. **Applying Algebra: Logs and Signal Strength[1]** – Cell phones, laptops, tablets, etc., often let you know how strong of a signal they have by displaying a certain number of bars. If you see 4 bars, you know you have a good signal; if there's only 1, you know you're in trouble. Did you realize these bars are really an application of logarithms?

We measure the strength of signals in a unit called dBm, or "decibels relative to a milliwatt."[2] As we touched on in Lesson 13.4, decibels are based on a logarithmic scale. In the case of phone and WiFi signals, we'll measure the power of the signal instead of sound intensity[3] and use a reference point of 1 mW, making the formula $D = 10\log\left(\dfrac{P}{1}\right)$, where P is in mW.

The bars on your electronic device are displayed based on the D value. On a 4G/LTE network,[4] the number of bars displayed is based on the D value according to the table shown.

D value	Bars
$\geq$–90 dBm	4
–91 to –105 dBm	3
<–105 dBm	2, 1, or a dead zone

Note: Negative dBm values just mean the D in the equation comes back negative . . . the P, or measurement of the power, is still positive . . . it's just a very small value. You'll see this as you answer the questions.

a. What is the minimum the power (P) could be in order to get 4 bars to display in a 4G/LTE network, if you need at least a D value of –90 dBm to get 4 bars on that network? Your answer should be in mW (i.e., milliwatts).

b. What will the signal strength be if the power (P) of the signal is 5×10^{-5} mW? Your answer should be in dBm (we won't get into how the units work out).

c. How many bars would the signal in 3b show on a 4G/LTE network?

1   See HyperPhisics, "Decibels," http://hyperphysics.phy-astr.gsu.edu/hbase/Sound/db.html, for information about the formula.
2   Metageek, "Understanding WiFi Signal Strength," https://www.metageek.com/training/resources/wifi-signal-strength-basics.html
3   ISA, "dB vs. dBm," InTech Magazine (November 2002), https://www.isa.org/standards-publications/isa-publications/intech-magazine/2002/november/db-vs-dbm/
4   Values taken from Signalbooster.com, "How to Measure Signal Strength in Decibels on Your Cell Phone?" (November 2019), https://www.signalbooster.com/blogs/news/how-to-measure-signal-strength-in-decibels-on-your-cell-phone

d. What will the signal strength be if the power (P) of the signal is 1×10^{-10} mW? Your answer should be in dBm.

e. How many bars would the signal in 3d show on a 4G/LTE network?

f. Graph $D = 10\log\left(\dfrac{P}{1}\right)$, the relationship we've been looking at, on a calculator with a horizontal scale of 0 to 0.0001 and a vertical one of –130 to 0 and draw the general shape in your notebook. The given scale on your calculator will show you values in the range of realistic inputs and outputs we have examined here.

The logarithmic function $D = 10\log\left(\dfrac{P}{1}\right)$ helps reduce very large changes in P to a very small change, making it easier to see on a graph ... and translate to signal bars on your electronic device.

See Lesson 7.3 for a reminder of how to graph two functions on the same calculator if needed.
Look at the "Transforming Functions Summary" at the very end of the chapter.
Look at the column labeled "Vertically" for each transformation type, as we looked at vertical transformations in this lesson. Consulting it can help you keep track of the different transformations to know how to solve the problems.

1. **Transforming Functions: Shifting Vertically**

   a. Shift $d(s) = 5s + 2$ vertically up by 4 by adding 4 to both sides of the function. The left side is done for you.

   $d(s) + 4 = $_____

   Example Meaning: The distance a robot travels as a function of the speed for a time of 5 minutes if it starts at a distance of 2 m; you want to rewrite the function to show that you started at a distance of an additional 4 m.

   b. Graph your answer to 1a at the same time as the original function, $d(s) = 5s + 2$, and use the graph to answer the question: what is the vertical coordinate of the y-intercept (i.e., the output for an input of 0) of each function?
   Hint: Rename the functions y rather than $d(s)$ and $d(s) + 4$ to input into the calculator.

   vertical coordinate of y-intercept of $d(s) = $_____

   vertical coordinate of y-intercept of $d(s) + 4 = $_____

   c. What does the output value of the transformed function (i.e., the distance) minus the output value of the original function for the same input values (i.e., the same speed) equal?
   Hint: Use the vertical coordinates you found in 1b, as those are the outputs for the same input of 0.

2. **Transforming Functions: Scaling Vertically**

   a. Scale $d(s) = 5s + 2$ vertically by 4 by multiplying both sides of the function by 4. The left side is done for you.

   $4d(s) = $_____

   Example Meaning: The distance a robot travels as a function of the speed for a time of 5 minutes if it starts at a distance of 2 m; you want to rewrite the function to see what would happen if the robot were going 4 times the distance it would be going in the function $d(s)$.

   b. Graph the $4d(s)$ you wrote in 2a on the calculator at the same time as the original function, $d(s) = 5s + 2$, and use the graph to answer the question: what is the vertical coordinate of the y-intercept (i.e., the output for an input of 0) of each function? Remember to use y to stand for the output of the functions when inputting into the calculator rather than $d(s)$ and $4d(s)$.

   vertical coordinate of y-intercept of $d(s) = $_____

   vertical coordinate of y-intercept of $4d(s) = $_____

c. What do the output value of the transformed function (i.e., the distance) divided by the output value of the original function for the same input values (i.e., the same speed) equal?
    Hint: Use the vertical coordinates you found in 2b, as those are the outputs for the same input of 0.

3. **Transforming Functions: Reflecting Vertically Across the x-axis**

    a. Reflect $d(s) = 5s + 2$ across the x-axis by multiplying both sides by –1. The left side is done for you.

    $-d(s) =$ _____

    Example Meaning: The distance a robot travels as a function of the speed for a time of 5 minutes if it starts at a distance of 2 m; you want to rewrite the function to see what would happen if the robot was at the exact opposite position all the time as it was in $d(s)$.

    b. Graph the reflection function you wrote in 3a on the calculator at the same time as the original function, $d(s) = 5s + 2$; what is the vertical coordinate of the y-intercept (i.e., the output for an input of 0) of each function?

    vertical coordinate of y-intercept of $d(s) =$ _____

    vertical coordinate of y-intercept of $-d(s) =$ _____

    c. How did the output value of the transformed function (i.e., the distance) for the same input values (i.e., the same speed) change?
        Hint: Use the vertical coordinates you found in 3b, as those are the outputs for the same input of 0.

    It was the same value, except multiplied by _____.

    Suggestion: Make flashcards or a note sheet for the different transformations and formulas covered in Lesson 14.1 to help you learn them.

1. **Basic Transformations** – Use the function $f(x) = 5x^2 + 2$ to solve these problems.
   Simplify all of your answers as much as possible. For example, rewrite $(x^2 + 3) + 2$
   as $x^2 + 5$. **Also, distribute the multiplication where you can.** For example, rewrite
   $2(x^2 + 1)$ as $2x^2 + 2$.

   a. Shift the function vertically up by 5; list the new function. Your answer should start
   "$f(x) + 5 =$."

   b. Graph the function you wrote in 1a on the calculator at the same time as the original
   function, $f(x) = 5x^2 + 2$; what is the vertical coordinate of the y-intercept (i.e., the
   output for an input of 0) of each function?

   vertical coordinate of y-intercept of $f(x) =$ _____

   vertical coordinate of y-intercept of shifted function = _____

   c. Scale the original function vertically by 5; list the new function. Your answer should start
   "$5f(x) =$."

   d. Graph the function you wrote in 1c on the calculator at the same time as the original
   function, $f(x) = 5x^2 + 2$; what is the vertical coordinate of the y-intercept (i.e., the
   output for an input of 0) of each function?

   vertical coordinate of y-intercept of $f(x) =$ _____

   vertical coordinate of y-intercept of scaled function = _____

   e. Reflect the original function across the x-axis; list the new function. Your answer should
   start "$-f(x) =$."

   f. Graph the function you wrote in 1e on the calculator at the same time as the original
   function, $f(x) = 5x^2 + 2$; what is the vertical coordinate of the y-intercept (i.e., the
   output for an input of 0) of each function?

   vertical coordinate of y-intercept of $f(x) =$_____

   vertical coordinate of y-intercept of reflected function = _____

2. **Understanding Transformations**
   Hint: While we've renamed the functions, look at what changed on the right side of them to
   determine the transformation applied.

   a. What transformation was applied to $f(x) = 2x^2 + 6$ to get $h(x) = -(2x^2 + 6)$?

   ○ vertical shift ○ vertical scale ○ reflection across the x-axis

   b. What transformation was applied to $f(x) = 2x^2 + 6$ to get $h(x) = 2x^2 + 3$?

   ○ vertical shift ○ vertical scale ○ reflection across the x-axis

   c. What transformation was applied to $f(x) = 2x^2 + 6$ to get $h(x) = x^2 + 3$?

   ○ vertical shift ○ vertical scale ○ reflection across the x-axis

3. **Recognizing Transformations**

   a. The black curve can be described by $f(x) = 7x^3 - 2$. What function describes the grey curve, given it is a transformation of the black curve using one of the transformations we've looked at?

   Hint: Look at how the outputs have changed for the same inputs.

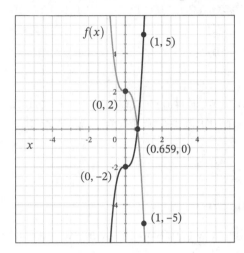

   b. The black curve can be described by $f(t) = 3\log(t)$. What function describes the grey curve, given it is a transformation of the black curve using one of the transformations we've looked at?

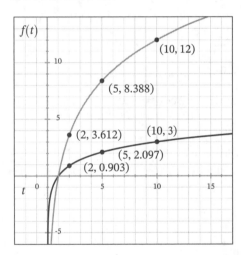

4. Algebra Applied

a. Suppose you knew that a population of 50 small fish in an aquarium tank that was growing *continuously* had grown to 400 in 3 years. Find the rate of growth. Do not round (i.e., leave as many decimals as your calculator can produce). Your answer should be in

the form $r = \dfrac{}{\text{year}}$, where the numerator is the value you calculate.

Hint: Think back to Chapter 12 and what formula was used for continuous growth. You'll then also need to use some of what you learned in the last chapter.

b. Using the rate you calculated in 4a, write a function describing the ending population as a function of time, given that the initial population is 50. Your answer should start "$P(t)$."

c. Suppose the aquarium wanted to see what the ending population would be at any given time *if they removed 100 fish* from the population at the end of that time. Write a new function $h(t)$ showing the ending population as a function of time. Note that this function will only be valid for a domain of $t \geq 1$, at which point there are at least 100 fish in the aquarium. Also, note that this function will really be a transformed version of the function you wrote in 4b!

d. Graph both $P(t)$ and $h(t)$ on a calculator. What does each transformed output minus the original output for that same input value equal?
Hint: Subtract the vertical value of the y-intercept of $P(t)$ from $h(t)$ to see; all the other outputs will have the same difference.

5. Skill Sharpening

a. Use the power rule to rewrite: $\log(3^{4t})$

b. Solve $20 = \log(t)$ for t.

c. Separate into two separate logarithms using the quotient rule: $\log\left(\dfrac{2a}{3}\right)$

Suggestion: Make flashcards or a note sheet for the different transformations and formulas covered in Lesson 14.2 to help you learn them. **Look ahead to the end of the chapter at the "Transforming Functions Summary."**
Unless otherwise specified, from now on, simplify any transformed functions as much as possible (including distributing any multiplication).

1. **Transforming Functions: Shifting Horizontally**

   a. Shift $d(s) = 5s + 2$ horizontally to the left by 4. Your answer should start "$d(s + 4) =$."

   Example Meaning: The distance a robot travels as a function of the speed for a time of 5 min if it starts at a distance of 2 m; you want to rewrite the function to show that the speed is actually some speed s in $\dfrac{\text{m}}{\text{min}}$ plus $4\,\dfrac{\text{m}}{\text{min}}$.

   b. Graph $d(s + 4)$ you wrote in 1a on the calculator at the same time as the original function, $d(s) = 5s + 2$, and use the graph to answer the question: what is the horizontal coordinate of the x-intercept (i.e., the input for an output of 0) of each function?
   Hint: Remember, rename the functions y to graph on a calculator.

   horizontal coordinate of x-intercept of $d(s) =$ _____

   horizontal coordinate of x-intercept of $d(s + 4) =$ _____

   c. What does the input value of the original function minus the input value of the shifted function that yields the same output value equal?
   Hint: Compare the horizontal coordinates of the x-intercepts to answer, as those are the inputs that yield an output of 0.

Note that we add to a function or its input to shift it. When we add to the input, it shifts it horizontally. When we add to the output, it shifts it vertically.

2. **Transforming Functions: Scaling Horizontally**

   a. Compress $d(s) = 5s + 2$ horizontally by 4. Your answer should start "$d(4s) =$."

   Example Meaning: The distance a robot travels as a function of the speed for a time of 5 minutes if it starts at a distance of 2 m; you want to rewrite the function to see what would happen if the robot were actually traveling at 4 times the speed represented by s.

   b. Graph the function you wrote in 2a on the calculator at the same time as the original function, $d(s) = 5s + 2$, and use the graph to answer the question: what is the horizontal coordinate of the x-intercept (i.e., the input for an output of 0) of each function?

   horizontal coordinate of x-intercept of $d(s) =$ _____

   horizontal coordinate of x-intercept of $d(4s) =$ _____

c. What does the input values of the original function (i.e., the speed) divided by those in the transformed function that yield the same output value (i.e., the same distance) equal?

d. Stretch $d(s) = 5s + 2$ horizontally by 4. Your answer should start "$d\left(\dfrac{1}{4}s\right) = .$"

Example Meaning: The distance a robot travels as a function of the speed for a time of 5 minutes if it starts at a distance of 2 m; you want to rewrite the function to see what would happen if the robot were actually traveling at $\dfrac{1}{4}$ times the speed represented by s.

e. Graph the function you wrote in 2e on the calculator at the same time as the original function, $d(s) = 5s + 2$, and use the graph to answer the question: what is the horizontal coordinate of the x-intercept (i.e., the input for an output of 0) of each function?

horizontal coordinate of x-intercept of $d(s) = $ _____

horizontal coordinate of x-intercept of $d\left(\dfrac{1}{4}s\right) = $ _____

f. What does the input values of the original function (i.e., the speed) divided by those in the stretched function that yield the same output value (i.e., the same distance) equal?

Note that we multiply to scale a function. When we multiply the input, it scales horizontally. When we multiply the output, it scales vertically.

3. **Transforming Functions: Reflecting Horizontally Across the y-axis**

   a. Reflect $d(s) = 5s + 2$ across the y-axis. Your answer should start "$d(-s) =.$"

   Example Meaning: The distance a robot travels as a function of the speed for a time of 5 min if it starts at a distance of 2 m; you want to rewrite the function to see what would happen if the robot were traveling at a negative instead of a positive speed.

   b. Graph the reflection function you wrote in 3a on the calculator at the same time as the original function, $d(s) = 5s + 2$, and use the graph to answer the question: what is the horizontal coordinate of the x-intercept (i.e., the input for an output of 0) of each function?

   horizontal coordinate of x-intercept of $d(s) = $ _____

   horizontal coordinate of x-intercept of $d(-s) = $ _____

   c. How do the input values of the transformed function (i.e., the speed) compare with those in the original that yield the same output value (i.e., the same distance) as in the original?
   It was the same value, except multiplied by _____.

Note that we take the opposite to reflect a function. When we take the opposite of the input, it reflects across the y-axis, making all the input values opposite of what they were. When we take the opposite of the output, it reflects across the x-axis, making all the output values opposite of what they were.

Remember, use the chart at the end of the chapter to help you. Remember that *horizontal* transformations affect the *input*, and *vertical* ones the *output*.

1. **Transformations** – Use the function $f(x) = 2x + 4$ to solve these problems.

   Note that these include vertical transformations! Note also that we'll no longer be reminding you how your answer should start, but continue to list the function in a way that shows the transformation to the original function on both sides of the equation unless otherwise indicated. For example, in 1a when you shift $f(x)$ horizontally to the right by 3, your answer should start "$f(x - 3) = .$"

   a. Shift the function *horizontally* to the right by 3; list the new function.

   b. Graph the function you wrote in 1a on the calculator at the same time as the original function, $f(x) = 2x + 4$. What is the horizontal coordinate of the x-intercept of each graph?

      horizontal coordinate of x-intercept of the original function: _____

      horizontal coordinate of x-intercept of shifted function: _____

   c. Looking at your answers to 1b, how did the x-intercept change in the shifted function? Graph the functions if you need to in order to answer.

      It shifted to the | ○ right   ○ left | by _____.

   d. Shift the original function *vertically* down by 3; list the new function.

   e. Graph the function you wrote in 1d on the calculator at the same time as the original function, $f(x) = 2x + 4$. Find the vertical coordinate of the y-intercepts of each, noticing that the shifted function's is 3 less than the original function's.

      vertical coordinate of y-intercept of the original function: _____

      vertical coordinate of y-intercept of shifted function: _____

   f. Compress the original function *horizontally* by 3; list the new function.

   g. Graph the function you wrote in 1f on the calculator at the same time as the original function, $f(x) = 2x + 4$. Using either the graph or the equations, find the inputs that yield an output of 10 in both the original and the scaled function.

      Input that yields a 10 in the original function: _____

      Input that yields a 10 in the compressed function: _____

   h. Stretch the original function *horizontally* by 3; list the new function.

   i. Graph the function you wrote in 1h on the calculator at the same time as the original function, $f(x) = 2x + 4$. Using the graph, find the inputs that yield an output of 10 in both the original and the scaled function.

      Input that yields a 10 in the original function: _____

      Input that yields a 10 in the stretched function: _____

j. Scale the original function *vertically* by 3; list the new function. This time, go ahead and rename the scaled function $h(x)$.

k. Graph the function you wrote in 1j on the calculator at the same time as the original function, $f(x) = 2x + 4$. Using the graph, find the outputs for when the input is 2.

Output when the input is 2 in original function: _____

Output when the input is 2 in scaled function: _____

l. Reflect the original function *horizontally*; list the new function.

m. Graph the function you wrote in 1l on the calculator at the same time as the original function, $f(x) = 2x + 4$. Using the graph, find the inputs that yield an output of 10 in both the original and the scaled function.

Input that yields a 10 in the original function: _____

Input that yields a 10 in the reflected function: _____

n. Reflect the original function *vertically*; list the new function. This time, go ahead and rename the scaled function $h(x)$.

o. Graph the function you wrote in 1n on the calculator at the same time as the original function, $f(x) = 2x + 4$. Using the graph, find the outputs for when the input is 2.

Output when the input is 2 in original function: _____

Output when the input is 2 in the reflected function: _____

2. **Understanding Transformations**

   Hint: To determine a horizontal or vertical change occurred, think through whether the input or the output was adjusted. While we've renamed the transformed functions, look at what changed on the right side of the functions. Was the entire side (which equals the output) changed or just the input?

   a. What transformation was applied to $f(x) = 2x^2 + 6$ to get $h(x) = 2(x-1)^2 + 6$?

      O horizontal   O vertical *(choose one)*

      O shift   O scale   O reflection *(choose one)*

   b. What transformation was applied to $f(x) = 2x^2 + 6$ to get $h(x) = 2(3x)^2 + 6$?

      O horizontal   O vertical *(choose one)*

      O shift   O scale   O reflection *(choose one)*

   c. What transformation was applied to $f(x) = 2x^2 + 6$ to get $h(x) = \frac{1}{3}(2x^2 + 6)$?

      O horizontal   O vertical *(choose one)*

      O shift   O scale   O reflection *(choose one)*

3. **Recognizing Transformations**

   a. The black curve can be described by $f(t) = 20(1.02)^t$. What function describes the grey curve, given it is a transformation of the black curve using one of the transformations we've looked at?

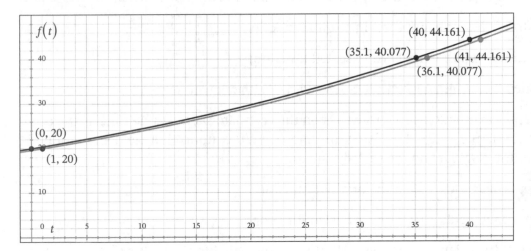

   b. The black curve can be described by $f(t) = 20(1.02)^t$. What function describes the grey curve, given it is a transformation of the black curve using one of the transformations we've looked at?

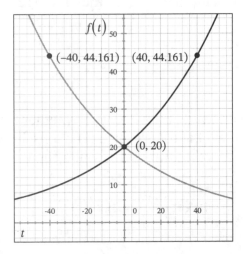

4. **Applying Algebra: Starlight** – On Worksheet 13.5B, we looked at finding the magnitude of starlight and saw we can express the magnitude using something called the Pogson scale. When the reference flux (normally represented by F_0) is 1, the formula for this becomes $m(F) = -2.5(\log(F))$, where F is the measurement of something called the flux density and the m stands for the magnitude.

   a. Compress the function horizontally by 100 by multiplying the input by 100, which will make each F value get the same output at $\frac{1}{100}$ of the original. **Be sure to use the product rule to simplify the transformed function as much as possible. Rename your final function $M(F)$.**

b. Using the function you found in 4a, find F when $M(F) = 45$.

> *And God made two great lights; the greater light to rule the day, and the lesser light to rule the night: he made the stars also. (Genesis 1:16)*

5. **Applying Algebra: Pepper Scale** – On Worksheet 13.6,[1] we looked at a hypothetical scale called the Pepper Scale that summarized the Scofield values of spiciness to a simple 0 to 4 scale using the formula $y = 1.39x - 2.94$. We can rewrite this using $P(s)$ to stand for y and x to stand for $\log(x)$ like this: $P(s) = 1.39\log(s) - 2.94$.

Spiciness	Scofield Scale Value s	Pepper Scale $P(s)$
Non Spicy	0 to 700	0 to 1
Mildly Spicy	700 to 3,000	1 to 2
Moderately Spicy	3,000 to 25,000	2 to 3
Highly Spicy	25,000 to 80,000	3 to 4
Very Highly Spicy	> 80,000	> 4

Suppose you want to change the Pepper Scale so that instead of a rating of 0 to 4, it uses a rating of 10 to 14. In other words, you want a $P(s)$ value (i.e., the output of the function) of between 0 and 1 to now equal between 10 and 11, a $P(s)$ value of between 1 and 2 to now equal between 11 and 12, and so forth. Transform the formula $P(s) = 1.39\log(s) - 2.94$ to show this.

1   See footnote on Worksheet 13.6 for the paper the idea of Scofield scale value ranges and comparisons with pungency (which we changed to spicy) came from.

1. **Specifying Transformations Without Words** – Find the transformed function requested. **Do not simplify.**

    a. Find $f(x-3)$ if $f(x) = 2x^2 + x$.

    b. Find $2f(x)$ if $f(x) = 2x^2 + x$.

    c. Find $-f(x)$ if $f(x) = 2x^2 + x$.

2. **Specifying the Transformation Without Knowing the Function** – Look back at Lessons 14.1 and 14.2 (or at the chart at the end of the chapter) as needed to figure out how to transform the functions in the specified manner.

    Example: Write a new function that equals $f(x)$ shifted down by 3.

    Answer: $h(x) = f(x) - 3$
    (We shift down by subtracting from the output, or $f(x)$.)

    a. Write a new function named $h(x)$ that equals $f(x)$ shifted to the left by 2.

    b. Write a new function named $h(x)$ that equals $f(x)$ shifted to the right by 10.

    c. Write a new function named $h(x)$ that equals $f(x)$ shifted vertically up by 10.

    d. Write a new function named $h(x)$ that equals $f(x)$ scaled vertically by 10.

    e. Write a new function named $h(x)$ that equals $f(x)$ compressed horizontally by 2.

    f. Write a new function named $h(x)$ that equals $f(x)$ stretched horizontally by 2.

    g. Write a new function named $h(x)$ that equals $f(x)$ reflected across the x-axis.

    h. Write a new function named $h(x)$ that equals $f(x)$ reflected across the y-axis.

3. **Finding Values**

    a. Find $f(-2)$ if $f(x-5) = 6x^2 + 2$.

    b. Find $f(4)$ if $f(3x) = 2x - 1$.

    c. Find $f(5)$ if $f(-x) = 3x + 5$.

    d. Find the input (i.e., x value) of $f\left(\dfrac{1}{3}x\right)$ that will produce an output of 10 if $f(6) = 10$.

    e. Find the input (i.e., x value) of $f(x-4)$ that will produce an output of 10 if $f(6) = 10$.

4. **Applying Algebra: Money in the Bank** – Suppose the amount of money you have in an account after a certain number of years varies according to the function $P(t) = \$400(1.02)^t$. Note that the interest is compounded annually.

a. Write a function based on $P(t)$ that shows what the interest is a year prior (i.e., a shift back in time of 1 year, which is a shift to the right horizontally). Part of it is given to you, but include that part in your answer.

   $P(t$ _____ $) =$ _____

b. At what number of years will the function you transformed in 4a equal $P(15)$?

   $t =$ _____ years

c. If instead the account has the interest compounded twice a year but the interest rate used each time remains 2% (that is, 2% is the interest rate used every 6 months when the interest is calculated), write a function showing how the ending balance will vary based on time. Part of it is given to you, but include that part in your answer.

   $P($ ___ $t) =$ _____

d. At what number of years will the function you transformed in 4c equal $P(15)$?

   $t =$ _____ years

1. **Transforming from a Graph**

   a. Suppose we have the points shown on the graph and know that y is a function of x, although we don't know exactly how. List what the points corresponding to these would be on a new function that is the same as this function except shifted to the left by 3. *Hint:* Copy the graph shown on graph paper and actually graph the new points — just draw them shifted 3 to the left.

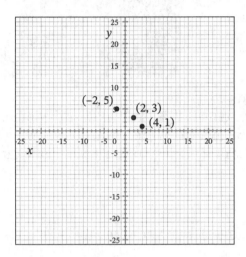

   b. Using the points you transformed in 1a, further transform them by first scaling them vertically by –5 and then reflecting them across the x-axis. *Hint:* Graph them on the graph you drew in 1a.

   c. Find the point that would correspond to $(2, -4)$ after the function it is on is compressed horizontally by 2. *Hint:* See the examples in the text for a reminder about compressing versus stretching horizontally.

   d. Find the point that would correspond to $(2, -4)$ after the function it is on is stretched horizontally by 2.

   e. Transform the point $(2, -1)$ which is part of a function by *first* reflecting it across the y-axis, *then* compressing it horizontally by 3, and *finally* shifting it vertically by –3. *Hint:* Use graph paper to draw the point and the transformations if needed.

2. **More Recognizing Transformations** – The black curve can be described by $f(x) = 5x^2 + 3x$. What function describes the grey curve, given it is a transformation of the solid curve using one of the transformations we've looked at? Try trial and error if you don't know how the function was transformed.

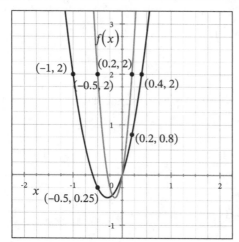

3. **Skill Sharpening: Mastering the Language** – Find the transformed function requested.

   a. Find $f(x-4)$ if $f(x) = 5^x$.

   b. Find $6f(x)$ if $f(x) = 5^x$.

   c. Find $2f(-x)$ if $f(x) = 5^x$

4. **Skill Sharpening: Finding Values**

   a. Find $f(5)$ if $f(5x) = \log(x)$.

   b. Find $f(4)$ if $f(x-1) = 3\log(5^{3x})$.

5. 🎯 **Challenge Problem: Interest** – Suppose that the ending balance of money in a bank can be described by the function $P(t)$, where $P(t)$ is the ending balance and t is the time.

   a. Write a function describing the ending balance if an additional $400 is added to the ending balance that does not change based on time, since it doesn't earn interest. Your answer should start "$P(t) +$." *Hint:* It doesn't matter that you don't know what $P(t)$ equals. You can still show how this additional $400 will affect it.

   b. Say that according to the function $P(t)$, the bank has $500 in it at one point. What value would it have if it were following the function in 5a instead?

   c. Say instead that you have a function $P(r)$ that describes the ending balance as a function of the rate. If the rate is decreased by 0.005, what will the new input (i.e., r value) be that yields 2,000 if $P(0.04) = 2,000$? *Hint:* You need to first find the transformed function and then find the r value that will make the parentheses of that function equal 0.04.

1. **Composite Functions and Transformations**

   a. If $f(x) = x^2 + x + 3$ and $g(x) = x - 3$, find $f(g(x))$.

      $f(g(x)) = $ _____

   b. Look closely at $f(x)$ and $f(g(x))$ in problem 1a. What type of transformation were you really applying to $f(x)$ when you found $f(g(x))$?

      ○ horizontal   ○ vertical *(choose one)*

      ○ shift   ○ scale   ○ reflection *(choose one)*

   c. If $f(x) = 2x^2 + 3x + 2$ and $g(x) = 2x$, find $f(g(x))$.

      $f(g(x)) = $ _____

   d. Look closely at $f(x)$ and $f(g(x))$ in problem 1c. What type of transformation were you really applying to $f(x)$ when you found $f(g(x))$?

      ○ horizontal   ○ vertical *(choose one)*

      ○ shift   ○ scale   ○ reflection *(choose one)*

   e. If $f(x) = 2x^2 + 3x + 2$ and $g(x) = 2x$, find $g(f(x))$.

      $g(f(x)) = $ _____

   Note that 1c and 1e used the same functions, except we swapped which we used as the input to the other.

   f. Look closely at $f(x)$ and $g(f(x))$ in problem 1e. What type of transformation were you really applying to $f(x)$ when you found $g(f(x))$?

      ○ horizontal   ○ vertical *(choose one)*

      ○ shift   ○ scale   ○ reflection *(choose one)*

   g. If $f(x) = 5x + 3$ and $g(x) = 3x$, find $f(g(x))$.

      $f(g(x)) = $ _____

   h. Look closely at $f(x)$ and $f(g(x))$ in problem 1g. What type of transformation were you really applying to $f(x)$ when you found $f(g(x))$?

      ○ horizontal   ○ vertical *(choose one)*

      ○ shift   ○ scale   ○ reflection *(choose one)*

   i. If $f(x) = 5x + 3$ and $g(x) = 2x$, find $g(f(x))$.

      $g(f(x)) = $ _____

j. Look closely at $f(x)$ and $g(f(x))$ in problem 1i. What type of transformation were you really applying to $f(x)$ when you found $g(f(x))$?

    ○ horizontal   ○ vertical *(choose one)*

    ○ shift   ○ scale   ○ reflection *(choose one)*

Both of the following problems relate to topics you may have never heard about before. And that's okay! You don't have to understand the science involved to use math to solve them . . . but you're getting a glimpse into how what you're learning applies.

2. ◎ **Challenge Problem: Normal Distribution** – Since we looked at the normal distribution formula as an example of a complicated function that we can break up in order to better examine the relationship, let's look at an application of that formula.

   a. Use a calculator to graph the normal age distribution of a hypothetical survey where the average age surveyed (μ) was 20 and the standard deviation (σ) was 2 years, where the distribution function is given by the formula $f(x) = \dfrac{1}{\sqrt{2\pi}\sigma}e^{\frac{-(x-\mu)^2}{2\sigma^2}}$. Make your scale on your y-axis 0 to 1, and on your x-axis 0 to 30. Draw the general shape in your notebook.

   b. Given that the vertical axis represents the probability density and that the *ratio* between two probability densities tells you how much more probable a specific answer to the survey is to be one result versus the other, see how much more probable it is that a specific person surveyed on this particular survey will be 20 years old than 22 years old. It is _____ times more probable that a person on this survey will be 20 to 22 years old.

3. **Applying Algebra: Electrons** – In measuring how electrons occupy energy levels in semiconductors, a distribution known as the Fermi-Dirac distribution is used.[1] Here is an equation for the distribution for a particular system: $h(x) = \dfrac{1}{e^{x-3}+1}$, where x is the energy of the electron in its current state. When combined with other functions, this distribution tells you how easy it is for electrons to flow in the semiconductor. Let's break this function down into separate functions. Note that we can do so different ways! Which way we picked would depend on what we were trying to separate out in order to better examine.

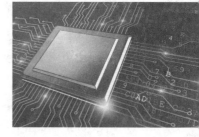

Hint: Think about what $g(x)$ would have to equal in order to end up at the function $h(x)$.

   a. Let's think of $h(x)$ as $f(g(x)) = \dfrac{1}{g(x)}$. If we do that, what would $g(x)$ equal?

   b. Let's think of $h(x)$ as $f(g(x)) = \dfrac{1}{g(x)+1}$. If we do that, what would $g(x)$ equal?

   c. Let's think of $h(x)$ as $f(g(x)) = \dfrac{1}{e^{g(x)}+1}$. If we do that, what would $g(x)$ equal?

---

1   Formula for Fermi-Dirac distribution can be found in Donald A. McQuarrie, *Statistical Mechanics* (Sausalito, CA: University Science Books, 2000), p. 164.

This worksheet is designed to be a review day, as we've covered a lot of material lately. Take some time to look back over the first five lessons of Chapter 14 and make sure you've understood transforming functions. **Also, look ahead to the chart at the end of the chapter on transforming functions as well, as it will help you review the key information.**

1. **Transformations and Composite Function Review**

   a. If $f(x) = \log_3(x)$ and $g(x) = 3^x$, find $g(f(x))$. Be sure to simplify as much as possible, using what you know of logarithms to help you.

   $g(f(x)) = $ _____

   b. If $f(x) = \dfrac{x^2}{3}$ and $g(x) = \log(x)$, find $g(f(x))$. Use the quotient rule to list your answer as two separate logarithms and the power rule to move any exponents out of the logarithms.

   $g(f(x)) = $ _____

   c. Find $2f(x + 3)$ if $f(x) = 3x^2 + x$. You do not need to simplify.

   d. Write a new function $h(x)$ that equals $f(x)$ shifted to the left by 3.

   e. Write a new function $h(x)$ that equals $f(x)$ compressed horizontally by 3.

   f. Write a new function $h(x)$ that equals $f(x)$ scaled vertically by $\dfrac{1}{3}$.

   g. Find $f(6)$ if $-f(x - 3) = 4x^2 + 2$.

   h. If the point $(-1, 3)$ is part of a function and that function is *first* shifted to the left by 4 and *then* reflected across the y-axis, find the corresponding point on the transformed function.

   i. The solid curve can be described by $f(x) = x^3 + 4$. What function describes the grey curve, given it is a transformation of the black curve using one of the transformations we've looked at?

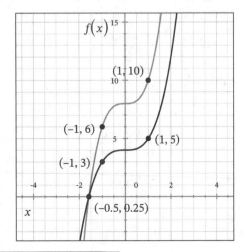

2. **Applying Algebra: Exploring the Price of Tea in China** – It's time to explore the age-old question of, "What does that have to do with the price of tea in China?" Let's say that the price of tea in China is a function of the number of tea leaves shipped to the U.S. and can be described by $d(p) = 52(1.05)^p - 52$, where $p \geq 0$. $d(p)$ is the dollars to buy and ship tea leaves between China and the U.S., and p is the pounds of tea leaves shipped (it grows exponentially with how much tea is shipped).

Note that these relationships are purely hypothetical!

a. Let's say that a trade agreement lowers the price of tea shipped such that 100 pounds are given free with every shipment. Write a transformed function describing this. **Write the entire transformed function (including the part given) as your answer.**

$d(p) = 52(1.05)^p - 52$, where $p \geq 0$ (original function)

$d(p\underline{\hspace{1.5cm}}) = \underline{\hspace{2.5cm}}$, where $p \geq 100$ (transformed function)

b. Use the following graph of the functions from 2a to answer the question: If you pay the same amount of dollars (d), how many more pounds of tea (p) will you get under the transformed function than you would under the original function for any poundage shipped?

      _____ lb more tea

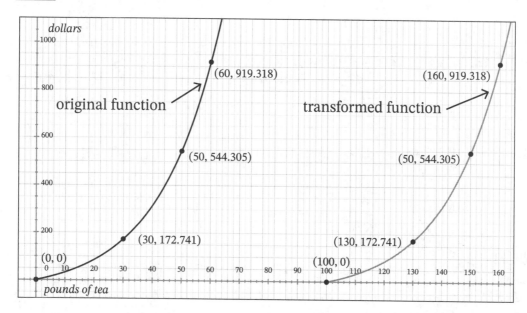

c. Let's say that instead there's an agreement between China and the U.S. to raise the standard base shipping price between China and the U.S by \$500 (i.e., if 0 pounds are shipped, \$500 is still owed). Transform the original function to show this. **Write the entire transformed function (including the part given) as your answer.**

$d(p) = 52(1.05)^p - 52$, where $p \geq 0$ (original function)

$d(p)\underline{\hspace{1.5cm}} = \underline{\hspace{2.5cm}}$, where $p \geq 0$ (transformed function)

d. Use the graph given of the functions from 2c to answer this question: How much more will the same number of pounds cost you under the transformed function than under the original?

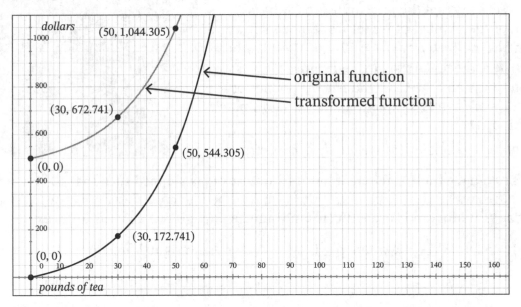

e. Let's say that the price of tea is increased by multiplying the pounds of tea by a certain scaling factor. The graph shows the original $d(p)$ function and the resulting function with the new prices. Figure out what function describes the new relationship between the price and pounds of tea. Notice that for the same dollar amount, you now get fewer pounds of tea.

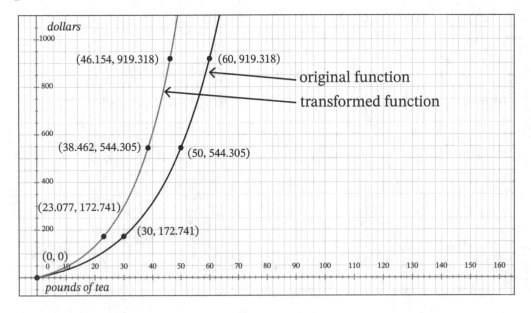

1. **Understanding Piecewise Functions** – The following function gives hypothetical values for a rocket's mass at various points (rockets lose mass as they travel). Use it to answer the questions.

$$m(t) = \begin{cases} 1{,}000 \text{ kg} & \text{if } t \le 0 \\ 1{,}000\,(0.97)^t, & \text{if } 0 < t \le 60 \\ 1{,}000(0.97)^{60}\,(0.999)^{t-60}, & \text{if } 60 < t \le 360 \\ 1{,}000(0.97)^{60}\,(0.999)^{300}, & \text{if } t > 360 \end{cases}$$

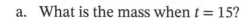

a. What is the mass when $t = 15$?

$m(15) \approx$ _____

b. What is the mass when $t = 60$?

$m(60) \approx$ _____

c. What is the mass when $t = 360$?

$m(360) \approx$ _____

d. 🎯 **Challenge Problem:** The majority of the mass of a rocket tends to be the fuel used to launch it. If all the mass that is lost during the first 360 seconds of this launch is from the fuel burning, what percent of the original mass at time $t = 0$ does the fuel make up? *Hint:* You can use whatever method you've learned for finding the percent; one formula is $Percent = \dfrac{Percentage}{Base}$, where *Percentage* is the mass in kg of fuel lost and *Base* is the original mass of the rocket.

2. **More Understanding Piecewise Functions** – What would you have to add to this piecewise function to show that for values less than 0, $x = 5$?

$$f(x) = \begin{cases} 2x + 5, & \text{if } x \ge 0 \\ \underline{\hspace{2cm}} \end{cases}$$

3. **Working with Piecewise Functions** – Given

$$f(t) = \begin{cases} 0, & \text{if } t \le 0 \\ -5t, & \text{if } 0 < t < 1 \\ -5t, & \text{if } 1 \le t \le 6 \\ 5t - 35, & \text{if } 6 < t \le 9 \end{cases}$$

the velocity function we looked at in the text for Lesson 14.6, what is the velocity when $t = 6.1$? Be sure to simplify.

$v(6.1) =$ _____

4. **Applying Algebra: Interest That Changes** – Suppose your bank account has a graduated interest tier, where your interest depends on the balance. The interest for average daily balances less than $5,000 is 1%, the interest for balances from $5,000 to $20,000 is 2%, and the interest for balances over $20,000 is 3%. In all cases, annual interest rates are given, but the interest is compounded monthly.

a. Rewrite this piecewise function describing how the ending balance varies based on the starting balance, leaving time as an unknown. When you rewrite it, fill in the missing places so as to accurately reflect the problem. The first row is done for you.[1]

$$P(P_i) = \begin{cases} P_i\left(1 + \dfrac{0.01}{12}\right)^{12t}, \text{ when } P_i < \$5,000 \\ \underline{\hspace{3cm}}, \text{when } P_i \underline{\hspace{2cm}} \\ \underline{\hspace{3cm}}, \text{when } P_i \underline{\hspace{2cm}} \end{cases}$$

b. Use the function you wrote in 4a to find $P(P_i)$ after $t = 4$ years if an initial balance of $5,000 was deposited and no withdrawals or deposits were given. Round your answer to the nearest cent.

$P(4) \approx \underline{\hspace{2.5cm}}$

c. Use the function you wrote in 4a to find the time (t) in years it will take to grow an initial deposit of $20,500 to $25,000, assuming no further withdrawals or deposits were made.

5. **More with Transforming Functions**

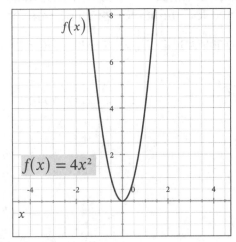

$f(x)$

$f(x) = 4x^2$

x

a. Which rewritten equation would result in shifting the function shown by 8 vertically upward?

○ A. $h(x) = 4x^2 + 8$ ○ B. $h(x) = 4(x + 8)^2$ ○ C. $h(x) = 8(4x^2)$

b. Which rewritten equation would result in reflecting the function shown across the x-axis?

○ A. $h(x) = -(4x^2)$ ○ B. $h(x) = 4(-x)^2$ ○ C. $h(x) = 4x^2 + 8$

---

1   Notice that we're simplifying the problem some and just viewing the tiers as based on the P_i, the beginning balance. This will hold true provided that the average daily balance stays close enough to the beginning balance and doesn't jump into another tier. We made sure this was the case on problems.

6. **More with Transforming Functions** – Use the function $f(x) = \log(5x)$ to solve these problems. After performing any transformation, **apply the product rule and calculate any logarithm you can.**

   a. Shift the function *horizontally* by 10 to the left.

   b. Shift the function *vertically by 10 upward.*

7. **Skill Sharpening**

   a. Separate into three different terms: $\log(abc)$

   b. Rewrite so there is no exponent in the expression: $\log(g^{4x})$

   c. Write a new function $h(x)$ that equals $f(x)$ scaled vertically by 10.

   d. Find the value of $f(2)$ if $-f(x-2) = 5x + 3$

   e. Say you know the point $(2, 4)$ is part of a function. If you transform the function by *first* reflecting it across the y-axis and *then* compressing it horizontally by 5, what will the corresponding point on the transformed function be?

   f. Again, say you know the point $(2, 4)$ is part of a function. This time, find the resulting point if the function is *first reflected across the x-axis* and *then stretched* horizontally by 5.

> *Be sure to keep reviewing transforming functions. They will be on the quiz, and you will not be allowed to look at the book or your notes.*

1. **Power Functions** – List any power functions. Note that in a power function, only one term can have the input in it, and the input is *not* in the exponent. Otherwise, if the input is raised to any real number, it's a power function!

   Example: List the power functions.

   $\bigcirc f(x) = \dfrac{1}{x^4}$ $\bigcirc f(t) = 5e^x$ $\bigcirc f(x) = 5x^{0.5}$ $\bigcirc f(x) = 5x^5 + 2x$

   Answer: $f(x) = \dfrac{1}{x^4}$ and $f(x) = 5x^{0.5}$

   Notice that we did *not* list $f(t) = 5e^x$, as the x was an exponent (which makes it an exponential function), nor did we list $f(x) = 5x^5 + 2x$, as there were two terms with an x (and power functions only have one term with the input). But the rest were power functions!

   Now it's your turn!

   $\bigcirc f(x) = 5x^5 + x$ $\bigcirc f(x) = x^{0.4} + 3$ $\bigcirc f(x) = 4x^2 + 3$

   $\bigcirc f(x) = x^{-b}$ $\bigcirc f(x) = 6^{3x}$ $\bigcirc f(x) = 4x^2 + 3x$ $\bigcirc f(x) = x^{0.1}$

2. **Reviewing Absolute Value** – Simplify as much as possible. Treat unknowns as variables that could be positive or negative. If you cannot simplify, just write the original expression again.

   a. $|-6 + 3|$

   b. $|5x - x|$

   c. $|18|$

   d. $|-a|$

   e. $|-5x|$

   f. $|-x^2 - 3x^2|$

   g. $|-2x^3 - x^3|$

   h. $|-7 + 3|$

   i. $|-5x^{3x} - 4x^{3x}|$

   j. $|-x^6 + x^4|$

3. **Working with Absolute Value Functions**

   a. If $f(x) = 2|x^2 - 15|$, find $f(2)$.

   b. If $f(x) = 2|x^2 - 15|$, find $f(4)$.

   c. Evaluate for when $x = -2$: $|3x|$

d. If $f(x-1) = 3|\log(x)|$, find $f(3)$.

e. If $-5f(x) = 2|-\log(x)|$, find $f(5)$.
   Hint: Find $-5f(x)$ for when $x = 5$, and then divide both sides by -5.

4. **Applying Algebra: Strain Rates** – Suppose we measured the viscosity (think thickness) of a certain mixture of corn starch and water and found the viscosity to be 1 mPa $\cdot$ s (we read these units as millipascal seconds) when no strain is applied, 85 mPa $\cdot$ s when a strain rate of 10 Hz is applied, and 1,357 mPa $\cdot$ s when a strain rate of 100 Hz is applied. If the viscosity represented by $n(\dot\gamma)$, varies based on the strain rate $(\dot\gamma)$ according to the power function $\eta(\dot\gamma) = a\dot\gamma^b + \eta_0$, find the values for a, b, and η_0 for this particular fluid. The questions below will help you. In this problem, you can ignore units for simplicity.

   a. Write three equations by plugging in the viscosity measurements as $n(\dot\gamma)$ and the strain rate as the $\dot\gamma$ in the power function $\eta(\dot\gamma) = a\dot\gamma^b + \eta_0$. Leave a, b, and η_0 as unknowns.

   Equation 1: _____

   Equation 2: _____

   Equation 3: _____

   b. Your three equations are really a system of equations! You can use the information in each equation to find the overall function for the corn starch/water solution by using the system of equations to find a, and b, and η_0. Note that this will take many steps and require applying many things you've learned, but you have all the skills you need!

   $a \approx$ _____ $b \approx$ _____ $\eta_0 \approx$ _____

   c. Plug the values you found in 4b into the relationship $\eta(\dot\gamma) = a\dot\gamma^b + \eta_0$, thereby writing the equation that describes this particular cornstarch fluid.

Notice how you were able to solve a system of equations using a combination of different skills you've learned. You now have a lot of "tools" in your mathematical toolbox!

5. **Transformation Time**

   a. Stretch horizontally by –3: $f(x) = 4\log(x)$.

   b. Compress horizontally by –3: $f(x) = 4\log(x)$.

   c. Scale vertically by –2: $f(x) = 2\log(x)$

   d. Reflect horizontally: $f(x) = x^2 + 6x + 2$

   e. Reflect vertically: $f(x) = x^2 + 6x + 2$

   f. Transform the point $(1, -3)$ if it is part of a function that is *first* stretched horizontally by 2, *then* scaled vertically by –5, and *finally* reflected across the x-axis.

6. **More with Absolute Value and Power Functions**

   a. Write $h(x) = f(g(x))$ if $f(x) = |x| - 3$ and $g(x) = x^{-3} - 4$.

   $h(x) = f(g(x)) =$ _____

   b. Use graph paper to graph all three functions from 6a ($f(x)$, $g(x)$, and $h(x)$), labeling each one.

   c. Which of the functions from 6a is a power function?

   $\bigcirc f(x)$ $\bigcirc g(x)$

   d. Which of the functions from 6a is an absolute value function with a linear input?

   $\bigcirc f(x)$ $\bigcirc g(x)$

1. **Basic Trigonometry Review**

    a. Calculate $\sin(40°)$.

    b. Calculate $\cos(30°)$.

    c. Calculate $\tan(50°)$.

    d. ◎ **Challenge Problem:** In the picture, what is the approximate length of the side of the triangle marked x? **Be sure to include the appropriate unit of measure.**
    Hint: Think about what the different trigonometric angles equal $\left(\dfrac{opposite}{adjacent}, \dfrac{adjacent}{hypotenuse}, \dfrac{opposite}{hypotenuse}\right)$.
    Use this knowledge to set either the sine, cosine, or tangent of 56° equal to a ratio that includes x.

    e. ◎ **Challenge Problem:** In the drawing, what is the height of the lantern?

2. **Understanding and Expanding Trigonometry** – Graph $y = \sin(x)$ using a vertical scale of −2 to 2 and a horizontal scale of 0 to 400; also, make sure you're in degree mode. Using your graph and remembering that the horizontal axis gives the angle value, while the vertical one gives the sine of that angle, write down the requested values.

    a. $\sin(30°)$

    b. $\sin(60°)$

    c. $\sin(120°)$

    d. $\sin(150°)$

    e. $\sin(180°)$

    f. $\sin(210°)$

    g. $\sin(240°)$

    h. $\sin(270°)$

    i. $\sin(300°)$

    j. $\sin(330°)$

    k. $\sin(360°)$

3. **More Understanding and Expanding Trigonometry** – Picturing a triangle moving around a circle as was shown in Lesson 14.8, compare your answers in 2a, 2d, 2f, and 2j. How do they compare?

    ○ they are all the same   ○ they are the same absolute value

    Why do you think that is? _____

4. **More Understanding and Expanding Trigonometry** – The black curve can be described by $f(x) = \sin(x)$. What function describes the grey curve, given it is a transformation of the solid curve using one of the transformations we've looked at?

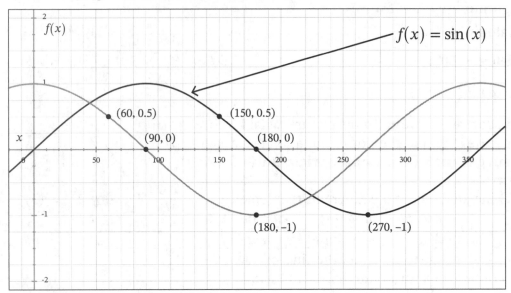

$f(x) = \sin(x)$

(60, 0.5)   (150, 0.5)
(90, 0)   (180, 0)
(180, −1)   (270, −1)

The transformed curve can also be described as $f(x) = \cos(x)$ — that is, the cosine function! The cosine function can be thought of as a transformed version of the sine function. It has been shifted horizontally to the left by a certain number of degrees (look at your answer to problem 4 to see how many).

5. **More Understanding and Expanding Trigonometry** – The following figures show the same triangle rotated around a circle. Find the ratio between the side adjacent (i.e., touching) the θ and the hypotenuse of 1 using division for each position; then use your calculator's cosine button to calculate the cosine of the labeled angle. You should get the same answer both ways.

a.

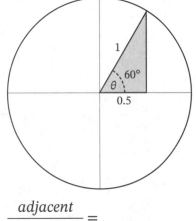

$$\frac{adjacent}{hypotenuse} = \underline{\hspace{2cm}}$$

$\cos(60°) = \underline{\hspace{2cm}}$

b.

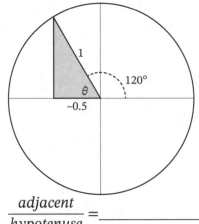

$$\frac{adjacent}{hypotenuse} = \underline{\hspace{2cm}}$$

$\cos(120°) = \underline{\hspace{2cm}}$

c.

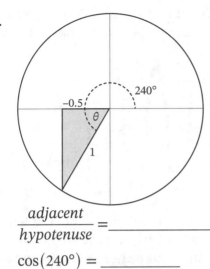

$$\frac{adjacent}{hypotenuse} = \underline{\hspace{3cm}}$$

$$\cos(240°) = \underline{\hspace{3cm}}$$

d.

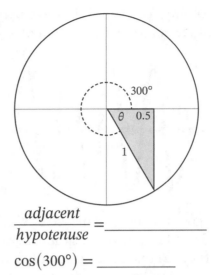

$$\frac{adjacent}{hypotenuse} = \underline{\hspace{3cm}}$$

$$\cos(300°) = \underline{\hspace{3cm}}$$

e. Look at your answers to 5a–5d. What do you notice about them all?

○ They are all the same.   ○ They are the same absolute value.

This is because these particular angles are really the same triangle with the same angle, just at different spots on the circle.

6. **Applying Algebra/Trigonometry: Light's Refraction[1]** – Have you ever noticed that if you put part of an object into water, it will look like the object bends at the water line? That's because the water slows the light down, changing the angle at which you see the part of the object that's submerged.

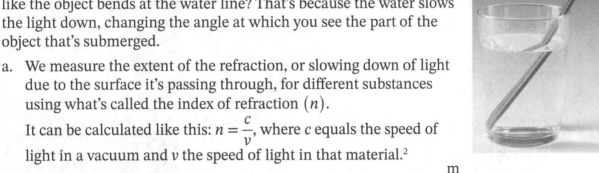

a. We measure the extent of the refraction, or slowing down of light due to the surface it's passing through, for different substances using what's called the index of refraction (n).

It can be calculated like this: $n = \dfrac{c}{v}$, where c equals the speed of light in a vacuum and v the speed of light in that material.[2]

Knowing this, that the speed of light in a vacuum is $299{,}792{,}458 \, \dfrac{\text{m}}{\text{s}}$, and that the index of refraction for air is 1.0003, find the speed (v) of light in air.

b. The refraction of light between two surfaces of two different materials/substances can be found using this relationship: $n_1 \sin(\theta_1) = n_2 \sin(\theta_2)$, where n_1 is the index of refraction for one material/substance and n_2 is the index of refraction for the other.[3] (*Note:* This is known as Snell's law.) Solve this relationship for n_2.
Hint: You can divide by the sine of an angle just like you can any other unknown. Only view $\sin(\theta)$ as a single unknown — the sine of the angle θ.

c. Given that the index of refraction for air is 1.0003, find the index of refraction for water (which would be n_2 if you view the value for the index of refraction of air as 1.0003) if the angle at which the light hits the water is 45° and the angle of refraction is 32.12842176°.

1   Randall D. Knight, *Physics for Scientists and Engineers with Modern Physics: A Strategic Approach* (Pearson, Addison Wesley, NY: 2004), p. 632 and 722.
2   Ibid., p. 722.
3   Ibid.

7. **Even More Applying Algebra/Trigonometry: Amplitude of a Light Wave** – We use the word "amplitude" to describe how tall or high a wave is at its maximum and minimum points.

amplitude 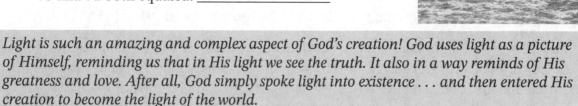 amplitude

Since the waves go up as high as they go down, it makes sense with amplitude to often only care about the absolute value of the amplitude. It turns out that if you have two waves with the same amplitude (a) that are not waving at the same time, but rather are off by the angle $\Delta\phi$ (in physics, we sometimes use two symbols to represent a single unknown), the total amplitude A of the resulting wave can be written using the following function:[4]

$$A(\Delta\phi) = \left|2a\cos\left(\frac{\Delta\phi}{2}\right)\right|$$

This particular equation is a composite function of a trigonometric function (cosine) into an absolute value function. That's right, we can combine trigonometric functions and absolute value functions.

a. Calculate the value of $A(\Delta\phi)$ if $a = 5$ and $\Delta\phi = 90°$.

b. Calculate the value of $A(\Delta\phi)$ if $a = 5$ and $\Delta\phi = 120°$.

c. Calculate the value of $A(\Delta\phi)$ if $a = 5$ and $\Delta\phi = 270°$.

d. Calculate the value of $A(\Delta\phi)$ if $a = 5$ and $\Delta\phi = 240°$.

e. Compare your answers in 7a and 7c as well as 7b and 7d.

7a and 7c both equaled: _____

7b and 7d both equaled: _____

Light is such an amazing and complex aspect of God's creation! God uses light as a picture of Himself, reminding us that in His light we see the truth. It also in a way reminds of His greatness and love. After all, God simply spoke light into existence . . . and then entered His creation to become the light of the world.

And God said, "Let there be light," and there was light. (Genesis 1:3; ESV)

Again Jesus spoke to them, saying, "I am the light of the world. Whoever follows me will not walk in darkness, but will have the light of life." (John 8:12; ESV)

---

4   Function from Ibid., p. 667.

8. **Skill Sharpening**

   a. Shift this function vertically by -4: $f(x) = \log(2x) + 8$. Then apply the product rule. Do not calculate any logarithms.

   b. Scale this function vertically by -4: $f(x) = \log(2x) + 8$. Do not simplify the expression/ rearrange the logarithm at all in your answer.

   c. Scale this function vertically by -4: $f(x) = |x + 3| + 3$. Do not simplify.

   d. Find the input value in $f(x + 8)$ that will yield an output of 30 if $f(5) = 30$.

   e. If $(-2, 5)$ is a point on a function, find the corresponding point on a function that has *first* been compressed by -3 horizontally and *then* reflected across the y-axis.

   f. If $(-2, 5)$ is a point on a function, find the corresponding point on a function that has *first* been stretched by -3 horizontally and *then* reflected across the y-axis.

   g. Find $f(g(x))$ if $g(x) = x^2 + 3$ and $f(x) = |x - 6|$.

   $f(g(x)) = $ _____

9. **More Skill Sharpening** – Solve for t.

   a. $700 = 30(0.02)^{5t}$

   b. $60 = 3\log(t)$ (Leave your answer as 10 raised to a power.)

Make sure you know how to transform functions — it will be on the quiz, and you will not be allowed to look back in your book.

1. **Reviewing** – Answer the following questions using this piecewise function.

$$f(x) = \begin{cases} 3x^3 + 2x \text{ if } x < 0 \\ 2x^3 \text{ if } 0 \leq x \leq 10 \\ \dfrac{2{,}000}{10^2}|x^2| \text{ if } 10 < x \leq 20 \\ \dfrac{2^2}{4}|x^3 - x + 20| \text{ if } x > 20 \end{cases}$$

   a. Can you simplify any of the "pieces" in this function?

      ○ yes   ○ no

      If so, simplify it. _____

   b. Evaluate for $f(-10)$.

2. **All About Transformations**

   a. Shift $f(x) = 6x^2 + 5x + 3$ to the right by 2. You do not need to simplify.

   b. Compress $d(s)$ (distance as a function of speed) *first* horizontally by 3, *then* scale vertically by 4, and *finally* reflect it over the y-axis.

   c. Notice how easy it would be to mistake your final answer to 2b as something other than function notation. This is one reason why it's often helpful to use $f(x)$ to show functions, regardless of what we're actually representing! Rewrite your answer to 2b, replacing s in the function with x, and d with f. Notice how this helps clue the reader in to the fact that it's a function.

d. The black curve can be described by $f(x) = 7x^2 - 3$. What function describes the grey curve, given it is a transformation of the black curve using one of the transformations we've looked at?

Hint: First use the quadratic formula to figure out the x-intercepts of the original function so you will have values to compare. Sometimes you have to use multiple concepts to solve a problem!

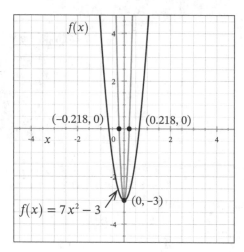

e. Given the point $(0, 5)$ that is part of the function $f(x)$, transform it by *first* shifting it horizontally to the left by 3, *then* scaling it vertically by 5, and *finally* reflecting it across the x-axis.

f. Find $f(x)$ if $f(g(x)) = 5^{x^2+2}$ and $g(x) = x^2 + 2$.

g. Find $4f(3)$ if $f(-2x) = 4x^2 + x$.

h. Given $f(x) = 4x$ and the transformed function $f(x + 2) = 4(x + 2)$, what input (i.e., x value) in the transformed function will yield the same output as an input of 20 does in the original?

3. ◎ **Challenge Problem: Damped Harmonic Oscillators** – Let's say you want to calculate the decibel value of the intensity of a sound wave in a damped harmonic oscillator (it's okay if you don't know what that is — it's something you might learn about down the road if you take a physics course or mechanical engineering course). Say $f(x) = 10\log(x)$ describes the decibel value, where x represents the intensity ratio.

a. Let's say we have another formula $g(x)$ that can help us calculate the intensity ratio. Replace x in $f(x) = 10\log(x)$ with $g(x)$.

b. In this case, let's say $g(x) = \dfrac{1}{16\left((x-4)^2 + \dfrac{1}{256}\right)}$. Use your answer to 3a to find $f(g(x))$.

Hint: You will need to use either the quotient or power rule to simplify after you find the composite function.

$f(g(x)) = $ _____

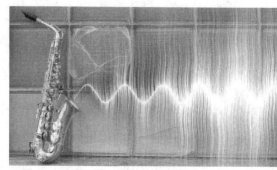

c. Find the approximate value of x when $f(g(x)) = 50$ using the formula you found in 3b.

4. **Applying Algebra/Trigonometry: Firing a Canon** – The maximum distance a cannon ball fired can reach is called its range. It turns out that the range is a function of the angle the cannon is tilted with respect to the horizon as follows when air resistance can be ignored:

$$R(\theta) = \frac{2v_0^2}{g}\left(\sin(\theta)\right)\left(\cos(\theta)\right)$$

Notice the use of trigonometric functions! In this problem, the value for the gravity constant is $g = 9.8\frac{m}{s^2}$ and for the initial velocity squared is $v_0^2 = 98\frac{m^2}{s^2}$.

a. Insert the values into the formula and simplify, keeping the units of measure.

b. Graph the function $R(\theta)$ for the domain $0° \le \theta \le 90°$ (that is, set your horizontal scale to 0 to 90) on a calculator and use it to answer these questions.

At what value of θ does the maximum of the function occur at?

$\theta_{max} =$_____

What is the maximum range of the function?

$R_{max} =$_____

Note: Make sure you have your calculator in degree mode and not radian mode, as you are inputting the angles in degrees (consult the manual if you don't know how to change it).

c. Say the military is considering buying a cannon with a range that is 3 times longer. Transform your simplified function from 4a to show the new cannon's range as a function of the launch angle (θ).

d. Say the military adds something to the cannon that lowers the actual angle by 10° from whatever angle the cannon says it is set at. Transform your simplified function from 4a to show the new cannon's range as a function of the set launch angle (θ).

Notice that trigonometry aids in problems that involve angles . . . and sines, cosines, and tangents are all based on angles in triangles. Because trigonometric functions help describe both angles and repetitive wave-like movement, they end up helping us describe many aspects of God's creation.

1. **Probability Problems**

   a. What is the probability of rolling a ⑤ on a special 8-sided die (i.e., an octahedron) on which there are 2 sides with a ⑤ and all the other sides do not have a ⑤?

      $P(⑤) =$ _____

   b. What is the probability of drawing a blue card from a deck of 30 cards, of which 15 are blue?

      $P(blue) =$ _____

      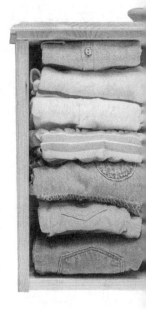

   c. If every day you randomly pick out a shirt from a drawer containing 7 different shirts (Shirts A, B, C, D, E, F, and G), what is the probability of wearing Shirt A on Sunday and Shirt B on Monday, provided you don't put any shirt back in the drawer after you wear it?

      $P(A \cap B) =$ _____

   d. If every day you randomly pick out a shirt from a drawer containing 7 different shirts (Shirts A, B, C, D, E, F, and G), what is the probability of wearing Shirt A on Sunday and Shirt B on Monday, provided this time that Sunday night you put your shirt back, as it was still pretty clean?
      Hint: The value you calculate for wearing Shirt B on Monday will be different than in the previous problem, as the number of shirts available on Monday morning will be different.

      $P(A \cap B) =$ _____

   e. Suppose you're drawing pieces of paper with symbols written on them out of a bowl. The bowl contains the 5 pieces of paper shown below. What is the probability of drawing a paper with an * on it on both of the first 2 draws, provided you don't put the paper back into the bowl?

      $P(*_1 \cap *_2) =$ _____

   f. Suppose again you're drawing pieces of paper with symbols written on them out of a bowl. The bowl contains the same 5 pieces of paper shown. What is the probability of drawing a paper with an * on it on both of the first 2 draws, provided that this time you *do* put the paper back into the bowl after each draw?

      $P(*_1 \cap *_2) =$ _____

2. **Connecting the Concepts** – While you should list probabilities in this course as fractions, they're often listed as percents instead. Convert the probabilities you calculated in problems 1a–1f to percents by completing the division in the fraction. For example, $\frac{1}{3} = 1 \div 3 \approx 0.33333 \approx 33.333\%$.

   a.

   b.

   c.

   d.

   e.

   f.

3. **Algebra Applied** – An apartment community held an event at which they handed out raffle tickets and gave out prizes. The prizes were drawn throughout the day, and tickets were continually handed out as people arrived. When a prize was drawn, that raffle ticket was removed and was no longer a ticket that could be drawn for a prize. Let's say the first prize was drawn after 50 tickets had been given out. What was the probability of winning?

1. **Understanding Adding Probabilities** – It's time to manually calculate the probability of rolling a ⚅(3) on one of two standard 6-sided dice to make sure you understand why the formula $P(A \cup B) = P(A) + P(B) - P(A \cap B)$ works. You will need this table.

A	B	A	B	A	B	A	B	A	B	A	B
1	1	2	1	3	1	4	1	5	1	6	1
1	2	2	2	3	2	4	2	5	2	6	2
1	3	2	3	3	3	4	3	5	3	6	3
1	4	2	4	3	4	4	4	5	4	6	4
1	5	2	5	3	5	4	5	5	5	6	5
1	6	2	6	3	6	4	6	5	6	6	6

a. As we saw in the lesson text, *probability of an event* $= \dfrac{\text{outcomes that produce event}}{\text{total possible outcomes}}$. The table shows all the total combinations of Die *A* and Die *B* that are possible. Count up all of these different total possible outcomes. How many are there altogether?

b. Out of the total outcomes, how many of these produce at least one ⚂(3)?

c. Based on your answers to 1a and 1b, what is the probability of rolling a ⚂(3) on either Die *A or* Die *B*?

$$P\left(\boxed{⚂}_A \cup \boxed{⚂}_B \right) = \underline{\hspace{2cm}}$$

d. What is the probability of rolling a ⚂(3) on Die *A*? Answer this by counting the number of outcomes that have *A* yielding a ⚂(3) and dividing that by the total number of outcomes (which you calculated in 1a).

$$P\left(\boxed{⚂}_A \right) = \underline{\hspace{2cm}}$$

e. What is the probability of rolling a ⚂(3) on Die *B*? Answer this by counting the number of outcomes that have *B* yielding a ⚂(3) and dividing that by the total number of outcomes (which you calculated in 1a).

$$P\left(\boxed{⚂}_B \right) = \underline{\hspace{2cm}}$$

f. Add your answers to 1d and 1e. Do you get the same answer as in 1c?

  ○ Yes   ○ No

g. What is the probability of rolling a ⚂(3) on *both* dice? Answer this by counting the number of outcomes that have both *A* and *B* yielding a ⚂(3) and dividing that by the total number of outcomes (which you calculated in 1a).

$$P\left(\boxed{⚂}_A \cap \boxed{⚂}_B \right) = \underline{\hspace{2cm}}$$

h. Now add your answers to 1d and 1e, but this time also subtract 1g from that sum. Does your answer match what you got in 1c?

○ Yes   ○ No

Notice that we have to add the probabilities of each event together and then subtract out the probability of *both* events taking place in order to accurately convey the probability of one *or* the other event taking place.

2. **Probability of Either Event**

a. Suppose you need to roll either a ⚂ *or* a ⚄ to win a game. You are rolling two dice. What is the probability of rolling either a ⚂ *or* a ⚄ on at least one of the dice?

b. Suppose you are drawing a card out of a 60-card deck containing 20 blue cards, 20 yellow cards, and 20 green cards. The deck also has 10 different shapes printed on the cards (one of which is a triangle, and another of which is a square), with each color having two of each shape (so 6 total of each shape in the deck). What is the probability of drawing either a blue card *or* a card with a triangle from a single draw if the deck is shuffled randomly?

c. Suppose you are drawing a card out of the deck of cards described in 2b. What is the probability of randomly drawing a card that has either a triangle *or* a square on it? *Hint:* Drawing a triangle or a square are mutually exclusive — you can't draw both a card with a triangle and a square in a single card since each card only has one shape.

3. **Probability Review** – Find these probabilities using what we discussed in the last lesson.

a. Let's say two people randomly draw a single card each from a bowl that contains 4 each of 3 different designs (polka dot, striped, and spotted) out of a hat. What is the probability of the two people both drawing a striped design, provided the first person does not put the design they drew back?

b. What is the probability of drawing a yellow marker randomly out of a bag with 6 markers three times in a row if there are 3 yellow markers total in the bag and the marker is put back into the bag after being drawn each time?

4. **Skill Sharpening**

    a. Transform $f(x)$ by *first* shifting it horizontally to the left by 3, *then* shifting it vertically down by 2, *then* reflecting it across the y-axis, and *then* scaling it vertically by -2.

    b. Find $f(3)$ if $-2f(x+2) = 5x^2 + 3$.

    c. The black curve can be described by $f(x) = 2\log(x)$. What function describes the grey curve, given it is a transformation of the black curve using one of the transformations we've looked at?

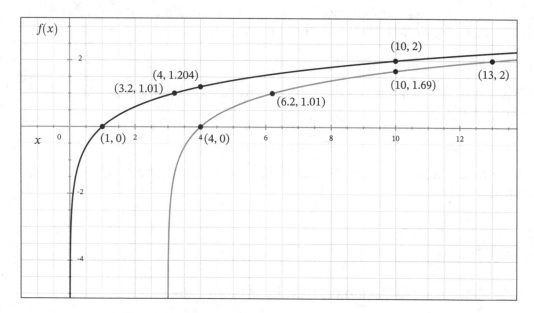

    d. If $(1, -2)$ is a point on a function and that function is stretched horizontally by 2, what point will correspond with this point on the transformed function?

    e. If $(1, -2)$ is a point on a function and that function is compressed horizontally by 2, what point will correspond with this point on the transformed function?

1. Factorial Fun

a. Rewrite using a factorial symbol and then simplify by calculating the product of all the multiplications (i.e., do not use the factorial button on your calculator):

   $6 \cdot 5 \cdot 4 \cdot 3 \cdot 2 \cdot 1 = $ _____ = _____

b. Rewrite using a factorial symbol and then simplify by calculating the product of all the multiplications (i.e., do not use the factorial button on your calculator):

   $4 \cdot 3 \cdot 2 \cdot 1 = $ _____ = _____

c. Rewrite using multiplication and then simplify by calculating the product of all the multiplications:

   $7! = $ _____ = _____

d. Rewrite using multiplication and then simplify by calculating the product of all the multiplications:

   $8! = $ _____ = _____

e. What does $0!$ equal?

f. Simplify without using the factorial button (show your work): $\dfrac{20!}{17!}$

g. Simplify without using the factorial button (show your work): $\dfrac{13!}{16!}$

h. Simplify without using the factorial button (show your work): $\dfrac{15!}{16!}$

i. Simplify without using the factorial button: $\dfrac{10!}{8!}$

j. Simplify without using the factorial button: $\dfrac{40!}{37!}$

k. Simplify without using the factorial button: $\dfrac{5!}{0!}$

l. Use a calculator to simplify: $67!$
   Hint: The calculator will show the answer in scientific notation. If your calculator gives an OVERFLOW error, try searching for a calculator online and inputting it there; some simpler calculators might not have enough decimal precision to calculate this large of a factorial.

m. Use a calculator to simplify: $40!$

2. **Applying Algebra** – You agree to a salary that is the factorial of how many years you have worked times your salary from the previous year. Your initial salary in year 1 is $20,000.

   a. What should the last two lines of this piecewise function be to finish showing the first 5 years in factorial form?

   $$f(t) = \begin{cases} \$20{,}000 \text{ if } t < 1 \\ \$20{,}000 \times 1! \text{ if } 1 \leq t < 2 \\ \$20{,}000 \times 1! \times 2! \text{ if } 2 \leq t < 3 \\ \underline{\hspace{3cm}} \\ \underline{\hspace{3cm}} \end{cases}$$

   b. Here, we've simplified the 2nd and 3rd lines of the piecewise function from 2a by completing the multiplication. Do the same to the last two lines that you wrote in 2a.

   $$f(t) = \begin{cases} \$20{,}000 \text{ if } t < 1 \\ \$20{,}000 \text{ if } 1 \leq t < 2 \\ \$40{,}000 \text{ if } 2 \leq t < 3 \\ \underline{\hspace{3cm}} \\ \underline{\hspace{3cm}} \end{cases}$$

   $20,000 might seem like a low wage at first, but after just four years of working, you should find that this job will make you a millionaire. Too bad no real salary raise schedule uses factorials.

3. **Probability Time**

   a. Find the probability of drawing the first 2 letters of the alphabet in order out of a hat containing all 26 letters.

   b. Find the probability of drawing all 26 letters in the alphabet in order out of a hat containing 1 of each letter.
   Hint: Look at your answer to 3a. Notice that the denominator for the 2nd draw decreased by one integer since there was one less letter to pull from. Applying this same thinking, you can use a factorial to easily calculate the probability of drawing all 26 letters in order!

   c. What is the probability of drawing *either* an A or an L on the first draw from a hat containing all 26 letters?

4. **Skill Sharpening**

   a. If $f(x) = 3^{x+5}$ and $g(x) = (x)!$, what does $g(f(x))$ equal?

   $g(f(x)) = $ _____

   b. If $f(x) = x + 5$ and $g(x) = (3^x)!$, what does $g(f(x))$ equal?

   $g(f(x)) = $ _____

   Notice the factorials in 4a and 4b. We can view a factorial as a function, provided the domain is restricted to integer input values. If you take higher-level math courses, you might learn about more general forms of the factorial function for non-integer inputs (these are called Gamma functions). Note also that $g(f(x))$ was the same value in both 4a and 4b — each problem just broke down the function differently.

c. Given the point $(3, 2)$ that is part of the function $f(x)$, find the corresponding point in the function $f(x - 3)$.
    Hint: While you haven't seen this exact wording before, you have all the skills you need to solve it!

d. Transform $f(x) = 3x^2 + x - 3$ by *first* shifting it horizontally by 3 to the left and *then* reflecting it across the x-axis. Do not expand any squared binomial terms.

e. Find the input of $f(x - 6)$ that will produce an output of 5 if $f(7) = 5$.

f. If $(-2, 3)$ is a point on a function and that function is *first* scaled vertically by 2, *then* stretched horizontally by 3, and *then* reflected across the y-axis, what point will correspond with this point on the transformed function?

You may want to make flashcards for the permutation and combination formulas, along with the typical way to show permutations and combinations without repetition: P_k^n and $\binom{n}{k}$. Remember that different orders of the same values are different permutations but the same combination.

1. **Permutations** – Simplify. Do not use the permutation or factorial buttons on your calculator. Show your work.

   a. Find P_3^{15}.
   Hint: This means "15 permutate 3" . . . meaning you want to find the number of *permutations* possible from 15 objects when you choose 3 of them.

   b. Find P_4^{20}.

   c. If you have 6 letters to play with, how many different ways can you rearrange those letters into 5-letter arrangements if you are limited to only using each letter once?

   d. If you have 6 letters to play with, how many different ways can you rearrange those letters into 5-letter arrangements if you can use each letter as many times as you want?

   e. If you are making a word puzzle game and want each row of your puzzle to have 5 letters on it, how many different ways could you write that row, given that you could choose from the 26 letters of the alphabet, if you are limited to only using each letter once on a row (i.e., you can't use the same letter more than once)?

   f. If you are making a word puzzle game and want each row of your puzzle to have 5 letters on it, how many different ways could you write that row, given that you could choose from the 26 letters of the alphabet, if you can use each letter as often as you like (i.e., you can repeat the same letter more than once)?

2. **Combinations** – Simplify. Do not use the combination, permutation, or factorial buttons on your calculator. Show your work.

   a. $\binom{15}{3} =$ _____
   Hint: This is a way of showing a *combination* — you want to find the number of *combinations* possible from 15 objects when you choose 3 of them.

   b. $\binom{20}{4} =$ _____

   c. If a card in a game has 6 different options of what it can do and the user gets to pick 2 different options, how many different combinations of options could the player have? Don't count separate orders of the options — only separate combinations.

   d. In the scenario in 2c, how many different combinations could the player have if he or she is allowed to pick the same option more than once?

e. If a store is running a sale where you get 3 books free when you buy a package and there are 10 books to choose your free books from, how many different combinations of books could you pick, provided you pick 3 different books?

f. In the scenario in 2e, how many different combinations of books could you pick if you could repeat and get multiple of the same book?

3. **Permutations and Combinations** – Solve the following problems.

a. $\binom{40}{6}$

b. $\binom{50}{10}$

c. P^{50}_{10}

d. An ice-cream store offers 8 different topping choices, and customers get to pick 2 free ones. How many different combinations of toppings could you top your ice cream with using the free topping choices, provided you get different toppings and don't repeat a topping?

e. An ice-cream store offers 8 different topping choices, and customers get to pick 2 free ones. How many different ways could you top your ice cream using the free topping choices, counting what order you put the toppings on as separate ways (for example, you could put sprinkles and then chocolate sauce, or chocolate sauce and then sprinkles, and those different choices are counted differently), provided you get different toppings and don't repeat a topping?

f. In the situation in 3d, if you can repeat a topping (getting double the normal amount), how many different combinations of toppings could you get?

g. In the situation in 3e, if you can repeat a topping (getting double the normal amount), how many different ways could you top your ice cream using the free topping choices?

h. 10 athletes are competing for 1st, 2nd, and 3rd place. How many different ways could these top 3 positions end up?

i. 10 athletes are competing for 3 spots on a trip to a special sports camp. How many different combinations of athletes could end up going?

j. Say a group votes to put 3 different people on a specific team. There are 6 people nominated, and the group has to vote. The nominees getting the top 3 votes will make it on the team, with the person with the highest vote serving 3 years, the person with the second-highest vote serving 2 years, and the person with the third-highest vote serving 1 year. How many different ways can this election turn out?

k. Say a group votes to put 3 different people on a specific team. There are 6 people nominated, and the group has to vote. How many different combinations of people could the final team have?

1. **Sequences**

   a. Find the first 3 values of the sequence $a_n = \log(n)$, where $n \geq 1$. You can use a table like the one below to help you.

n	a_n
1	
2	
3	

   b. Find the first 3 values of the sequence $c_n = n - 5$, where $n \geq 1$. You can use a table like the one below to help you.

n	c_n
1	
2	
3	

   c. Find the 30th term of the sequence in 1b.

      $c_{30} =$ _____

   d. Find the 20th term of the sequence $d_n = n + 3$, where $n \geq 1$.

      $d_{20} =$ _____

   Notice how having a formula where the unknown is the value's position in the sequence lets us find a term without calculating all the terms!

2. **Describing Sequences Algebraically** – Find the pattern in these sequences, describe them algebraically, find the next 3 terms, and confirm your algebraic description works. Be sure to include "where $n \geq 1$" in your algebraic descriptions so anyone looking at it knows at what value to start numbering the positions in the sequence, but do not simplify your algebraic descriptions.

   a. Find the pattern in this sequence and describe the sequence algebraically; then write the next 3 terms: {10, 20, 30, . . . }

      Pattern: _____

      Algebraic Description: _____

      Next 3 Terms: _____

b. Check your work to 2a by calculating the requested values using the algebraic description you wrote in 2a. **Show your work.**

$a_1 =$

$a_2 =$

$a_3 =$

c. Find the pattern in this sequence and describe the sequence algebraically; then write the next 3 terms: {9, 18, 36, ... }

Pattern: _____

Algebraic Description: _____

Next 3 Terms: _____

d. Check your work to 2c by calculating the requested values using the algebraic description you wrote in 2c. **Show your work.**

$a_1 =$

$a_2 =$

$a_3 =$

e. Find the pattern in this sequence and describe the sequence algebraically; then write the next 3 terms: {12, 15, 18, ... }

Pattern: _____

Algebraic Description: _____

Next 3 Terms: _____

f. Check your work to 2e by calculating the requested values using the algebraic description you wrote in 2e. **Show your work.**

$a_1 =$

$a_2 =$

$a_3 =$

g. Find the pattern in this sequence and describe the sequence algebraically; then write the next 3 terms: $\left\{ \dfrac{1}{4}, \dfrac{1}{8}, \dfrac{1}{16}, \ldots \right\}$

Pattern: _____

Algebraic Description: _____

Next 3 Terms: _____

h. Check your work to 2g by calculating the requested values using the algebraic description you wrote in 2g. **Show your work.**

$a_1 =$

$a_2 =$

$a_3 =$

1. **Sequences**

   a. Find the first 3 values in the sequence $d_n = n - 4$, where $n \geq 1$.
      Hint: You can use a table to help you. Note that d is being used here instead of a to stand for the different terms in the sequence.

   b. Find the 20th value in the sequence given in 1a.

   c. Find the 15th value in the sequence $t_k = k + \ln(3)$, where $k \geq 1$.
      Hint: k is another popular letter to use to stand for the index, or the term's position in the sequence.

   d. Find the first 3 values in the sequence $a_n = a_{n-1} - 2$, where $a_1 = 50$.

   e. Find the next 3 values of the sequence $a_n = 2a_{n-1}$, where $a_1 = 2$ and $n \geq 1$. How the first 3 values were found is shown in the middle column below to help you. You can use a table like the one below to help you find the next 3 values.

      $\{2, 4, 8, \dots\}$

n		a_n
1	Value for a_1 was given to us.	2
2	$a_2 = 2a_{2-1} = 2a_1 = 2(2)$	4
3	$a_3 = 2a_{3-1} = 2a_2 = 2(4)$	8
4		
5		
6		

   Note that we couldn't just find a term in this sequence without calculating the values before it, as the unknown is not the value's position in the sequence, but rather the previous value in the sequence. Nonetheless, it still gives a formula that computers can take and use to calculate values. (They just need to be told to keep calculating until they get to the term needed.)

   The particular sequence in 1e could have been rewritten as $a_n = 2^{n+1}$, but for the problem, we wrote it as a recursive sequence to give you practice with that type of sequence.

2. **Describing Sequences Algebraically** – Find the pattern in these sequences, describe them algebraically, and find the next 3 terms. Be sure to check your work! Include "where $n \geq 1$" in your algebraic descriptions so anyone looking at it knows at what value to start numbering the positions in the sequence, but do not simplify your algebraic descriptions.

   a. Find the pattern in this sequence and describe the sequence algebraically:
      $\{5, 10, 15, \dots\}$, then find the next 3 terms.

      Pattern: _____

      Algebraic Description: _____

      Next 3 Terms: _____

b. Find the pattern in this sequence and describe the sequence algebraically: {20, 10, 5 . . . },
then find the next 3 terms.

Pattern: _____

Algebraic Description: _____

Next 3 Terms: _____

c. Find the pattern in this sequence and describe the sequence algebraically:
{100, 95, 90, . . . }, then find the next 3 terms.
Hint: You can have negative values for the difference in the formulas.

Pattern: _____

Algebraic Description: _____

Next 3 Terms: _____

d. Find the pattern in this sequence and write the next 3 terms:
{4, 8, 7, 11, 10, 14, 13, . . . }
(You do not need to describe this sequence algebraically.)

Pattern: _____

Next 3 Terms: _____

3. **Applying Algebra: Exploring the Fibonacci Sequence**

a. The seeds in a sunflower are arranged in spiral
patterns, with some spiraling one way and the rest the
other direction. The number of spirals in each direction
is always approximately neighboring numbers in the
Fibonacci sequence. If there are 55 spirals in direction
A, how many will there be in direction B if there are
more spirals in direction B than A?
Hint: Look at the table in Lesson 15.6 with the first
9 Fibonacci numbers and find 55 there; then use the
formula given there to calculate the next term in the
sequence.

b. Is the Fibonacci sequence an arithmetic sequence, a
geometric sequence, or neither?

4. **Probabilities, Combinations, and Permutations**

a. When playing a card game with a 100-card deck, how
many different possible hands of 20 can be made
assuming each card is distinct?

b. Find $\binom{6}{2}$.

c. Suppose you decide to try a different meal each night for 14 days. You look through a
cookbook and find 18 meals you want to make. How many different combinations could
you decide to plan out the next 14 days' worth of meals if you don't repeat a meal and the
order of the meals doesn't matter?

d. Suppose you are meal planning and have 18 meals you want to make. How many different ways could you decide to plan out the next 14 days' worth of meals if you're okay with repeating meals an unlimited number of times and the order of the meals doesn't matter?

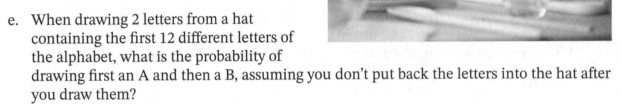

e. When drawing 2 letters from a hat containing the first 12 different letters of the alphabet, what is the probability of drawing first an A and then a B, assuming you don't put back the letters into the hat after you draw them?

f. In the same situation described in 4e, what is the probability of drawing *either* an A *or* a B on the first draw?

5. **Skill Sharpening**

a. The black curve can be described by $f(t) = 6e^t$. What function describes the grey curve, given it is a transformation of the black curve using one of the transformations we've looked at?

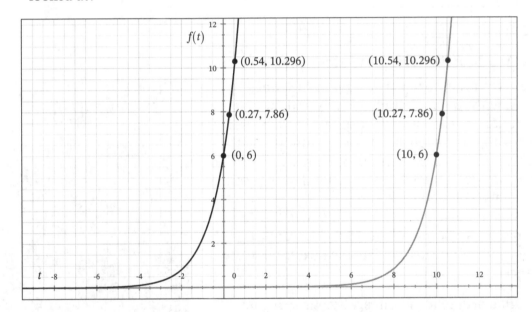

b. At what value would the point (2, 6) correspond to in a transformed function if the original function was *first* scaled vertically by 3 and *then* stretched horizontally by 2?

c. Find the value of $f(-2)$ if $-2f(x-8) = 5x^2 + 2x$.

1. **Starting the Index at 0** – Find the requested values. Note that these indices (i.e., the numbering of the sequences) start at 0.

    a. Find the first 3 values of the sequence $a_n = 5^n$, where $n \geq 0$.
    Hint: Use a table like the one shown to help you.

n	a_n
0	
1	
2	

    b. Find next 3 values of the sequence $a_k = k - 2$, where $k \geq 0$.
    Hint: Use a table like the one shown to help you.

k	a_k
0	
1	
2	

    c. Find the 11ᵗʰ term of the sequence in 1b. Your answer should start "$a\_ =$," where there's a subscript where the _ is identifying that this is the 11ᵗʰ term of the sequence.
    Hint: Be careful! If the first term is 0, then what position is the 15ᵗʰ term going to be in?

    d. Find the 15ᵗʰ term of the sequence $t_n = 2n - 1$, where $n \geq 0$. Your answer should start "$t\_ =$," where there's a subscript where the _ is identifying that this is the 15ᵗʰ term of the sequence.

2. **Describing Sequences Algebraically Starting at 0** – Use the formulas below that are based on numbering the positions starting at 0 instead of 1. Note that these are the same sequences you looked at in 2a and 2b on Worksheet 15.5 . . . only this time, you're describing them using an index starting at 0.

    Arithmetic Formula: $a_n = a_0 + dn$, where $n \geq 0$

    Geometric Formula: $a_n = a_0 r^n$, where $n \geq 0$

    a. Find the pattern in this sequence and describe the sequence algebraically:
    {10, 20, 30, . . . }. Do not simplify your algebraic description.

    Pattern: _____

    Algebraic Description: _____, where $n \geq 0$

    b. Check your work to 2a by calculating the requested values using the algebraic description you wrote in 2a. **Show your work.**

    $a_1 =$

    $a_2 =$

    $a_3 =$

c. Find the pattern in this sequence and describe the sequence algebraically: $\{9, 18, 36, \ldots\}$. Do not simplify your algebraic description.

Pattern: _____

Algebraic Description: _____, where $n \geq 0$

d. Check your work to 2c by calculating the requested values using the algebraic description you wrote in 2c.

$a_1 =$

$a_2 =$

$a_3 =$

Stop and compare your answers to problem 2a–2d with the answers to 2a–2d on Worksheet 15.5. Notice that both formulas accurately described the same sequence, only they used a different convention for the index.

3. **More Describing Sequences Algebraically Starting at 0** – Use the formulas below that are based on numbering the positions starting at 0 instead of 1. Be sure to specify in your algebraic descriptions that $n \geq 0$, but do not simplify your algebraic descriptions.

Arithmetic Formula: $a_n = a_0 + dn$, where $n \geq 0$

Geometric Formula: $a_n = a_0 r^n$, where $n \geq 0$

a. Find the pattern in this sequence and describe the sequence algebraically: $\{3, 5, 7, \ldots\}$

Pattern: _____

Algebraic Description: _____

b. Check your work to 3a by calculating the requested values using the algebraic description you wrote in 3a.

$a_1 =$

$a_2 =$

$a_3 =$

c. Find the pattern in this sequence and describe the sequence algebraically:
$$\left\{ \frac{1}{3}, \frac{1}{9}, \frac{1}{27}, \ldots \right\}$$

Pattern: _____

Algebraic Description: _____

d. Check your work to 3c by calculating the requested values using the algebraic description you wrote in 3c.

$a_1 =$

$a_2 =$

$a_3 =$

4. **Understanding Pascal's Triangle** – Complete a drawing of Pascal's triangle (through Row 12). You'll find the first 8 rows for you below. Copy it into your notebook, then complete your drawing there.

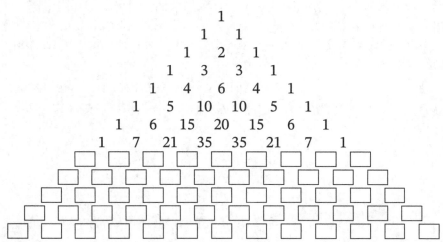

5. **Using Pascal's Triangle** – Remember, the top row of the triangle is 0 . . . and the first value in each row is in position 0. **Do this problem with your parent/teacher.**

a. Demonstrate how you can use Pascal's triangle to find $\binom{10}{3}$.

b. Demonstrate how you can use Pascal's triangle to find the number of different ways the first day of a 3-day competition could be structured if there are 12 athletes who need to compete and each day there's time for 5 athletes to compete.

Remember, if we're using n to represent the index and $n \geq 0$, the 3rd term is found when $n = 3 - 1 = 2$, and the 10th term is found when $n = 10 - 1 = 9$. Subtracting 1 accounts for having started numbering at 0 instead of 1. When we start at a position of 1, though, we don't have to adjust like this; the 10th term will be when $n = 10$.

Keep in mind that we start numbering the rows and positions at 0 in Pascal's triangle. This means that row 5 is really the 6th row down from the top. Likewise, position 5 is really the 6th value over from the left.

```
                    1
                 1     1
              1     2     1
           1     3     3     1
        1     4     6     4     1     Row 5, Position 5
     1     5    10    10     5    (1)
  1     6    15    20    15     6     1
1     7    21    35    35    21     7     1
```

1. **Miscellaneous Sequences** – Note that these problems could have the index start at either 0 or 1; look at the domain to see.

   a. Find the 10th term in the sequence $a_n = 5 + n$ if $n \geq 1$.

   b. Find the 10th term in the sequence $a_n = 5 + n$ if $n \geq 0$.

   c. Find the 8th term in the sequence $d_k = 5k$ if $k \geq 1$.

   d. Find the 8th term in the sequence $d_k = 5k$ if $k \geq 0$.

2. **Using Pascal's Triangle** – Draw the necessary rows of Pascal's triangle in your notebook and circle the answer on the triangle.

   a. $\binom{5}{4}$

   b. $\binom{5}{2}$

   c. $\binom{3}{2}$

3. **Understanding Check** (Problem may be done orally with parent/teacher.)

   a. Explain in your own words what you found in problem 2b.

   b. ◎ **Challenge Problem:** Give a real-life example for what the problem in 2c could represent. It is fine to use an example from the text or a worksheet, only substituting these values into it.

4. Applying Algebra: Exploring Harmonics

a. Given that the harmonic sequence can be described algebraically as $h_n = \dfrac{1}{n+1}$, where $n \geq 0$, what is the 12th harmonic?

b. If we want to find the actual values in the harmonic sequence (as opposed to just the relationship between the fundamental wavelength and a harmonic), we would use this formula:[1] $\lambda_n = \lambda_0 \left(\dfrac{1}{n+1} \right)$, where $n \geq 0$.

   Use this formula to find the wavelength of the first 5 terms in the sequence if the fundamental tone's wavelength λ_0 is 1.559 m (which is the wavelength for the A below middle C on a piano at standard atmospheric conditions).

5. More Applying Algebra: Fibonacci Sequence

a. When we start numbering positions at 0, the Fibonacci sequence can be written like this: $F_n = F_{n-1} + F_{n-2}$ for $n \geq 2$ and $F_1 = 1$ and $F_0 = 1$. Given that $F_{12} = 144$ and $F_{13} = 233$, what is the 15th term in the Fibonacci sequence?
   Hint: Remember, $n \geq 0$ here.

b. Now calculate the 15th term using the formula written when we start counting the index at 1, $F_n = F_{n-1} + F_{n-2}$ for $n \geq 3$ and $F_2 = 1$ and $F_1 = 1$. When we start numbering the positions at 1, $F_{13} = 144$ and $F_{14} = 233$. Notice that you get the same answer!

Don't get confused by the $n \geq 2$ and $n \geq 3$. This description of the Fibonacci sequence only works for the 3rd position onward (the first two values are given to us, as they don't follow the same pattern). However, we can tell the positioning is starting at 0 based on the values given for F_0 in the formula from 5a . . . and starting at 1 based on the F_1 given in the formula in 5b.

6. Probabilities, Combinations, and Permutations

a. If a surgery has been successful 9 out of 12 times, estimate what the probability is that it will be successful in the future based on the past occurrences?

b. If a computer game is programmed to randomly display 10 different tiles, 2 of which have a smiley face on the back, what is the probability that the first 2 tiles you flip over will both be smiley faces assuming you don't flip the tiles back over after you've flipped them?

c. In the computer game described in 6b, what is the probability of a specific tile having a smiley face *or* a hat if there are 10 tiles, 2 have smiley faces, 2 of the non-smiley face tiles have hats, 0 tiles have both smiley faces and hats, and none of the tiles have yet been revealed?

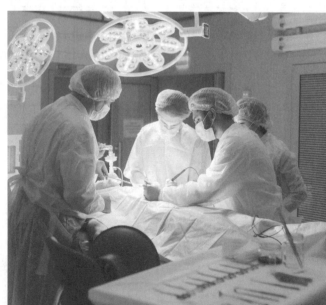

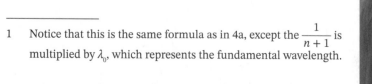

d. Say the tiles in the computer game in 6b (so 10 tiles, 2 of which have smiley faces) are color coded on the back as well, such that there are 4 orange tiles, 1 of which has a smiley face. What is the probability of a tile being either orange *or* having a smiley face?

e. Suppose you got on a game show where you had to pick 3 boxes out of 8 boxes. How many different combinations of boxes could you pick (i.e., each box is distinct, you can't pick the same box twice, and the order you pick doesn't matter)?

f. Suppose the coach of a baseball team has 10 pitchers that are eligible to play in a game. He picks one to start, one to be the 1st backup, and another to be the 2nd backup. How many different ways could he put this pitching lineup together?

g. How many different ways could a 9-digit telephone number be made if each digit could be one of 10 numbers (the numbers 0 through 9)?

7. **Skill Sharpening**

a. The black curve can be described by $f(x) = -5x^2 - 2x + 4$. What function describes the grey curve, given it is a transformation of the black curve using one of the transformations we've looked at?

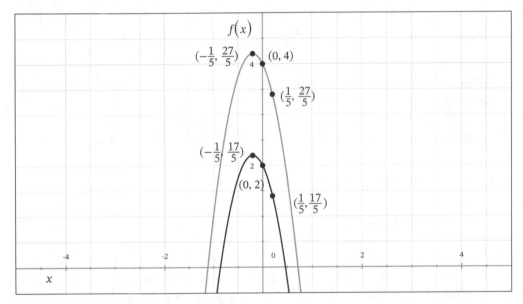

b. What would the function be if instead we'd shifted the original curve shown in 7a horizontally to the right by 2? Do not simplify (just plug in the values to shift the input).

c. Copy the black curve given on the graph in 7a on graph paper, adding to it the general shape of shifting the black curve shown in 7a horizontally to the right by 2.

1. **Understanding Summation**

   a. Find the sum of the first 5 terms in the sequence $\{3, 9, 15, \ldots\}$.
      Hint: First find the next 2 values by figuring out the pattern!

   b. Find the sum of the first 3 terms in the sequence $a_n = 7(2)^n$, where $n \geq 0$

2. **Using Summation Notation**

   $$\sum_{n=7}^{10} n - 3$$

   a. Find the values of the elements in the position where $n = 7$ through $n = 10$ (we're stopping at $n = 10$ since that's the number on top of the summation sign, telling us it's the value we want to sum to).

      $a_7 = $ _____

      $a_8 = $ _____

      $a_9 = $ _____

      $a_{10} = $ _____

   b. Sum up the values you found in 2a to evaluate the requested sum.

3. **Using Summation Notation** – Find the requested sum. Remember, start by finding the values of the terms in the sequence in the positions requested, and then sum them!

   $$\sum_{n=1}^{5} 7n$$

1. **Using Summation Notation** – Find the requested sums. Remember, start by finding the values of the terms in the sequence in the positions requested, and then sum them.

   a. $\displaystyle\sum_{n=0}^{3} 7n^2$

   b. $\displaystyle\sum_{k=2}^{6} a_0 + 4k,$ where $a_0 = 3$ *Hint:* Notice the use of k instead of n to number the terms in the sequence that we are summing.

   c. $\displaystyle\sum_{i=1}^{3} a_0 5^i,$ where $a_0 = 3$ *Hint: i* here is the index variable, not the imaginary number.

   d. $\displaystyle\sum_{n=3}^{6} a_n,$ where $a_n = 4 - 3n$ *Hint:* Notice that this time the series was defined as the sum of a_n, and then we were given the definition of a_n. This is another way of writing the series below: $\displaystyle\sum_{n=3}^{6} 4 - 3n$

2. **More with Describing Sequences**

   a. Which problem(s) in problem 1 were summing an arithmetic sequence? List as many as apply.

       O 1a   O 1b   O 1c   O 1d

   b. Which problem(s) in problem 1 were summing a geometric sequence? List as many as apply.

       O 1a   O 1b   O 1c   O 1d

   c. Find the pattern in this sequence and describe it algebraically: $\{6, 11, 16, 21, \ldots\}$; then sum the first 7 terms. You can pick whether to start numbering the positions at 0 or 1. Do not simplify your algebraic description.

       Pattern: _____

       Algebraic Description: _____, where $n \geq$ _____

       Sum of First 7 Terms: _____

   d. Find the 6th term in the sequence $a_n = 5n^2 + 2$, where $n \geq 0$.

       a____ = _____

   e. Find the 6th term in the sequence $a_n = 5n^2 + 2$, where $n \geq 1$.

       a____ = _____

3. **Applying Algebra: Series and Annuities**[1] – Use the formula below to find the value of these annuities given the information. Remember from what was in the text that you're really summing a sequence!

$$P_t = d\left(\frac{(1+r)^{t+1} - 1}{r}\right),$$ where d = the amount being deposited each time, r = the interest rate used each time, and t = the number of times the interest is calculated.

   a. Calculate the value of an annuity into which $1,000 is being deposited each year at the end of 4 years if the annual interest rate is 8%. Round your answer to the nearest cent.

   b. Calculate the value of an annuity at the end of 4 years into which you're paying $500 each month if the *annual* interest rate is 18% but it is compounded *monthly*. Round your answer to the nearest cent.
   Hint: Remember that the t you need in the formula is the number of times the interest is compounded (i.e., calculated), and the interest rate you need is the rate used when it's compounded.

4. 🎯 **Challenge Problem: Finding the Center of Mass**[2]

center of mass

In physics, we sometimes need to calculate what we call the center of mass. Picture a football rotating while being thrown through the air for a minute. The center of mass is the invisible point around which the ball rotates.

While in the case of a ball, it will be the center of the ball, since the mass is all evenly distributed around that point, it might not be so obvious where the center of mass is for other objects. For example, if a chair were to fall out of a window and rotate through the air while falling, around what point would it rotate? The point of rotation, or center of mass, can be found by finding the mass of the different parts of the chair times the position of those parts (some parts, like the seats, have more mass than others, like the legs) and dividing that by the total mass. We can actually think of this as a series! The series below describes how to find where just the horizontal center of mass is (we'd have to also calculate the vertical and the depth centers of mass using a similar formula).

$$c = \frac{1}{M}\sum_{n=1}^{N} m_n x_n$$

The M here stands for the total of all the masses, and the N for the number of different masses we're summing. Okay, let's apply this. Suppose you had 3 balls tied to a rod. The mass and center positions of the balls are listed in the table below and shown in the picture. What is the horizontal center of mass of the entire rod and ball system (i.e., what is c)?

2   Formula based on Randall D. Knight, *Physics for Scientists and Engineers with Modern Physics: A Strategic Approach* (Pearson, Addison Wesley, NY: 2004), p. 374, and David Halliday, Robert Resnick, and Jearl Walker, Fundamentals of Physics, 7th ed. (USA: John Wiley & Sons, 2005), p. 203.

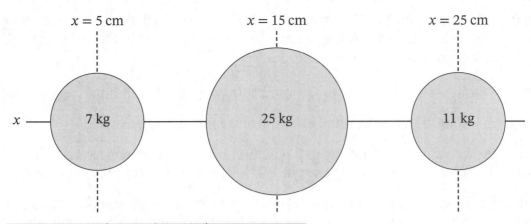

$x = 5$ cm $x = 15$ cm $x = 25$ cm

x — 7 kg — 25 kg — 11 kg —

n	m	x
1	7 kg	5 cm
2	25 kg	15 cm
3	11 kg	25 cm

Hint: Add up 7 kg, 25 kg, and 11 kg to find M and insert it into the formula. Since there are 3 masses, insert 3 for N into the formula. Then sum up the sequence for the positions the formula now specifies and multiply that sum by $\frac{1}{M}$. You can find the values of m and x for the different positions using the table. For example, the value for m_1 can be found in the m column of the table in the row labeled "1"; the value for x_1 can be found in the x column.

5. **Probabilities, Combinations, and Permutations** – 3 winners are chosen at random from all of a store's customers who have spent $500 or more in a month, which total 100 customers. The first winner will receive a $100 shopping spree, the next a $50 shopping spree, and the third a $25 shopping spree. Each customer can only win a maximum of one prize.

   a. How many different outcomes could there be?

   b. What is the probability of the eldest of three sisters winning the $100 dollar shopping spree, the next oldest sister winning the $50 shopping spree, and the youngest sister winning the $25 shopping spree, assuming all the sisters have spent $500 or more at the store during the month to become eligible.

   c. What is the probability of *any* of the 3 sisters winning the $100 shopping spree?

   d. If all 3 prizes were $50 instead, how many different outcomes could there be? Note that the order now doesn't matter.

   e. Find $\binom{4}{2}$ using Pascal's triangle.

1. **Using the Binomial Theorem** – Expand the given polynomials, demonstrating how you used the binomial theorem to do so. Be sure to simplify your final answer and watch out for any negative signs!

   a. $(x + 3)^6$

   b. $(x - 2)^4$

   c. $(x + 2)^3$

   d. Go back and solve $(x + 2)^3$ without the binomial theorem, but by manually multiplying out $(x + 2)(x + 2)(x + 2)$. You should get the same answer! **Show your work.**

   e. $(x + 2)^4$

   f. $(2a + c)^3$ *Hint:* In this case, the x in the binomial theorem equals $2a$.

   g. $(t + 7)^3$

2. 🎯 **Challenge Problem: Applying Algebra to Probability** – Suppose you had a weighted die where the probability of rolling a 🎲 is $(1 - x)$. What is the probability in terms of x of rolling a 🎲 four times in a row? Give your answer so it contains an expanded binomial, using the binomial theorem to help you.

3. **Applying Algebra**

   a. If you go on to study thermodynamics and explore energy in more depth, you'll learn that we use the formula

   $$\Omega = \frac{N!}{n!(N - n)!}$$ to calculate what is called the

   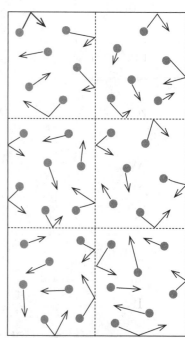

   multiplicity (Ω) of molecules. In this example, the multiplicity represents a "closed container"[1] with n compartments that have a large number of gas molecules bouncing around inside between the containers; in this case, N is the number of molecules. (Don't worry about what the multiplicity is exactly.) Note that this formula is really a combination. In fact, we could rewrite it like this:

   $\Omega = \binom{N}{n}$. If this is the case, what is the initial multiplicity

   (Ω) of 60 molecules (N) all on the inside of a closed container with $n = 10$ compartments?

A real system would have many times more molecules. Most typical gas molecule systems in a container the size of an average room in a house have more than 10^{27} molecules in it (that is a number called an octillion, *or a* billion billion billion), *but not all calculators can handle those large numbers, so we gave smaller numbers. Yet God is overseeing all of these molecules, though numbering more than we can easily count in just one room of one house, consistently enough for us to calculate their multiplicity!*

---

1   Based on Donald McQuarrie, *Statistical Mechanics* (Sausalito, CA, USA: University Science Books, 2000), p. 22.

b. The probability of the system being in a given configuration is $P = \dfrac{1}{\Omega}$. Calculate this probability for the system described in 3a.

c. The entropy of the system is $S = k_B \ln(\Omega)$, where k_B is the Boltzmann constant with value $1.38064852 \times 10^{-23}\,\dfrac{J}{K}$. Calculate this entropy.

Note: $\dfrac{J}{K}$ is a unit of measure called joules per kelvin.

Reminder! The quiz is open book. You can consult your textbook and notes on it. So just make sure you understand how to use the various concepts covered.

1. **Sequences, Series, and More**

   a. Find the 15th element in this sequence: $a_n = 3^n + 2$, where $n \geq 0$.

   b. Describe this sequence algebraically:
      $\{5, 7, 9, \ldots\}$
      (You may have n start at either 0 or 1; just be sure to specify which you did. Do not simplify your algebraic description.)

      $a_n = $ _____, where $n \geq$ _____

   c. Find the requested sum: $\sum_{n=3}^{5} 6n$

   d. Find $\binom{10}{2}$.

2. **Probability Time**

   a. When playing a card game with a 30-card deck, where there are the numbers 1 to 6 in each of 5 different colors (red, blue, yellow, green, and purple), what is the probability of drawing either a 4 *or* a purple card?

      $P(4 \cup purple) = $ _____

   b. In the situation described in 2a, what is the probability of drawing 2 purple cards in a row?

      $P(1st\ purple \cap 2nd\ purple) = $ _____

   c. What is the probability of drawing either a 4 or a purple card if the following are the only 9 cards in the deck from which you're drawing? (That is, find $P(4 \cup purple)$.)
      the blue 4
      the blue 5
      the red 2
      the purple 3
      the purple 5
      the purple 6
      the green 3
      the yellow 2
      the yellow 1

3. **The Binomial Theorem** – Use the binomial theorem to expand $(3b - d)^4$. Note that since you have unknowns, your answer will as well!
   Hint: Plug 3b in for x and $-d$ for y, as those are the values in the place of x and y in the binomial theorem.

4. **The Dangers in Gambling**

   a. Consider a big-dollar lottery that sells tickets with 5 numbers, each of which can have a value of from 1 to 50 each. The winning number is chosen by drawing balls from a bin; there are 50 balls total (numbered 1–50). Say the lottery requires your ticket to match the 5 values chosen in the lottery drawing *in the same order they are chosen*. Calculate the number of possible outcomes such a lottery could have if the numbers drawn do not repeat (that is, once a ball/number is chosen, it's not put back so it can't be chosen again).
   Hint: You're really finding a permutation here. There are 50 numbers possible, and you need exactly 5 in a specific order from that 50.

   b. Sometimes these lotteries will allow the order you get the numbers in to not be the same as the lottery drawing. If the numbers still don't repeat, how many possible outcomes would there be in this scenario for the same number of digits and the same possible values as in 4a?
   Hint: How can you calculate total possible outcomes when the order doesn't matter?

   c. The probability of winning the grand prize for a single lottery ticket is 1 divided by the total number of possible outcomes. What is the probability of winning if the lottery follows the rules in 4a? Give your answer in scientific notation.

      $P_{4a} \approx$ _____

   d. What is the probability of winning if the lottery follows the rules in 4b? Give your answer in scientific notation.

      $P_{4b} \approx$ _____

   e. What is the probability of winning the lottery following the rules in 4b if you buy 50 different tickets?

      $P_{4b \text{ with 50 tickets}} \approx$ _____

   > Some lotteries have even lower probabilities than those listed here. For example, the Mega Millions lottery[1] has 6 numbers, each of which can have a value from 1 to 70 that cannot be the same as the others, plus another one with a value from 1 to 25. While in that lottery the 6 numbers can be in any order, the extra ball has to have the exact value! To be fair, they do offer lower prizes, but there's still only about a $\frac{1}{37}$ or about 2.703% probability of winning even the cost of the ticket back — which means you're likely to lose money 36 times out of 37 times you play, and even then only win back the cost of one ticket!

   f. Given that the probability of getting struck by lightning in your lifetime[2] is $P_{\text{Lightning}} \approx \frac{1}{15,300}$, is it more likely that you'll get struck by lightning or win a lottery by buying a single ticket based on the probabilities you calculated in 4c, 4d, and 4e?
   Hint: Convert the probability of lightning to scientific notation to compare more easily.

   ---

   1   Mega Millions, "How to Play," https://www.megamillions.com/How-to-Play.aspx
   2   National Weather Service, "How Dangerous Is Lightning?", https://www.weather.gov/safety/lightning-odds

How many tickets would you need to buy in order for your probability of winning to be equal to or greater than the probability of getting struck by lighting based on the grand prize scenario given in 4a? Round your answer to the nearest whole ticket.

Hint: Remember that we find the probability by taking $\dfrac{E}{T}$, where E is the outcomes that produce the event we're looking at and T the total possible outcomes. So set $\dfrac{1}{15,300}$, the probability of being struck by lightning, equal to $\dfrac{E}{T}$. Substitute the total possible outcomes you found in 4a for T and solve for E to find the number of tickets you need to buy in order for the probability to equal the probability of being struck by lightning (each ticket gives you a single chance at the desired outcome, so E will be the number of tickets needed).

> *Hopefully the problem above gives you an idea into how easy it is to lose money in gambling. Despite the probability of losing, according to one resource, "as many as 23 million Americans go into debt because of gambling and the average loss is estimated to be around $55,000."*[3] *The Bible's warning about the love of money piercing with many griefs is one many can testify to the truth of. While losing money is certainly one of those griefs, living chasing the love of money has griefs of its own on spiritual levels also. The discontent and love of money it breeds can rob of us the joy of contentment in Christ and resting in Him for provision.*
>
> > *Keep your life free from love of money, and be content with what you have, for he has said, "I will never leave you nor forsake you." (Hebrews 13:5; ESV)*

---

3   Max Fay, "Gambling and Debt" (Debt.org), https://www.debt.org/advice/gambling/

While this worksheet focuses on Chapters 1–6 and miscellaneous "mechanics" covered elsewhere in the curriculum, note that we've included some problems that utilize other concepts too. Hopefully you'll get a feel for how all the "tools" you've been learning connect together.

If you're not sure how to solve a problem, use the Table of Contents or the Index in the Student Textbook *to figure out where the concept was taught and review that concept.*

1. **Simplifying Algebraic Expressions**

   a. Simplify: $\dfrac{\frac{x}{3}}{\frac{2}{15}}$

   b. Simplify: $\dfrac{(16 \text{ m}^4)^{\frac{1}{4}}}{\frac{-7 \text{ m}}{s^2}}$

   Note: Here m stands for the unit of meters and s for the unit of seconds.

   c. Simplify without using a calculator: $\sqrt{-24}$ (Do not approximate any square roots that are not integers.)

   d. Simplify, specifying what x cannot equal: $\dfrac{\sqrt{-6}\sqrt{-8}x^2x^3}{\left(4x^{\frac{1}{2}}\right)^3}$ (Do not approximate any square roots that are not integers.)

   e. Simplify, specifying what x cannot equal: $\dfrac{x^2 - x - 20}{x + 4}$

   f. Simplify, factoring out any common factors: $4e^{3t} + 5e^{2t}$

   g. Rewrite using a fractional exponent and simplify: $\sqrt{\dfrac{b^{4x}}{a^{2x}}}$

   h. Find $f(t)g(t)$ if $f(t) = 2^{4t}$ and $g(t) = 4^{2t}$.

   i. Find $f(x) + g(x)$ if $f(x) = 5x^4$ and $g(x) = 2x^2$. Factor out any common factors.

   j. Simplify using the product rule, calculating any logarithms you can: $\log_2(3x)$

   k. Simplify using the power rule, calculating any logarithms you can: $\log_4(2^x)$

   l. Simplify: $4i\left(\dfrac{i^2}{i^5}\right)$ *Note: i* here represents the imaginary number.

   m. Simplify: $4x - (-x + 3) - y^3\left(y^{\frac{1}{4}} - 2\right) + 3y^3$

   n. Simplify, factoring out any common factors: $\dfrac{3a^2}{b} + 2ab^{-2} + (3a)^2$

2. **Applying the Mechanics to Finding Unknowns** – Find the requested unknowns.

   a. Solve the inequality for b: $\dfrac{-b}{3} > 5$

   b. Solve for x: $-5x^2 = -6y$, where $y = -2$ (Do not approximate any square roots that are not integers.)

   c. Solve for x in terms of d: $\dfrac{5x}{2+d} = 30$

   d. Find the value of both x and y:

      $2x - 4y = -10$

      $-x + 3y = 7$

      $x =$ _____ $y =$ _____

   e. Suppose you know that $y = ax$ and that $c = a^2x$. Find c in terms of x and y only.
      Note: This problem is very similar to a real-life one related to power, voltage, and current you'll encounter on the final exam, so make sure you understand how to solve!

3. **Mastering the Language: Sets, Sequences, and Series** (Chapter 3 and Chapter 16)

   a. If set $A = \{5, 2, -1\}$ and set $B = \{2, 3\}$, what is $A \cap B$?
      Your answer should be in the form of $A \cap B = \{\quad\}$.

   b. With the sets described in 3a, what is $A \cup B$?
      Your answer should be in the form of $A \cup B = \{\quad\}$.

   c. Use symbols to show that x needs to be a real number less than 2.
      Your answer should be in the form of $x \in$ _____ $\cap \, x <$ _____.

   d. If $x \notin \mathbb{I}$, can x equal $\sqrt{-4}$?

      ○ yes   ○ no

   e. Identify the pattern and describe this sequence algebraically: $\{6, 10, 14, \ldots\}$. You may decide whether to start counting the positions at 0 or 1.
      Your answer should be in the form of $a_n =$ _____, where $n \geq$ _____.

   f. Find this series:

      $$\sum_{n=1}^{5} 3^n$$

4. **Applying Algebra** – These problems may use a variety of skills and are designed to test your ability to think through situations and apply the skills you've learned.

   a. Suppose that there's a rectangle with an area of 40 ft². The width of the rectangle is 5 ft. The length is 5 ft + x. Find the value of x, given that the area of a rectangle equals the length times the width.

b. Suppose you sell baked goods at a farmer's market. Suppose one hour you sold 4 loaves of bread, 10 muffins, and 30 cookies for a total of $74. The next hour you sold 5 loaves of bread, 2 muffins, and 10 cookies for $44. The third hour you sold 1 loaf of bread, 15 muffins, and 50 cookies for $86. What was the price of a loaf of bread, a muffin, and a cookie?

bread = _____

muffin = _____

cookie = _____

c. Suppose volunteers handing out bagged lunches start with 10 bags of chicken sandwiches, 5 bags of turkey sandwiches, and 20 bags of roast beef sandwiches. If the bags are all mixed together and the volunteers randomly grab a bag, how probable is it that they'll give the first 2 people a roast beef sandwich?

$P(R_1 \cap R_2) \approx$ _____

d. Suppose a game uses a regular 6-sided die that has been altered so that the sides with 1, 2, and 3 are painted red while the other 3 sides are all black. How probable is it that a roll will be either a 3, 4, or 5 *or* a black number?

$P(3, 4, \text{or } 5 \cup black) =$ _____

5. **More Applying Algebra: Torque** – When objects are rotating, they're under what we call torque (τ), which is basically a way of describing "the 'effectiveness' of the force at causing an object to rotate about a pivot"[1] — that is, how much it's being pulled into a circular motion.

a. Find the force (F) on an object if the torque is 50 N • m (N • m is a unit called "newton meters"), the radius (r) is 5 m, and the angle between the force direction and the radial direction (ϕ) is 40°. The torque (τ) on an object equals $rF\sin(\phi)$, or $\tau = rF\sin(\phi)$.

b. The net torque on an object equals the "sum of the torques due to the applied forces"[2] (these forces can pull in different directions); it can be expressed like this:

$$\tau_{net} = \sum_i \tau_i$$

Notice that there's no value at the top of the $\sum$; this means you should sum up *all* of the values. In this case, the τ_i is specifying a series made up of all the different torques. Find the net torque (τ_{net}) on an object if there is a torque from a force of 20 N at an angle (ϕ) of 90°, a torque from a force of 15 N at an angle (ϕ) of 180°, and a torque from a force of 10 N at an angle (ϕ) of 240°. All of the forces are applied at a radius of 10 m.
Hint: This problem is not as hard as it sounds! Simply plug the values given here into the formula from 5a to find the different torques, and then add them all together (i.e., find their sum). Notice that we're applying $\sum$ to something you wouldn't at first think of as a sequence. A lot of what you've learned applies in many different ways.

1   Randall D. Knight, *Physics for Scientists and Engineers with Modern Physics: A Strategic Approach* (Pearson, Addison Wesley, NY: 2004), p. 377.
2   Ibid., p. 379.

While this worksheet focuses on Chapters 7–12, note that we've included some problems that utilize concepts covered in other chapters too. Hopefully you'll get a feel for how all the "tools" you've been learning connect together.

1. **About Functions in General** (Chapter 7)

   a. If we're looking at how our electricity bill for the month (B) depends on the amount of electricity we use that month (E), which is the independent variable?

   $\bigcirc E$ $\bigcirc B$

   b. Use function notation to write $d = 5t + 2$ to show d (distance) as dependent on t (time).

   c. Graph the function in 1b on a calculator. Given the meaning of the problem, the y-intercept represents

   _____.

   d. Given the meaning of the problem, the x-intercept represents _____

   _____.

   e. If $f(x) = 5x$ and $g(x) = 2x^2$, find $f(x)g(x)$.

   f. If $f(x + 6) = x^2 + 12$, find $f(9)$.

2. **More Identifying Functions** – List the function that corresponds with the graph. **Do not use a graphing calculator.**

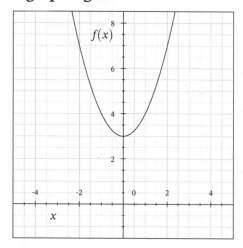

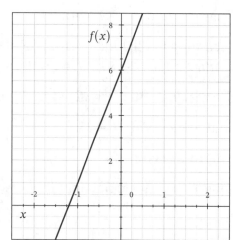

   a.

   $\bigcirc$ A. $f(x) = 5^x + 3$

   $\bigcirc$ B. $f(x) = x^2 + 3$

   $\bigcirc$ C. $f(x) = x^2 + 4x$

   b.

   $\bigcirc$ A. $f(x) = 10x - 1$

   $\bigcirc$ B. $f(x) = 5x + 6$

   $\bigcirc$ C. $f(x) = 10x + 6$

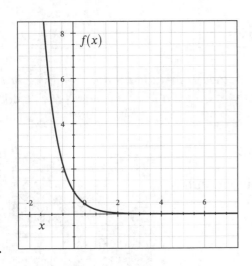

c.

○ A. $f(x) = 5^{-x}$

○ B. $f(x) = 5^x$

○ C. $f(x) = e^x$

3. **Polynomial Functions**

   a. $f(x) = 5x^2 + 3x + 2$ is

      ○ even   ○ odd   ○ neither.

   b. $f(x) = 5x + 3$ is

      ○ even   ○ odd   ○ neither.

   c. $f(x) = 5x^2 + 2$ is

      ○ even   ○ odd   ○ neither.

   d. According to the fundamental theorem of algebra, how many roots (including repeat and complex roots) does $f(x) = 5x^7 + 5x^6$ have?

   e. Use the quadratic formula to find the roots of the function in 3a.

   f. Find the roots of $x^2 - 25$.

4. **Rational Function**

   a. Rewrite as a single fraction: $f(x) = \dfrac{5x + 6}{2 + x} + 3x$

   b. Simplify $\dfrac{x^2 + 10x + 25}{x^2 + 8x + 15}$. Be sure to include what x does not equal.

   c. At what value of x does the function in 4b have an asymptote?

   d. At what value of x does the function in 4b have a discontinuity?

5. **Other Functions**

   a. Solve for t: $30 = \log_3(5t)$

   b. Transform $f(x) = 5x + 6$ horizontally to the right by 5.

c. If you are given $(-2, 0)$ as a point on a function that is *first* stretched horizontally by 4 and *then* reflected across the x-axis, what point on the transformed function corresponds with this point?

d. If given $-3f(x + 3) - 2 = 10x^2 + 5x - 2$, find $f(4)$.

e. The black curve can be described by $f(x) = 4x^2 + 3x - 20$. What function approximately describes the grey curve, given it is a transformation of the black curve using one of the transformations we've looked at?
Hint: Start by finding the approximate x-intercepts of the black curve so you will have points to compare!

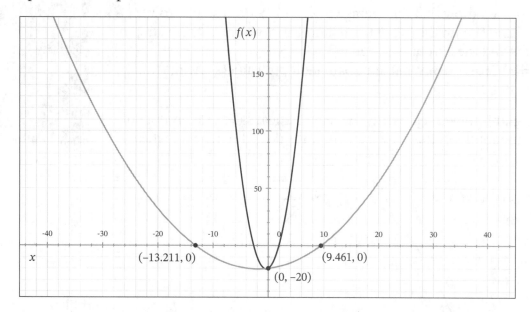

6. **Other Concept: Inequalities** – While inequalities are not functions, they're important! Graph the solution to $y \leq 5x + 2$ and $y \geq \log(x) + 5$. The functions themselves are shown for you; copy their general shape to your notebook and shade the appropriate region.

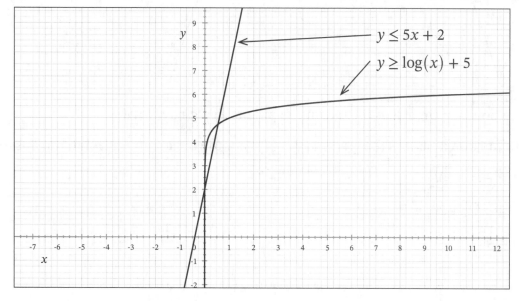

7. **Applying Algebra** – These problems use a variety of skills and functions and test your ability to apply what you've learned in real-life settings.

a. Find the input that would yield the peak output of a machine if the output follows the function $f(x) = -4x^2 + x + 5$.

$$x_{\text{min|max}} = \underline{\hspace{2cm}}$$

b. Let's say you bought an MP3 album with 30 podcasts on it. Each day, you plan to listen to 2 podcasts, without repeating any. How many different combinations of podcasts could you pick to listen to on the first day?

c. Let's say we know that the average price of a certain stock grows with time (t) with the following relationship, where t is measured in months and the output is in dollars: $P(t) = 4t^2 + 4t - 20$. What approximate input value(s) yield(s) an output of 0?

d. If the graph shown represents the hypothetical sales of a product over time (in months), after how many months does it reach its highest level of sales?

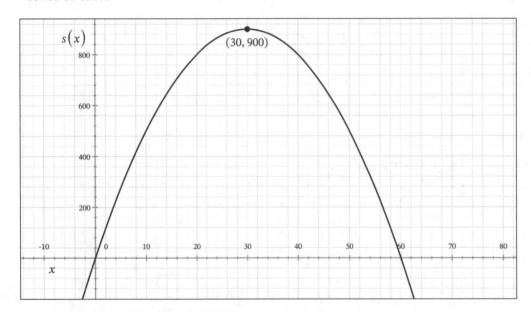

e. At what points in time does the sale of the product in 7d have 0 sales?

f. Which function describes the graph in 7d? (Do not use a graphing calculator to answer.)

○ $s(t) = -t^2 + 60t$

○ $s(t) = -5t^2 + 20t + 5$

○ $s(t) = 4e^{5t}$

g. 🎯🖥 **Challenge Problem:** The hypotenuse of a certain right-angled triangle is 10 ft greater than side b, and 3 ft greater than side a. What are the approximate lengths of each side? Because you will end up needing to use the quadratic formula, you'll end up with two possible values for one side. Use the one that makes all of the sides of the triangle positive.
Hint: Use the knowledge that $a^2 + b^2 = c^2$ (i.e., the Pythagorean theorem).

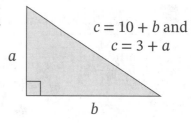

$a \approx$ _____ $b \approx$ _____ $c \approx$ _____

h. How much will a population of 1,000 grow to after 1 year at a continuous growth rate of $\dfrac{0.00068}{\text{day}}$? Round a year to 365 days.

i. If you borrow \$30,000 at an annual interest rate of 19%, compounded daily, how much will you owe when the loan becomes due in 5 years, assuming you make no payments on the loan along the way? Round a year to 365 days and round your answer to the nearest cent.

j. Find the time it will take a mushroom population of 400 to grow to 600 at a continuous growth rate of $\dfrac{0.00068}{\text{day}}$.

k. Let's say that the miles a car is driven on average per month can be expressed as $m(x) = 3x - 12$ (where x represents the deliveries made), and the gallons it uses on average per month can be expressed as $g(x) = x^2 - x - 12$, where x again represents the deliveries made. Write a rational function showing its miles per gallon as a function of deliveries x. Be sure to simplify as much as possible and to specify what x cannot equal.
Hint: You've been given one function that describes the miles and another the gallons. You've been asked to find miles *per* gallon, or $\dfrac{\text{miles}}{\text{gallon}}$.

l. Suppose you have 40 tasks on your to-do list. You decide to pick, work on, and complete 5 of them each day. You make a list each day of the tasks you'll do, in order. On the first day, how many different ways could you structure your list?

m. Suppose you bought 24 bales of hay for \$150 total. If a part of those cost \$10 a bale and the rest \$5 a bale, how many bales did you buy at each price?

_____ bales at \$10

_____ bales at \$5

Many of these problems are similar to those used on the chapter quizzes. If you forget how to solve a problem, you might look at the similar problems there or consult the Key Skills for the chapter.

1. **Reviewing Logarithms** (Chapter 13)

    a. Find $\ln(40)$.

    b. Find $\log_4(20)$.

    c. Solve for t: $\$1{,}400 = \$100(1.02^{0.5t})$

    d. Simplify to a single logarithm (do not calculate on a calculator): $\log(58) + \log(2)$.

    e. Rewrite as separate logarithms, calculating the logarithm where you can: $\log_2(6x)$.

    f. Rewrite using the power rule without an exponent: $\log(6^t)$.

    g. Rewrite $f(t) = 2e^{2t}$ as a linear expression. Take the logarithm in base e of both sides, apply the product rule, and calculate/simplify any logarithm you can. Express the log of the output as y.

    h. Find x^2 if $\log(x) = 5$.

    i. Rewrite as separate logarithms, calculating the logarithm where you can: $\log\left(\dfrac{40}{x}\right)$.

    j. How long will it take $\$3{,}500$ to grow to $\$7{,}000$ if it earns interest at an annual rate of 4.5%, compounded every 6 months? Remember that the formula for compound interest is $P(t) = P_i\left(1 + \dfrac{r}{n}\right)^{nt}$, where the r is the annual rate, n the number of times the interest is calculated each year, and t is the number of years.

    k. Solve for x: $50 = \log_2(x^5)$

2. **Reviewing More with Functions** (Chapter 14)

    a. Find $g(h(x))$ if $h(x) = \dfrac{7x + 5}{2}$ and $g(x) = (7\sin(40°))^x$.

    $g(h(x)) = $ _____ (Do not simplify.)

    b. Find $f(-8)$ if $f(2x + 4) = 5|x - x^2|^3$.
    Hint: This problem looks a little more challenging as it combines multiple skills. Just remember to break it down step by step.

    c. Reflect the function $f(x) = 5x + 3$ across the x-axis, listing the transformed function.

d. Find the functions that describe the two grey curves given that the black curve can be described by $f(x) = x^2 + 3x$ and that the grey curves are transformations of the black curve using one of the transformations we've looked at. You do not need to simplify the transformed functions.

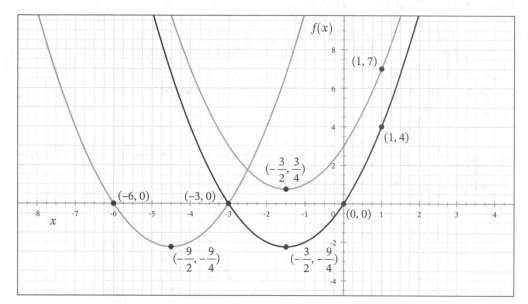

Function of grey curve with no x-intercept: _____

Function of grey curve with two x-intercepts: _____

e. Show how you would write the transformation of the general function $f(x)$ with the following steps: *First* scale $f(x)$ vertically by 10, *then* reflect it across the y-axis, and *then* shift it horizontally to the right by 3.

f. If $(2, 8)$ were part of a function and that function was *first* compressed horizontally by 4, *then* scaled vertically by 2, and *then* reflected across the x-axis, what point in the new function will correspond with this point in the original?

g. Find the power (P) of a particle if $P = Fv\cos(\theta)$, F is the net force on the particle of $10 \text{ kg} \cdot \dfrac{m}{s^2}$, v is a velocity of $5 \dfrac{m}{s}$, and θ is 50°. Include units in your answer.[1]

h. Suppose you have money growing in a bank according the function $P = \$500(1.05)^t$. You have an additional \$500 at home besides whatever is in the bank. This gives you $P_{total} = \$500(1.05)^t + \$500$. Identify how we could describe how adding the \$500 transforms the function.

    ○ horizontal shift   ○ vertical shift   ○ horizontal scale   ○ vertical scale

3. **Reviewing Probability, Combinations, Permutations, Sequences, and Series** (Chapter 15)

a. Find $\begin{pmatrix} 7 \\ 3 \end{pmatrix}$.

---

1   Formula from Randall D. Knight, *Physics for Scientists and Engineers with Modern Physics: A Strategic Approach* (Pearson, Addison Wesley, NY: 2004), p. 329.

b. When rolling two 6-sided dice, how many different permutations of values on the two dice can you get? Note that in this case, repetition is allowed.

c. How many different results can you get from rolling two dice *if you exclude rolling doubles* (i.e., you disallow repetition)?

d. Suppose that in a game, players play with two standard dice. The sum of the dice determines how the game proceeds. What is the probability of rolling a combined sum of 7 on the two dice? The table below shows the different possible combinations you could get from two dice.

$P(7) =$ _____

Die A	Die B	Sum	Die A	Die B	Sum	Die A	Die B	Sum
1	1	2	1	3	4	1	5	6
2	1	3	2	3	5	2	5	7
3	1	4	3	3	6	3	5	8
4	1	5	4	3	7	4	5	9
5	1	6	5	3	8	5	5	10
6	1	7	6	3	9	6	5	11
1	2	3	1	4	5	1	6	7
2	2	4	2	4	6	2	6	8
3	2	5	3	4	7	3	6	9
4	2	6	4	4	8	4	6	10
5	2	7	5	4	9	5	6	11
6	2	8	6	4	10	6	6	12

e. In the situation described in 3d, what is the probability of rolling either a sum of 7 *or* a sum that is 7 or greater?

$P(7 \cup \geq 7) =$ _____

f. Find the 15th value in this sequence: $d_k = 2(3^k)$, where $k \geq 0$.

g. Express this sequence algebraically: $\{5, 15, 45, \ldots\}$. You may decide whether to start counting the positions at 0 or 1. Your answer should be in the form of

$a_n =$ _____, where $n \geq$ _____.

h. Find the requested sum: $\displaystyle\sum_{k=8}^{10} 2^{k+1}$

Note that other concepts may be covered on the test. Be sure to read through the Chapter Synopsis and look over the quizzes for Chapters 13–15! Note that the binomial theorem will not be on the test.

You are allowed to bring a single sheet of paper with notes on it to the test with you. *We suggest writing on it formulas or notes from these 3 chapters you think you might need.*

Quizzes and Tests

Intentionally left blank

| Principles of Algebra 2 | Scope: Chapter 1 | Day 9 | Quiz 1 | Total score: |
| | Setting the Foundation | | | ____ of 100 |

You are allowed to use a calculator on this quiz. However, calculators that can solve algebraic expressions are not allowed (or if used, that feature should not be used).

These are unit conversion ratios you may need:

5,280 ft = 1 mi   100 cm = 1 m   60 s = 1 min

1 ft ≈ 30.480 cm   1 yd = 3 ft   60 min = 1 hr

On all quizzes or tests, unless otherwise indicated or instructed, you are not allowed to consult any other notes or resources.

1. **Understanding Check** – Write an equal sign between any of these expressions that you can tell are equal.
   Each problem is worth 2 points.

   a. $5ab$ $ab5$

   b. $3\left(\dfrac{a}{x}\right)$ $\dfrac{3a}{x}$

   c. $3\dfrac{m}{s}$ $\dfrac{3\ m}{s}$

   d. $a7$ $7a$

   e. $a(7x)$ $7ax$

2. **Skill Testing** – Simplify. When asked to add fractions, give your answer as a single fraction.
   Each problem is worth 9 points.

   a. $\dfrac{x}{-a}\left(\dfrac{-3a}{b}\right)$

   b. $\dfrac{\dfrac{6x}{3b}}{2}$

   c. $\dfrac{6a}{b} - \dfrac{-5c}{d}$

   d. $15\dfrac{m}{s} + 3\dfrac{ft}{min}$; give your answer in $\dfrac{m}{s}$.

   e. $\dfrac{4\dfrac{yd}{min}}{-2\dfrac{ft}{min}}$; solve so that all of the units cancel out, leaving you with a unitless answer.

   f. $-xy$ if $x = -2$ and $y = -1$

   g. $15\ ft\left(\dfrac{5\ s}{3\ ft}\right)$

3. **Applying Algebra** – Have you ever noticed how heavier bowling balls, if thrown at the same speed as lighter ones, are more powerful in knocking down the pins, but that you can throw a light ball faster and still knock them down with the same or more power? There's a property called momentum that describes this. Momentum (p) equals the mass (m) times the velocity (v), or $p = mv$. (Mass is related to weight, and velocity is like speed but includes direction.) Use this information to answer the questions. Be sure to include the units in your answer (for 3a and 3b, leave units in those given; for 3c, convert to $kg \dfrac{mi}{hr}$ to do the comparison).

Each problem except 3c is worth 9 points; problem 3c is worth 9 points if correct and no points deducted if wrong or skipped.

a. What is the momentum (p) of a ball with a mass (m) of 5 kg if it's thrown at a velocity (v) of $16\dfrac{mi}{hr}$?

b. What is the momentum (p) of a ball with a mass (m) of 6 kg if it's thrown at a velocity (v) of $17\dfrac{ft}{s}$?

c. 🎯 **Challenge Problem for Extra Credit:** Which ball (the one in 3a or the one in 3b) has the greater momentum, and by how much?

d. If we want a ball to have a ratio of momentum to velocity of 3 to 2, what should we make the velocity if the momentum is 10? Units have been left off, so you can leave them off in your answer.

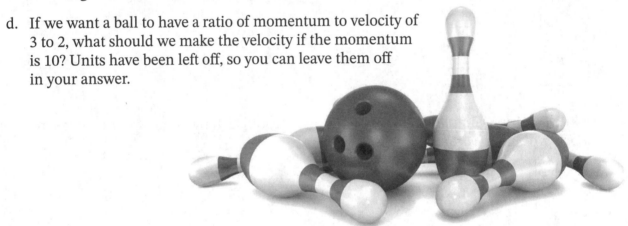

You are allowed to use a calculator on this quiz. However, calculators that can solve algebraic expressions are not allowed (or if used, that feature should not be used).

1. **Skill Checking** – Simplify or follow instructions in parentheses.
   Each problem is worth 5 points.

   a. $\dfrac{\frac{8x^2}{x^{-5}}}{3}$

   b. $\left(x^4\right)^6$

   c. $\left(4.0 \times 10^{-6}\right)\left(2.0 \times 10^8\right)$

   d. $\left(b^{\frac{1}{2}}\right)^3$

   e. $y^5 y^3 y^{-2}$

   f. $\left(a^2\right)^2$

   g. $-(-x)^2$

   h. $-(-x^2)$

   i. $\dfrac{1}{-c}\left(\dfrac{1}{-c}\right)$

   j. $\sqrt{c}\sqrt{c}$

   k. $-2^2(-3)^2$

   l. $\sqrt{50}$ (Find the value on a calculator.)

   m. $4^{\frac{2}{5}}$ (Find the value on a calculator.)

   n. the positive and the negative square root of 450 (Find the value on a calculator.)

2. **Algebra Applied**
   Each problem is worth 10 points.

   a. The weight (W) of an object equals its mass (m) times the acceleration due to gravity on the object (g), which we use letters to express like this: $W = mg$. What is the weight of an object that has a mass of 60 kg on earth where the acceleration due to gravity is $9.807\dfrac{\text{m}}{\text{s}^2}$? Be sure to watch your units.

   b. Using the information in problem 2a, calculate the weight of that same object on the moon where the acceleration due to gravity[1] is approximately $1.6\dfrac{\text{m}}{\text{s}^2}$.

---

1   Gravity measurement for the moon is from NASA, "What is Gravity" (n.d.), https://settlement.arc.nasa.gov/teacher/lessons/bryan/microgravity/gravback.html, accessed 10/8/19.

c. Rewrite your answer to problem 2a using negative exponents to express any units that are in the denominator as units in the numerator.

d. When an object is traveling in a circle, we get what's known as centripetal acceleration. If you've ever ridden a ride at an amusement park that turned in circles quickly, you may have felt a pull on your body towards the center. This is known as centripetal acceleration. This acceleration (a_c) equals the object's tangential velocity (v) squared divided by the radius of the circle it's traveling (r), which we use letters to express like this: $a_c = \dfrac{v^2}{r}$. If a person is on an amusement ride traveling in a circular path and his velocity (v) is $4\,\dfrac{m}{s}$ and the radius (r) of the circle he's traveling is 10 m, what is the centripetal acceleration (a_c) on him?

Principles of Algebra 2	Scope: Chapter 3 Numbers and Sets	Day 34	Quiz 3	Total score: ____of 100

You are allowed to use a calculator on this quiz. However, calculators that can solve algebraic expressions are not allowed (or if used, that feature should not be used).

1. **Skill Testing**
   Each problem is worth 10 points.

   a. If set $A = \{6, 10, 11\}$ and set $B = \{11\}$, what is $A \cap B$?

   $A \cap B = \{$_____$\}$

   b. Rewrite as an imaginary number: $\sqrt{-16}$

   c. Simplify: $5i \left(\dfrac{3i^2}{i} \right)$

   d. Use symbols to show that x needs to be an element of all natural numbers and must be greater than 3.

   x_____$\cap \, x >$_____

   e. Simplify without a calculator: $\sqrt{-44}$

   f. Simplify without a calculator: $\dfrac{\sqrt{-28}}{\sqrt{7}}$

   g. Simplify without a calculator: $\sqrt{3} \sqrt{-6}$

   h. Simplify without a calculator: $\sqrt{-10} \sqrt{-2}$

2. **Application Checking**
   Each problem is worth 10 points.

   a. If a search engine is trying to find all results that contain *Dogs* ∪ *Leashes*, describe the set of results.

   $a_0 = $ *Should You Walk Your Dogs on a Leash?*

   $a_1 = $ *Dogs Are Amazing Pets*

   $a_2 = $ *Leashes Should Be Legislated*

   $a_3 = $ *Buy New Leashes for Dogs*

   Dogs ∪ *Leashes* = {   }

   b. Using the same possible results, what would a search engine using *Dogs* ∩ *Leashes* be?

   Dogs ∩ *Leashes* = {   }

Intentionally left blank

You are allowed to use a calculator on this quiz. However, calculators that can solve algebraic expressions are not allowed (or if used, that feature should not be used).
Note that 1 yd = 36 in = 3 ft and 1 m = 100 cm.

1. **Skill Testing** – Solve for x. On problem 1c, your answer will still contain an unknown. *Each problem is worth 10 points.*

   a. $-3x = -12$

   b. $\dfrac{x^6}{x^4} = 81$

   c. $2x = -\dfrac{5ab}{2}; b = -4$

   d. $64 = \dfrac{8x^3}{x}$

   e. $-4x > 40$

   f. $-\dfrac{-x}{3} < 2$

   g. $-\dfrac{1}{2}x < \dfrac{-2}{-3}$

2. **Algebra Applied**[1]

   Each problem is worth 10 points: 5 for the correct answer, and 5 for setting up the problem the correct way.

   a. Some strings are thick; others are thin. We can describe the "thickness" by looking at how much mass, or material, there is per length. We call this the linear density (μ) of the string. It can be represented like this: $\mu = \dfrac{m}{L}$. If the length (L) of a certain stretch of string is 50 cm and the density is $0.008\,\dfrac{\text{kg}}{\text{m}}$, what is its mass?

   b. When you shake a string, it forms a wave. That wave travels through the string at a positive speed that "depends on both the string's linear density μ and the tension T_s [think of tension as how tightly you've stretched the string] in the string."[2] The relationship looks like this: $s = \sqrt{\dfrac{T_s}{\mu}}$.

   Find the speed (represented by s) if the tension is $5\,\text{kg}\,\dfrac{\text{m}}{\text{s}^2}$ and the linear density is $0.008\,\dfrac{\text{kg}}{\text{m}}$.

---

1   The formulas in 2a and 2b come from Randall D. Knight, *Physics for Scientists and Engineers with Modern Physics: A Strategic Approach* (Pearson, Addison Wesley, NY: 2004), p. 614 and 615.
2   Randall D. Knight, *Physics for Scientists and Engineers with Modern Physics: A Strategic Approach* (Pearson, Addison Wesley, NY: 2004), p. 615.

c. Suppose you are trying to get a dress made. You need 45 inches of fabric, plus 3 feet of trim. If the fabric costs $4 a yard, and the trim costs $2 a yard, how much will it all cost you, if you also have to pay a friend labor of $10 an hour and she estimates it will take 5 hours?

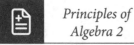

	Principles of Algebra 2	Scope: Chapter 5	Day 56	Quiz 5	Total score: ____of 100
		Solving More In-depth Problems			

You are allowed to use a calculator on this quiz. However, calculators that can solve algebraic expressions are not allowed (or if used, that feature should not be used).

1. **Skill Checking**

   Each problem is worth 10 points.

   a. Simplify: $2x - (x + 6) - y^4\left(y^{\frac{1}{2}} - 3\right) + 2y$

   b. If $x = 4y^{-1}$ and $\frac{1}{2}y = 18x$, find y.

   c. Solve for x: $\dfrac{5x - 2}{y} = 10y$

   d. Simplify, factoring out common factors: $\dfrac{5x^2}{y} + 3xy^{-1} + (2x)^2$

   e. Solve for x: $\dfrac{2x}{3 + y} = 20$

   f. If $y - 2x = -11$ and $x - 2y = c$, find an equation solved for x that only includes the unknowns x and c and does *not* include y.

2. **Application Checking**

   Each problem is worth 20 points.

   a. The surface area of a cylinder equals the circumference (C) of the base times the height (h), plus 2 times the area of the base (B), or $A = Ch + 2B$. The area of the base equals πr^2. The circumference equals $2\pi r$. Use substitution and factoring out common factors to write a more specific equation for finding the surface area of a cylinder that does not include C or B.

   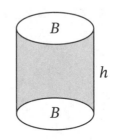

   b. In examining the order God placed within light, one equation we look at is this: $a = 2\left(m + \dfrac{1}{2}\right)\pi$. This is useful to help us describe something called destructive interference, which sometimes happens when multiple lightwaves are combined into one (the waves "interfere" with each other). Let's say that we know a is 3π. Find the value of m.[1]

---

1   Equation from Randall D. Knight, *Physics for Scientists and Engineers with Modern Physics: A Strategic Approach* (Addison Wesley, San Francisco, CA: 2004), p. 675.

Quiz 5 ∥369

3. 🎯 **Challenge Problem for Extra Credit**

Worth 20 points if correct and no points deducted if wrong or skipped.

On one of the worksheets in this chapter, we looked at this equation, which is called the dividend growth model.[2] Here's the equation in the way the finance book gives:

$P_0 = \dfrac{D_0(1 + g)}{R - g}$. Solve this equation for D_0 in terms of the other unknowns. **Distribute any multiplication in your answer that you can.**

---

2   Ross Westerfield Jordan, *Essentials for Corporate Finance* (New York: McGraw-Hill/Irwin, 2008), pp. 206.

| Principles of Algebra 2 | Scope: Chapter 6 — Unleashing Algebra: Solving Systems of Equations | Day 64 | Quiz 6 | Total score: _____ of 100 |

You are allowed to use a calculator on this quiz. You will need a calculator that can solve matrices (you may use an online one). However, calculators that can solve algebraic expressions are not allowed (or if used, that feature should not be used).

1. **Skill Checking** – Solve these systems of equations using any method you like.
   Each problem is worth 10 points.

   a. $2x - 3y = -7$

   $4x + y = 7$

   $x =$ _____ $y =$ _____

   b. $\frac{1}{2}x + \frac{1}{2}y = 3$

   $x - 2y = -6$

   $x =$ _____ $y =$ _____

2. **Applying Algebra**
   Each problem is worth 15 points.

   Suppose you are selling some items you make online. You sell scarves for $10, and blankets for $15. You want your total sales to be $175 a month. Now also suppose that it costs you $1 to make a scarf and $2 to make a blanket, and you only have $20 a month to spend on supplies.

   a. Write 2 equations with 2 unknowns (*s* representing the number of scarves and *b* the number of blankets you should make in a month to get $175 in sales, given the amount you have to spend on supplies).

   _____

   _____

   b. Solve the equations you wrote in 2a to figure out how many scarves and blankets to make. You can use any method you like.

   scarves to make = _____

   blankets to make = _____

3. **More Skill Checking**
   Worth 10 points.

   Suppose you know that $y + x = a$ and $2y + 3x = b$. Find a formula for what x equals *in terms of all of the other unknowns, including both a and b*, by first solving the first equation for y and substituting that into the second equation.

Quiz 6 // 371

4. **More Applying Algebra**

Each problem is worth 10 points.

a. Suppose you sell 5 pounds of tomatoes, 3 pounds of peaches, and 10 pounds of zucchini for $29 at your farm stand. To the next customer, you sell 2 pounds of tomatoes, 4 pounds of peaches, and 8 pounds of zucchini for $24. The third customer gets 0 pounds of tomatoes, 1 pound of peaches, and 2 pounds of zucchini for $5. If you sold the produce for the same price per pound each time, set up a system of 3 equations. You may use whatever letters you like to stand for the unknowns.

————————————————

————————————————

————————————————

b. Write Matrix A showing the coefficients of the unknowns in the equation you wrote in 4a, and Matrix B to show the values on the right side of the equations you wrote in 4a.

$$A = \begin{bmatrix} \square & \square & \square \\ \square & \square & \square \\ \square & \square & \square \end{bmatrix} \qquad B = \begin{bmatrix} \square \\ \square \\ \square \end{bmatrix}$$

c. Find the price per pound of each produce item by calculating $A^{-1}B$ on the calculator. Write your results as Matrix C.

$$C = \begin{bmatrix} \square \\ \square \\ \square \end{bmatrix}$$

d. What was the price per pound of the zucchini?

You are allowed to use a calculator on this quiz. However, calculators that can solve algebraic expressions are not allowed (or if used, that feature should not be used).

1. **Exploring Functions**

   Each problem is worth 10 points.

   Note: The first 6 problems in this section are based on the relationship between the "magnetic force between two parallel wires"[1] and the distance between them for a situation where the current of both wires is 80 Amps, and we're treating the length of each wire (l) as a constant; part 1g deals with the same scenario, except looks at the relationship between the force and the length of each wire, treating the distance between them as a constant.

   a. Rewrite $\dfrac{F}{l} = \dfrac{0.00064}{r}$ to show F as a function of r, treating l as a constant.

   b. Show the domain of the function you wrote in 1a. Your answer should start "$r \neq$."

   c. Show the range of the function you wrote in 1a. Your answer should start "$F(r) \neq$."

   d. Use a calculator to graph the function you wrote in 1a for when l is 6. In what 2 quadrants is the graph?

   ○ I   ○ II   ○ III   ○ IV

   e. What is the vertical asymptote(s) of the function you graphed in 1d?

   $r =$ _____

   f. Is the function you graphed in 1d even, odd, or neither?

   ○ even   ○ odd   ○ neither

   g. If $F(l) = 5l$, what is the x-intercept? You may graph to find the answer.

---

1   W. Thomas Griffith and Juliet Brosing, *The Physics of Everyday Phenomena: A Conceptual Introduction to Physics*, 6th ed. (New York: McGraw-Hill, 2009), p. 286

2. **Functioning with Functions** – For these problems, $f(x) = 2x$, $g(x) = 3x^2 + x$, and $h(x) = 2x^2$.

Each problem is worth 6 points.

a. Find $g(x) - f(x)$.

b. Find $f(x)g(x)$.

c. Find $g(f(x))$.

d. Find $f^{-1}(x)$ or explain that the inverse is not a function.

e. Find $h^{-1}(x)$ or explain that the inverse is not a function.

3. ◎ **Challenge Problem for Extra Credit**

Each problem is worth 4 points if correct and no points deducted if wrong or skipped.

Suppose you're coordinating a turkey food drive. Since each turkey cost $10, the number of turkeys you can give away equals the dollar amount of donations received divided by 10. Historical data shows that the dollar amount of donations received depends on the amount spent on advertising in such a way that it is usually 5 times what was spent on advertising.

a. Set up a function showing how the number of turkeys (t) you can give away depends on the dollar amount of donations received (d).

b. Set up a function showing how the dollar amount of donations received (d) depends on what was spent on advertising (a).

c. Set up a composite function showing the number of turkeys (t) as a function of the amount spent on advertising (a).

d. Use the function you wrote in 3c to find the number of turkeys if $500 was spent in advertising.

You are allowed to use a calculator on this quiz. However, calculators that can solve algebraic expressions are not allowed (or if used, that feature should not be used).

Below are formulas you may or may not need on the quiz:

General form of linear functions : $f(x) = mx + b$

Slope of linear functions: $m = \dfrac{y_2 - y_1}{x_2 - x_1}$

y-intercept of linear functions: $b = \dfrac{y_1 x_2 - y_2 x_1}{x_2 - x_1}$

General form of quadratic functions: $f(x) = ax^2 + bx + c$

$x_{\text{min|max}}$ of quadratic functions $= -\dfrac{b}{2a}$

Vertex form of quadratic functions: $f(x) = a(x - h)^2 + k$

1. **Term Time** – For each expression, list **all of these words** (polynomial, monomial, binomial, and/or trinomial) that describe it (some can be described by more than one word!). In these expressions, both a and x are variables.

   Each problem is worth 4 points.

   a. $2a^3 + 3a$

   b. $5x + 2 + a$

   c. $\dfrac{5a}{x} + x^3$

   d. $\dfrac{2a}{3}$

2. **More Term Time** – For each expression, list **all of the words** from the words listed that describe it (some can be described by more than one word!).

   Each problem is worth 2 points.

Linear Function	First-Degree Polynomial	Fourth-Degree Polynomial
Quadratic Function	Second-Degree Polynomial	Fifth-Degree Polynomial
Cubic Function	Third-Degree Polynomial	

   a. $y(x) = x^2 + 3$

   b. $d(s) = 8s + 5$

   c. $f(x) = x^4 + x + 2$

   d. $f(x) = x^3 + 2x$

3. **Odd and Even** – Look back at the functions in problem 2 and identify if each one is odd or even or neither.

    Each problem is worth 4 points.

    a.   ○ Even   ○ Odd   ○ Neither

    b.   ○ Even   ○ Odd   ○ Neither

    c.   ○ Even   ○ Odd   ○ Neither

    d.   ○ Even   ○ Odd   ○ Neither

4. **Exploring Functions**

    Each problem is worth 10 points.

    a. Say you have been examining some statistical data and found a line of best fit to describe that data. If that line goes through points (2, 9) and (3, 21), find the slope of the line.

    b. Find the *y*-intercept of the line described in 4a.

    c. Suppose that a particular college discovered that the retention rate of students in a class varied with the length of the class (*l*, in minutes) according to this function:
    $r(l) = -\frac{1}{20}l^2 + 4l + 2$. What length of class resulted in the highest retention rate? Note that this can be answered by finding the maximum point of the function.

    _____ minutes

    d. In the situation described in 4c, what was the highest retention rate achieved?

    e. Suppose instead that a particular college discovered that the retention rate of students in a class varied with the length of the class (*l*, in minutes) according to this function:
    $r(l) = -\frac{1}{6}(l - 20)^2 + 70$. What length of class resulted in the highest retention rate?

    _____ minutes

    f. In the situation described in 4e, what was the highest retention rate achieved? Give your answer as a percent.

5. **Applying the Distributive Property** – Distribute the multiplication.

    Each problem is worth 5 points.

    a. $(x - 4)^2$

    b. $5(a + 3)(a - 4)$

You are allowed to use a calculator on this quiz. However, calculators that can solve algebraic expressions are not allowed (or if used, that feature should not be used).

1. **Factoring Quadratic Expressions** – Factor the right side of these functions without using the quadratic formula. If possible, do this section orally with your parent/educator.
    Each problem is worth 5 points.

    a. $f(x) = x^2 + 8x + 16$

    b. $f(s) = 2s^2 + 40s + 200$

    c. $g(t) = t^2 + 7t + 10$

    d. $f(x) = x^2 - 7$

    e. $f(h) = h^2 + 3$

    Note: Problem 1e is a function based on calculating rotational moments of inertia.

2. **Recognizing Specific Quadratic Expressions** – List as many options as apply.
    Each problem is worth 3 points.

    a. Which of the expressions you factored was a perfect square?

    ○ 1a   ○ 1b   ○ 1c   ○ 1d   ○ 1e

    b. Which of the expressions you factored was a sum of two squares?

    ○ 1a   ○ 1b   ○ 1c   ○ 1d   ○ 1e

3. **Identifying Roots** – Look at the factored expressions in problems 1a–1e and identify what the roots are, specifying if any are repeated.
    Each problem is worth 5 points.

    a.

    b.

    c.

    d.

    e.

4. **More with Roots** – Find the roots of these expressions.
    Each problem is worth 10 points.

    a. $2x^2 + 10$

    b. $-4x^2 + 3x + 7$

5. **Recognizing Quadratic Functions** – Choose the correct function to describe the graph.
   Do not use a graphing calculator.
   Problem is worth 4 points.

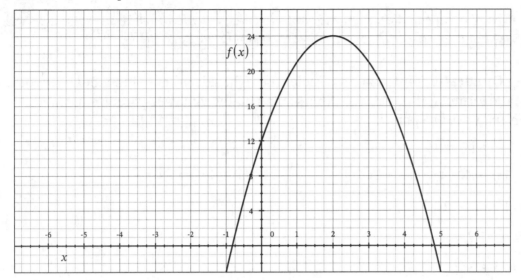

   A. $f(x) = -3x^2 + 12x + 12$ B. $f(x) = x^2 + 4x + 4$ C. $f(x) = -x^2 + 5x$

   ○ A   ○ B   ○ C

6. 📖 **More Applying Algebra** – A railway train traveled $5\,\dfrac{\text{mi}}{\text{hr}}$ slower
   than usual and was 1 hr late in making a run of 280 mi. How many
   miles per hour did it travel? The following steps will help you answer
   this question. Note that *distance = speed • time*.
   Each problem is worth 5 points.

   a. Write an equation showing the relationship between the distance,
      speed, and time of the train *if it ran at its normal speed*. Substitute s_n
      for speed and t_n for time to stand for the normal speed and time.

   b. Write an equation showing the relationship between the distance, speed, and time of the
      delayed train *in terms of* its normal speed and time (s_n) and (t_n). For example, the speed
      you'll use is $(s_n - 5)$, as the delayed speed is the normal speed *minus* $5\,\dfrac{\text{mi}}{\text{hr}}$.

   c. Solve the equation from 6a for s_n and substitute that value into the equation from 6b
      to solve for t_n. While you will get both a positive and negative value when you use
      the quadratic formula to solve for t_n, in this case, only list the positive value, as we're
      interested in a positive value for time.

   d. Use the value you found in 6c to find s_n, the train's normal speed. Your answer should be
      in miles per hour.

   e. Given your answers to the earlier questions and the information given at the start of this
      problem, what is the train's delayed speed and time?

      Train's delayed speed = _____

      Train's delayed time = _____

| Principles of Algebra 2 | Scope: Chapter 10 _____ More with Polynomials | Day 110 | Quiz 10 | Total score: _____ of 100 |

You are allowed to use a graphing calculator on the first part of this quiz. You will also need graphing paper.

1. **Fundamental Theorem of Algebra** – Identify the total number of roots the following expressions have.
   Each problem is worth 8 points.

   a. $x^4 + 2x^2 - 8$

   b. $5x^5 + 4x^3$

2. **Finding Roots** – Find the roots for each expression in 1a and 1b. For 1a, find both the complex and real roots. For 1b, only find real roots.
   Each problem is worth 8 points.

   a.

   b.

3. **Graphing Equalities** – List the input(s) and output(s) these functions share. Your answer should be one or more pairs of coordinates, such as $(5, -2)$.
   Each problem is worth 8 points.

   a. $f(x) = 7x + 3$ and $f(x) = 4x^2 + 2x - 3$

   b. $g(t) = -4.9t^2 + 5t$ and $f(t) = -5t$

4. **Applying Algebra** – Say two people are running a race. Runner A is currently 6 miles into the race, and Runner B is 3 miles into the race. If Runner B starts running at a consistent $5 \frac{\text{mi}}{\text{hr}}$, while Runner A slows to $2 \frac{\text{mi}}{\text{hr}}$, how long will it take for Runner B to overtake Runner A, and how many miles altogether will they have run? The following steps will help you answer this question.
   Know that $d(t) = st + d_{\text{start}}$.
   Each problem is worth 9 points.

   a. Write a function showing the relationship between the distance as a function of time for Runner A.

   b. Write a function showing the relationship between the distance as a function of time t for Runner B.

   c. Graph the functions you wrote in 4a and 4b. At what distance and time do the two runners meet?

      Distance = _____   *Time* = _____

   d. Use graphing paper to show the range of distances that are less than that of both runners for any given value of time.

5. **More Graphing Inequalities** – Choose the set of inequalities that accurately describes the graph.

   Each problem is worth 8 points.

   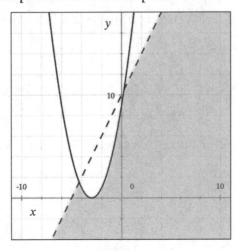

   A. $y \le x^2 + 6x + 9$ and $y > 2x + 10$ C. $y \ge x^2 + 6x + 9$ and $y < 2x + 10$

   B. $y \le x^2 + 6x + 9$ and $y < 2x + 10$ D. $y \ge 2(x^2 + 6x + 9)$ and $y < 2x + 10$

   ○ A   ○ B   ○ C   ○ D

6. **Even More Graphing Inequalities** – Copy the general shape of the graph shown and shade the appropriate region.

   Problem is worth 8 points.

   $y < -4.9x^2 + 5x$ and $y > -5x$

   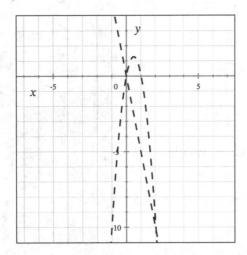

You are allowed to use a calculator on this quiz. However, calculators that can solve algebraic expressions are not allowed (or if used, that feature should not be used). A graphing calculator is not needed on the quiz.

1. **Skill Checking**
   Each problem is worth 9 points.

   a. Rewrite this function with a single fraction on the right: $f(x) = \dfrac{8x^2 + 3x + 5}{x + 2} + 3x$.

   b. Is there a value the input to the function in 1a cannot be?

      ○ Yes   ○ No

      If yes, what? Your answer should start "$x \neq$."

      _____

   c. At what value(s) will the output of the function you wrote in 1a be 0?

   d. Complete the division in this rational expression: $\dfrac{10x^2 + 42x + 8}{x + 4}$.

   e. Solve for x: $\dfrac{x(2x^2 - 6)}{3x} = 0$.

   f. Complete the division in this rational expression: $\dfrac{5x^2 + 3x + 3}{-x + 1}$.

   g. What value can x not equal? Specify it using a $\neq$ sign. $\dfrac{5x^4 + 3x^2 + 2}{-x + 1}$

   h. Find the roots, approximating your answers on a calculator where needed: $\dfrac{2x^4 - 9x^2 + 4}{x + 2}$

   i. Simplify: $\dfrac{x^2 - 16}{x^2 + 3x - 4}$. Be sure to specify what x does not equal.

2. **Springs** – The formula for finding the energy of a specific spring is $E = \dfrac{1}{2}(8)x^2 + 15$, where x is the distance between where it starts and ends. Suppose you want to divide this energy by the energy of another object whose energy equals $x + 2$ in order to find the ratio of their energies as a function of x.
   Problem 2a is worth 3 points; each part of 2c is worth 2 points; each other problem is worth 4 points.

   a. Finish writing a function describing the ratio of the energies of the spring and the other object as a function of x (which in this case is representing a displacement distance).

      $E_{\text{Ratio}}(x) = $ _____

b. Looking at your answer to 2a, is there ever a time when the ratio of the energies equals 0? Answer no if there are no real roots to the function.

    ○ Yes   ○ No

c. Based on your answer to 2a, are there any values x cannot be?

    ○ Yes   ○ No

    If so, what value(s) can x not equal? Your answer should start "$x \neq$."

    _____

d. Complete the division in the function you wrote in 2a, getting a partial fraction.

e. We can rewrite the original equation as $E = \frac{1}{2}kx^2 + U$. If the units of E and U are $kg \cdot \frac{m^2}{s^2}$ and the units of x are m, then find the units of k (the constant $\frac{1}{2}$ has no units).

Here are some of the exponential growth formulas we looked at in Chapter 12. You may or may not need them all on this quiz.

$$P(t) = P_i g^{ct} \qquad P(t) = P_i (1 + r)^t$$

$$P(t) = P_i e^{rt} \qquad P(t) = P_i \left(1 + \frac{r}{n}\right)^{nt}$$

You are allowed to use a calculator on this quiz. However, calculators that can solve algebraic expressions are not allowed (or if used, that feature should not be used). You do not need a graphing calculator.

Each problem is worth 10 points.

1. **Skill Checking** – When simplifying, factor out all common factors.

   a. Find $\dfrac{f(x)}{g(x)}$ if $f(x) = e^{15x}$ and $g(x) = e^{2x}$.

   b. Find $f(x)g(x)$ if $f(x) = 4^{2x}$ and $g(x) = 16^x$.

   c. Find $f(x) - g(x)$ if $f(x) = 3e^{3x}$ and $g(x) = 6e^{2x}$.

   d. Simplify: $(3y)^4 \left(\dfrac{x}{y}\right)^3$

   e. Simplify: $5a^6 + a^2$

   f. Simplify: $\sqrt{\dfrac{a^{2x}}{b^{2x}}}$

2. **Applying Algebra**

   a. Let's say that a small town's population has been growing exponentially such that it was 30,000 one year and 40,000 the next. If it's 40,000 now, what will it be after 7 years if this rate continues?

   b. If you take out a $10,000 loan to start a business at a 10% annual rate compounded monthly, how much will you owe if you pay back the loan after 6 months, assuming the loan allows an early pay back? Round to the nearest cent.

   c. If the continuous exponential growth rate of a certain population is 50% per year, how much will a population of 300 grow to in 5 years?

3. **Rules Expressed with Algebra** – Write an example using actual values of this rule in action by substituting actual values for each of the letters given (use 10 for m and 5 for n) and then simplifying as much as possible: $\dfrac{m}{n^{-1}} = mn^1$

You are allowed to use whatever calculator you like on the quiz.

1. **Understanding and Working with Logarithms**

   Each problem is worth 5 points.

   a. Find $\ln(20)$.

   b. Find $\ln(0)$.

   c. Find $\log_3(20)$.

   d. Solve for t: $400 = 200(4^{0.005t})$

   e. Simplify to a single logarithm: $\log(a) - \log(b)$

   f. Rewrite as separate logarithms, calculating the logarithm where you can: $\log_4(8x)$

   g. Use the power rule to rewrite without an exponent: $\log(a^8)$

   h. Use the power rule to rewrite with an exponent: $3\ln(a)$

   i. Solve for x: $6 = \log_3(x^3)$

   j. Rewrite $f(t) = 3e^{5t}$ as a linear expression by taking the logarithm of both sides, applying the product rule, simplifying any logarithms you can, replacing the logarithm of $f(t)$ with y, and calculating any logarithms you can.

   k. Find x^2 if $\log(x) = 3$.

   l. Rewrite as separate logarithms, calculating the logarithm where you can: $\log_3\left(\dfrac{8}{x}\right)$

   m. If $y = \log(3x)$ is a log scale, where y is really the logarithm of the actual output $f(x)$, what is the *actual output* when $x = 15$?

   n. Solve for t: $60 = 10(e^{0.07t})$

   o. Find $\log_2(502)$.

2. **Applying Algebra: The *pH* Scale**[1] – The *pH* scale, which is a common way of measuring how acidic or basic a substance is, has values from approximately 0 to 14, and the values can be computed based on the formula $pH = -\log(H)$, where H stands for the concentration of H^+ ions in the water. **Note that *pH* is a single unknown — it doesn't mean *p* times *H*.** *pH* is equal to 7 for neutral water. Liquids with *pH* values higher than 7 are called bases and liquids with *pH* values lower than 7 are called acids.

Problems 2a and 2b are worth 5 points each; the bonus questions are worth 1 point each.

a. Find the *pH* level of baking soda, given that H is 0.000000001.

b. **Bonus Question:** Based on your answer in 2a, is baking soda an acid or a base?

   ○ acid   ○ base

c. Find the pH level of distilled vinegar, given that H is 0.004.

d. **Bonus Question:** Based on your answer in 2c, is distilled vinegar and acid or a base?

   ○ acid   ○ base

3. **More Applying Algebra** – Suppose you have two separate experiments you want to conduct. The first experiment has to be finished before you start the second. In the first, you want a population of 100,000 bacteria to die off to a population of 20,000 bacteria, at a rate of 6% per day. In the second, you want the resulting population of 20,000 bacteria to die off to a population of 5,000, at a rate of 12% per day. You will need to use this formula for exponential growth: $P_f(t) = P_i(1 - r)^t$.

Each problem is worth 5 points.

a. Solve to find the time needed for the first experiment, in terms of a logarithm (don't actually calculate the value of the logarithm).

b. Solve to find the time needed for the second experiment, in terms of a logarithm (don't actually calculate the value of the logarithm).

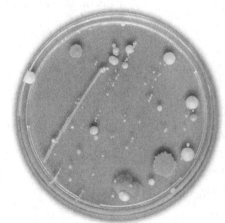

c. Find how many days the whole experiment will take by adding the times you calculated in 3a and 3b. Calculate the value this time.

---

1   See "What Is the pH Scale?", Math in the Physical Sciences: Chemistry and Math, https://www.papertrell.com/apps /preview/The-Handy-Math-Answer-Book/Handy%20Answer%20book/What-is-the-pH-scale/001137022/content /SC/52cb016e82fad14abfa5c2e0_default.html

You are allowed to use whatever calculator you like on the quiz.

Each problem is worth 5 points.

1. **Skill Testing**

    a. Find $f(g(x))$ if $f(x) = \log(x)$ and $g(x) = 7x^3$. Leave your answer as a single logarithm.

    $f(g(x)) = $ _____

    b. Find $f(-6)$ if $f(x - 3) = 4|2x^3| - 3$.

    c. Simplify: $|x^2| - 3|x^3| - 4|-5|$

    d. The black curve can be described by $f(x) = x^2 + 3$. What function describes the grey curve, given it is a transformation of the black curve using one of the transformations we've looked at?

    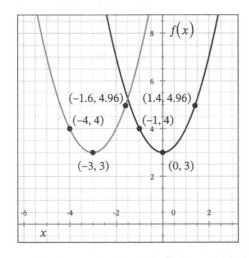

    e. If the point $(1, -2)$ is part of a function that is *first* compressed horizontally by 2 and *then* reflected across the x-axis, what will the corresponding point on the new function be?

    f. If the point $(3, -5)$ is part of a function that is *first* scaled vertically by 5 and *then* reflected across the y-axis, what will the corresponding point on the new function be?

    g. Shift the function $f(x) = 2x^2 + 3x + 2$ vertically *down* by 5.

2. **Applying Algebra: Firing a Cannon** – The relationship between the range and the angle at which a cannon is fired when air resistance can be neglected is

    $$R(\theta) = \frac{2v_0^2}{g}(\sin(\theta))(\cos(\theta)).$$

    Calculate the range $R(\theta)$ for when $\theta = 35°$, v_0 is $5\dfrac{\text{m}}{\text{s}}$, and $g = 9.8\dfrac{\text{m}}{\text{s}^2}$.

3. **Applying Algebra: Running** – The distance a runner goes in 5 hours depends on his or her speed according to the function $d(s) = 5s$, assuming the distance he or she starts at is 0.

   a. Shift this function vertically down by 6.

   b. How does the function in 3a change the runner's starting distance from the original function?

      Starting distance in original function: _____

      Starting distance in shifted function: _____

      Change: _____

   c. Compress $d(s) = 5s$ horizontally by 2.

   d. At what speed now does the runner, running according to the compressed function in 3c, go the same distance as he or she used to go with a speed of 10 miles per hour? Be sure to include the unit of measure in your answer.

4. **More Applying Algebra: Running** – Say a runner changes the speed at which he or she runs throughout a race, making the distance traveled take on the piecewise function shown.

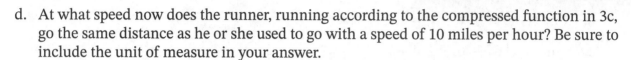

$$d(t) = \begin{cases} 0\,\dfrac{\text{mi}}{\text{hr}}, \text{ if } t \le 0 \text{ hr} \\[2mm] \left(3\dfrac{\text{mi}}{\text{hr}}\right)t, \text{ if } 0 \text{ hr} < t \le 1 \text{ hr} \\[2mm] \left(4\dfrac{\text{mi}}{\text{hr}}\right)(t - 1 \text{ hr}) + 3 \text{ mi}, \text{ if } 1 \text{ hr} < t \le 2 \text{ hr} \\[2mm] \left(2\dfrac{\text{mi}}{\text{hr}}\right)(t - 2 \text{ hr}) + 7 \text{ mi}, \text{ if } 2 \text{ hr} < t \end{cases}$$

   a. What is the runner's distance after 1 hour?

   b. What is the runner's distance after 3 hours?

5. **More Applying Algebra: More Running** – Suppose a runner's distance varies based on his or her speed for the 3 hours he or she runs according to the function $d(s) = 3s$.

   a. Write a function showing the distance as a function of speed if the runner's speed is decreased by 1 mile an hour.

   b. What kind of transformation was applied in 5a?

      ○ horizontal   ○ vertical *(choose one)*

      ○ shift   ○ scale   ○ reflection *(choose one)*

   c. Write a function showing the distance as a function of speed if the distance the runner travels is increased by 2, since he or she ran 2 miles before the 3-hour clock this function is tracking started.

   d. What kind of transformation was applied in 5c?

      ○ horizontal   ○ vertical *(choose one)*

      ○ shift   ○ scale   ○ reflection *(choose one)*

6. **More Applying Algebra: Richter Scale** – Use this formula (which is the Richter scale relationship for earthquakes when the denominator equals 100) to answer the questions:

$$M_L(A) = \log\left(\frac{A}{100}\right).$$

a. Suppose that there are issues with the amplitude reading machine, such that it reports each amplitude reading (A in the formula) as 1,000 less than it really is. Transform the function to account for this and still get accurate readings.

b. What kind of transformation was applied in 6a?

   ○ horizontal   ○ vertical *(choose one)*

   ○ shift   ○ scale   ○ reflection *(choose one)*

Intentionally left blank

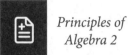

Principles of Algebra 2	Scope: Chapter 15	Day 173	Quiz 15	Total score: ____ of 100
	Functions and Formulas That Help Us Count, Find Probabilities, and Generate Sequences			

This quiz is open book, meaning you can consult your textbook and any notes you took to help you answer the questions. You are also allowed to use any calculator you like.

1. **Probability, Permutations, and Combinations**

   Each problem is worth 10 points.

   a. What is the probability of rolling three ⚁'s in a row on a standard 6-sided die?

   $P(⚁ \cap ⚁ \cap ⚁) = $ _____

   b. What is the probability of rolling either a ⚁ or a ⚂ on a standard 6-sided die?

   $P(⚁ \cup ⚂) = $ _____

   c. What is the probability of rolling either a ⚁ or a number greater than 4 on a standard 6-sided die?

   $P(⚁ \cup > 4) = $ _____

   d. In a white elephant gift exchange, everyone draws a random number that determines the order in which they get to pick a gift. What is the probability of drawing the number that gives the first pick in a white elephant gift exchange if you are the second person to draw a number, the first person did not draw the first pick, and there are 30 different people playing?

   e. Let's say you are a football coach. You have 6 players who can play wide receiver, but only need 2 in the game at a given time: one to play on the left side and one to play on the right side. How many different ways could you assign your wide receivers for each play, assuming they can all play either left or right?
   Note: A player playing the left position is different than a player playing the right position.

   f. Let's say you bought an MP3 album with 12 songs on it. You listen to 5 songs randomly. If the software you're playing the songs on only plays each song a single time when playing them randomly, how many different combinations of songs could you end up with (i.e., we don't care about the order the songs are played in)?

   g. Suppose again that you bought an MP3 album with 12 songs on it. You listen to 5 songs randomly. If the software you're playing the songs on allows repeats when playing randomly, how many different combinations of songs could you end up with?

   h. Find $\binom{8}{4}$.

2. **Sequences and Series**

   Each problem is worth 5 points.

   a. Find the 20th element in this sequence: $a_n = 6n + 2$, where $n \geq 0$.

   b. Describe this sequence algebraically:
      $\{3, 7, 11, \dots\}$
      (You may have n start at either 0 or 1; just be sure to specify which you did.)

      $a_n = $ _____, where $n \geq$ _____

   c. Find the requested sum: $\sum\limits_{n=2}^{6} 5^n$

3. **The Binomial Theorem** – Use the binomial theorem to expand $(x - 4)^5$.

   Problem is worth 5 points.

You are allowed to use a calculator on this test. However, calculators that can solve algebraic expressions are not allowed (or if used, that feature should not be used).

1. **Skill Checking**

   Each problem is worth 5 points.

   a. Simplify: $\left(x^{\frac{1}{2}}\right)^4$

   Example Meaning: Taking the square root of a speed and then raising that to the fourth power.

   b. Simplify: $(6)\dfrac{\left(4\ \text{in}^2\right)^{\frac{1}{2}}}{4\ \text{in}^2}$

   c. Simplify: $-\dfrac{-\left(x^3\right)^{-3}}{x^4}$

   d. Simplify: $\left(\dfrac{3xy^3}{dy}\right)\left(-\dfrac{2d^{-2}}{x}\right)^2$

   e. Solve this equation for x in terms of y (you will still have y as another unknown in the problem) given that $b = 2^{\frac{3}{3}}$:

   $8x^2 = 16yy^3y^0b$

   $x = \underline{\hspace{2cm}}$

   f. Rewrite using the imaginary unit: $\sqrt{-30}$

   g. Simplify: $\sqrt{-10}\,\sqrt{-6}i$

   h. Simplify: $5i^3(3i)$

   i. If set $A = \mathbb{N}$ and set $B = \{-2,\ \dfrac{1}{2},\ 1\}$, $A \cap B = \underline{\hspace{2cm}}$.

   j. Is 3.5 an element of the set represented with a $\mathbb{N}$?
      ○ Yes   ○ No

   k. If $x \notin \mathbb{I}$, can $x = 2i$?
      ○ Yes   ○ No

   l. Solve this inequality for x : $\dfrac{1}{3}x^3x^{-2} < -4$

2. **Application Checking**

   Each problem is worth 10 points.

   a. Given that *distance* = *speed* (*time*), or $d = st$, how many miles per *hour* would you have to go in order to travel −400 miles (i.e., 400 miles in the opposite direction) in 360 *minutes*?

   b. You know that *distance* = *speed* (*time*), or $d = st$. Let's say that in a particular setting the speed (*s*) equals 2*x*. Write an equation showing what the distance equals that does not use the letter *s*.

   c. Let's say that you have 3 hours to finish an exam. There are 20 questions on the exam. On average, you have to solve each problem in less than how many *minutes*?

   $x < $ _____

   d. Let's say that you need $200 a month to cover your rent, plus twice that amount to cover your portion of your college tuition and other miscellaneous expenses. If you can only work 20 hours a week, how much per hour do you need to make to at least pay all your expenses? Assume there are exactly 4 weeks in a month (i.e., don't worry about partial weeks for months with more than 28 days).

3. 🎯 **Challenge Problem for Extra Credit**

   Problem is worth 10 points if correct and no points deducted if wrong or skipped.

   Use the formula $-\dfrac{F_t r^2}{G m_1} + m_2 = m_3$ to find m_3 when m_2 is 50 kg, r is 6 m, m_1 is 100 kg, G is

   $6.674 \times 10^{-11} \dfrac{\text{m}^3}{\text{kg} \cdot \text{s}^2}$, and F_t is 5.105×10^{-11} N. *Note:* $1 \text{ N} = 1\dfrac{\text{kg} \cdot \text{m}}{\text{s}^2}$.

You are allowed to use a calculator on this test. However, calculators that can solve algebraic expressions are not allowed (or if used, that feature should not be used).

Below are formulas you may or may not need on the test:

General form of linear functions : $f(x) = mx + b$

Slope of linear functions: $m = \dfrac{y_2 - y_1}{x_2 - x_1}$

y-intercept of linear functions: $b = \dfrac{y_1 x_2 - y_2 x_1}{x_2 - x_1}$

General form of quadratic functions: $f(x) = ax^2 + bx + c$

$x_{min|max}$ of quadratic functions $= -\dfrac{b}{2a}$

Vertex form of quadratic functions: $f(x) = a(x - h)^2$

1. **Skill Testing**

    Each problem is worth 4 points.

    a. Solve for x: $\dfrac{3}{13}x + \dfrac{1}{2} = 3$

    b. Solve for x and simplify as much as possible: $3x + 3y(y + 2y) = 15$

    c. Simplify: $3x(2 + 2a) + 4a(2x + 3) + x$

    d. Solve for x: $\dfrac{\frac{1}{2}x}{5 - y} = 15$

    e. Distribute the multiplication: $4(x - 3)^2$

2. **Time Management**

   Each problem is worth 3 points.

   Suppose you have 40 minutes each day to work on craft projects. In that time, the first day you get 10 rows of a knitting project completed, 1 card made, and 10 bows tied. The next day you get 5 rows of the knitting project completed, 3 cards made, and 0 bows tied. The third day you get 2 rows of the knitting project completed, 3 cards made, and 6 bows tied. On average, how many minutes does it take to complete a row of knitting, make a card, and tie a bow? [1]

   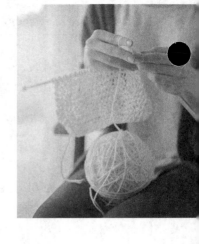

   a. Write 3 equations in 3 unknowns to describe this situation.

   b. How many minutes on average does it take to complete a row of knitting?

   c. How many minutes on average does it take to make a card?

   d. How many minutes on average does it take to tie a bow?

3. **Understanding Functions**

   Each problem is worth 4 points.

   a. Is $g(x) = \pm\sqrt{3x^4}$ a function?

      O Yes   O No

   b. For the function $f(x) = \dfrac{8}{x}$, what value does the domain *not* include? Your answer should start "$x \neq$."

   c. Find the inverse of the function in 3b. What value does its domain *not* include? Your answer should start "$y \neq$."

   d. Is the function in 3b a polynomial function?

      O Yes   O No

   e. Find the value of x at the minimum or maximum in the function $f(x) = 3x^2 + 3x - 6$.

      $x_{\text{min}|\text{max}} = \underline{\qquad\qquad}$

   f. Use your result from 3e to find the output at the minimum or maximum in the function $f(x) = 3x^2 + 3x - 6$.

   g. Find the maximum/minimum point of this function: $f(x) = -2(x+1)^2 + 3$

   h. Using a graphing calculator, graph $f(x) = (x - 5)(x + 3)$ and then draw the general shape in your notebook.

   i. The following is a _____-degree polynomial: $f(x) = 3x^7 + 3x^5$

---

1   Heavily adapted from a problem in Edwin Seaver and George Walton, *The Franklin Elementary Algebra* (Boston: William War & Co., 1882), p. 156

j. The function in 3i was

    ○ Even   ○ Odd   ○ Neither

k. For the function $f(x) = 10x$, finish completing the table showing the outputs for the inputs given.

	Domain (i.e., inputs)	Range (i.e., outputs)
1		
2		
3		

4. Force, Mass, and Acceleration

Each problem is worth 3 points.

The average force of an object equals its mass times its average acceleration, or $F = ma$. The average acceleration equals the velocity (think speed) minus the initial velocity divided by the time, or $a = \dfrac{v - v_0}{t}$.

a. Write a function in function notation showing the average force (F) as a function of the average acceleration (a).

b. Write a function in function notation showing the average acceleration (a) as a function of time (t).

c. Write a composite function in function notation showing the average force (F) as a function of time (t).

5. Working with Functions

Each problem is worth 5 points.

Given that $f(x) = x^2$ and $g(x) = x + 2$, find the requested information.

a. Find $f(x)g(x)$, if $f(x) = x^2$ and $g(x) = x + 2$.

b. Find $f(x) + g(x)$, if $f(x) = x^2$ and $g(x) = x + 2$.

c. Find $g(f(x))$ if $g(y) = y + 3$ and $f(x) = x^3$.

6. ◎ Challenge Problem for Extra Credit

Problem is worth 5 points if correct and no points deducted if wrong or skipped.

Say you know that after 10 seconds, a deer running away from the road at a constant speed is 40 ft away from the side of the road. 25 seconds later, so 35 total seconds since starting to track the distance of the deer, the deer was 50 ft away from the side of the road. View distance as a function of time, $d(t) = st + d_{start}$. Find the distance from the road that the deer started running, given that the deer started running at 0 seconds.

Intentionally left blank

Below are some formulas you may need on the test:

$$P(t) = P_i g^{ct} \qquad\qquad P(t) = P_i (1 + r)^t$$

$$P(t) = P_i e^{rt} \qquad\qquad P(t) = P_i \left(1 + \frac{r}{n}\right)^{nt}$$

You are allowed to use a calculator on the entire test. However, calculators that can solve algebraic expressions are not allowed (or if used, that feature should not be used).
You are NOT allowed to use a calculator to graph on problems 1a–5b.

Each problem is worth 5 points.

1. **Solve for x** – Note that there may be more than one solution.

   a. $x^2 - 6x + 9 = 0$

   b. $x^2 + 9 = 0$

   c. $5x^2 - 4x + 3 = 0$

   d. $\dfrac{x^2 - 16}{x + 4} = 0$

   e. $\dfrac{x^4 - 25x^2}{2 - x} = 0$

2. **More with Rational Functions**

   a. Complete the division: $\dfrac{x^4 - 16}{x^2 - 4}$

   b. Bonus question (worth 5 extra points): Is $x = -2$ a root of $x^4 - 16$?

      O Yes   O No

   c. Rewrite as a single fraction: $\dfrac{5x^2 - 3}{x - 3} - \dfrac{4}{x}$

3. **Simplifying Expressions** – Simplify the following expressions, factoring out any common factors.

   a. $2x^{3t} + 4x^{6t}$

   b. $40(2)^{3t} + 30(2)^{2t}$

4. **Miscellaneous**

   a. How many total roots does $x^4 - 2x$ have?

   b. Finish graphing the solution to $y \geq 5x$ and $y \leq x^2 + 3$ by copying the general shape in your notebook and shading the appropriate region.

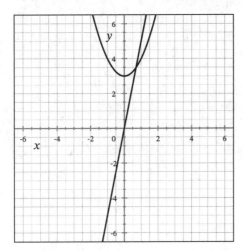

5. **Graph Recognition** – Choose the function that describes the graph.

   a.

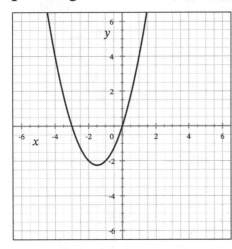

   A. $f(x) = x^2 + 3x$

   B. $f(x) = x^2 - 3x$

   ○ A   ○ B

   b.

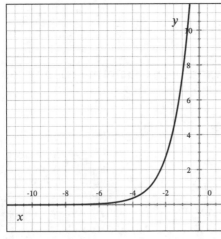

   A. $f(t) = 20e^t$

   B. $f(t) = 20e^{-t}$

   C. $f(t) = x^3 - 6$

   ○ A   ○ B   ○ C

c.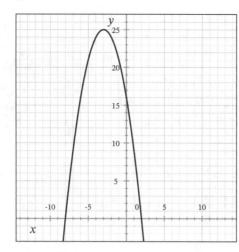

A. $f(x) = x^2 + 6x - 16$

B. $f(x) = -x^2 - 6x + 16$

○ A   ○ B

A graphing calculator is allowed on this part of the test.

6. **Applying Algebra: Growth and Decay**

   a. Suppose there's a population that grows exponentially from 40 to 70 in 5 hours. If the growth continues at the same rate, what will the population be in an additional 2 days from the point it was 70? Round your answer down to the nearest whole number.

   b. Suppose you invest $10,000 when you're 18. How much will the investment grow to by the time you're 33 if it earns 4% annual interest compounded monthly? Round to the nearest cent.

   c. A business' revenue in one year was $100,000. In the next year, it was $90,000. If the decline in revenue is exponential decay and it continues at this same rate, what will its revenue be in another 6 years? Round to the nearest cent.

7. **Even More with Rational Functions**

   a. Simplify: $\dfrac{x^2 - 16}{x + 4}$

   b. At what value of x is there a discontinuity in the expression $\dfrac{x^2 - 16}{x + 4}$, which is the same expression you simplified in 7a?

   c. At what value of x is there an asymptote in $\dfrac{x^4 - 25x^2}{2 - x}$?

8. **Applying Algebra: Sales** – Say a party shop makes an average of $30,000, and that the number of specialty helium balloon sales can be described by the function $s(p) = -p^2 + 100$, where $1 \leq p \leq 10$.

   a. Write a function $f(p)$ showing the ratio between the total the party shop makes and the number of specialty helium balloons that sell at the party shop. Include the entire function and domain, even the parts given below, in your answer.

   $f(p) =$ _____, where ____ $\leq p \leq$ ____

   b. In the ratio, is there a value that p cannot be that is within the domain?

   ○ Yes   ○ No

   If yes, what is it? Use a $\neq$ to show.

   c. Given the graph of $s(p)$ shown, if the domain didn't exist, at what prices would the sales be 0? (And now you know why we need the domain — the negative values don't make any sense in this scenario!)

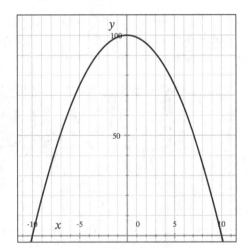

9. **Applying Algebra: More Sales** – In economics, there's something known as supply and demand. Suppose the supply for a certain product can be approximated by the function $y = -x + 20$, where y is the price of each product and x is the quantity of that product purchased. Also suppose the demand for a product (that is, how much people will want to buy the product) can be approximated by $y = x + 4$, where again the y is the price of each product and x is the quantity of that product available to purchase (i.e., quantity). We have omitted units for simplicity.

   a. At what quantity do the supply and demand curves intersect and what is the price at that quantity? This is known as the equilibrium point — at this quantity, the supply matches the demand, meaning the quantity available of the product is the same as the quantity desired of a product.

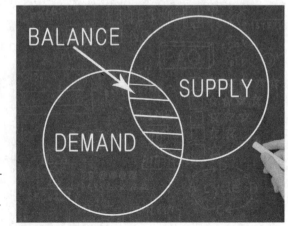

   Quantity at intersection: _____

   Price at intersection: _____

b. Copy the general shape of these graphs and shade the region showing the quantities that would result in a price that is greater than the demand quantity (i.e., where $y > x + 4$) but less than or equal to the supply quantity (i.e., where $y \leq -x + 20$).

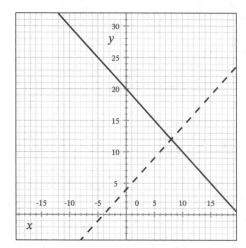

10. **Applying Algebra: Measuring** – The perimeter of a rectangular raised bed is 14 ft and its area is 10 ft². Find its length and its width. Know that the perimeter of a rectangle equals 2 times its length plus 2 times its width ($P = 2l + 2w$), while the area equals its length times its width ($A = lw$).

Start by writing out two equations — one for the perimeter and one for the area. You will have two unknowns, the length and the width. **But insert all values you know.**

Perimeter equation: _____

Area equation: _____

Use the equations given to find the length and then that value to find the width. You should find two values for the length; use the larger value.

length =_____   *width* =_____

Intentionally left blank

You may bring a single sheet of paper with notes on it to the test. *You may not consult any other resource. You are allowed to use any calculator you like on the test.*

1. **Skill Testing**

   Each problem is worth 4 points.

   a. Find $\binom{9}{4}$.

   b. Find $\log_5(45)$.

   c. Simplify to a single logarithm: $\log(x) + \log(y)$.

   d. Solve for x: $90 = \log(2x)$.

   e. Find $h(g(x))$ if $g(x) = 7x + 3$ and $h(x) = 5^x - 3$.

      $h(g(x)) = $ _____

   f. Transform $f(x) = 5x + 6$ by shifting it horizontally to the left by 5.

   g. Find x^3 if $\log(x) = 4$.

   h. Find $f(4)$ if $-f(x + 6) = 5|x^5|$.

   i. The black curve can be described by $f(x) = x^3 - 6$. What function describes the grey curve, given it is a transformation of the black curve using one of the transformations we've looked at?

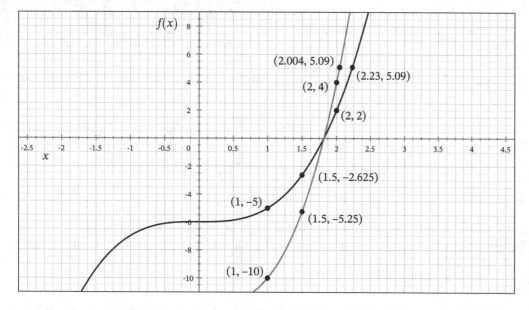

   j. *First* reflect $f(x)$ across the x-axis, *then* compress it by 0.3 horizontally, and *then* shift it horizontally to the right by 3.

   k. Complete the sentence: $f(x - 2)$ will yield the same output as $f(4)$ when $x = $ _____.

l. If (2, 5) is a point on a function that is *first* shifted horizontally to the left by 3, *then* stretched horizontally by 2, *then* scaled vertically by 3, and *then* reflected over the *y*-axis, what is the corresponding point on the transformed function?

m. Find the 50th value in this sequence: $a_n = 10(7^n)$, where $n \geq 0$.

n. Express this sequence algebraically: {5, 10, 15, . . . }. You may decide whether to start counting the positions at 0 or 1. Your answer should be in the form of

$a_n = $ _____, where $n \geq$ _____.

o. Find the requested series:

$$\sum_{k=17}^{20} 2 + k$$

2. **Application Testing**

Each problem is worth 4 points.

a. A grocery store often runs a special where you save $5 when you buy 5 different items involved in that special. There are usually more than 5 different kinds of items from which you can pick 5 to buy. Say there are 10 items that count for the special. How many combinations of 5 items could you put in your cart that would result in the savings, assuming you only want to buy 1 of each item?

b. Let's say a bride is planning her wedding. She has 7 bridesmaids, but only 2 of the bridesmaids can stand next to her on the stage on which she's getting married (the others will have to stand just below). How many different ways could she choose and arrange the 2 bridesmaids who will stand with her?
Note: The order they stand next to her matters.

c. 10 teams need to be ranked into 5 playoff ranking positions. How many different ways could the 5 teams be ranked?

d. In a deck of 25 cards with 5 cards that allow you to gain money and 7 option cards, 2 of which are also cards that allow you to gain money, what is the probability of drawing either a card that allows you to gain money *or* an option card?

$P(gain \cup option) = $ _____

e. How much time in seconds will it take for a virus population of 100,000 to shrink to a population of 10 if your immune system causes it to decay at a continuous rate of $\dfrac{-0.00025}{second}$? The formula to use is $P = P_0 e^{rt}$.

f. How long will it take a credit card debt to grow from $500 to $1,000 at an annual interest rate of 18% compounded monthly? The formula to use is $P = P_i\left(1 + \dfrac{r}{n}\right)^{nt}$.

g. Suppose a graphic artist decided to experiment with RGB color. In RGB, the color is specified using numbers to stand for the red (the R), green (the G), and blue (the B). The artist decides to increase the red (the R) value every few pixels[1] according to the sequence $C_n = 0 + 4^n$, where $n \geq 0$. Find the red value of the first 3 positions in this sequence.

h. Suppose the growth of a population can be described by this function: $f(t) = 4e^{0.003t}$, while the growth of another population can be described by the same function, only scaled vertically by 10. Write the function for the other population.

i. What is the probability of 3 children in a row ending up with blue eyes if there are 4 different gene permutations these particular parents could pass on, only 1 of which results in blue eyes?

j. Three tickets are chosen at random in a drawing at which 200 raffle tickets have been given out. The person with the first ticket chosen wins a $50 toy, the next a $25 toy, and the last a $5 toy. How many different outcomes could there be?

---

1   For example, the artist might decide that the first 5 pixels will be the value of the 1st term in this sequence, the next 5 the value of the 2nd term, and so forth.

Intentionally left blank

You are not allowed to consult any reference materials on Part 1 of the exam. You are also not allowed to use a graphing calculator, although simple or scientific calculators are allowed.

📚 *Problems marked with this symbol were adapted from School Algebra.*

1. **Simplifying Expressions** – Simplify the expressions below.

    Each problem is worth 2 points.

    a. $\dfrac{x^2 + 3x - 18}{x + 6}$ (Be sure to specify what x cannot equal.)

    b. $\log_3(5x)$ (Calculate any logarithm you can.)

    c. $\dfrac{2i(i^2 + 3i)}{(2i^2)^2}$, where i = the imaginary number (Your answer should include at least one fraction.)

    d. $5e^{2t} + 10e^{6t}$ (Factor out any common factors.)

    e. $5t - (-t^2) + t(-4 + 3a)^2 + 2a^0$

    f. $\sqrt{-5}\sqrt{-10}$ (Do not approximate any square roots that are not integers.)

2. **Miscellaneous Problems**

    Each problem is worth 2 points.

    a. Solve for x: $-c < \dfrac{x}{-3}$

    b. Solve for t: $\dfrac{5t}{t - 6} = 50$

    c. If set $A = \{4, 8, -30\}$ and set $B = \{-30, 3\}$, what is $A \cup B$? Your answer should be in the form $A \cup B = \{$ $\}$.

    d. Write an equation in function notation showing how your frequent flier account mile balance (b) varies based on or is dependent on the amount in dollars you spend on your credit card (s) if you earn 3 miles on every dollar spent. Do not write units in your answer.

    e. Rewrite as a single fraction, factoring out any common factors: $f(t) = \dfrac{2t + t}{3t + 6} - \dfrac{6t}{5}$

    f. Solve for x: $40 = \log(2x)$. Give your answer in scientific notation.

    g. How many roots (including real and repeat) does $x^5 + 4x - 3$ have?

    h. Find the roots of $-4x^2 + 3x - 7$.

    i. Transform $f(x) = 2x^2 + 6x$ horizontally to the left by 2. Simplify the transformed function as much as you can.

j. Is $x^2 + 3x - 6$ odd, even, or neither?

    ○ odd   ○ even   ○ neither

k. Find x and y:

$$2x + 3y = 4$$

$$\frac{1}{2}x - \frac{3}{4}y = -2$$

l. Find $f(2)$ if $-2f(x + 8) = 5x^2 + x + 2$.

m. Find $y(x)z(x)$ if $y(x) = 4^{3t}$ and $z(x) = 2^{6t}$. Simplify your answer as much as possible. You should give your final answer as a number raised to an unknown.

n. The black curve can be described $f(x) = x^2 + 3x + 3$. Which function describes the grey curve, given it is a transformation of the solid curve using one of the transformations we've looked at?

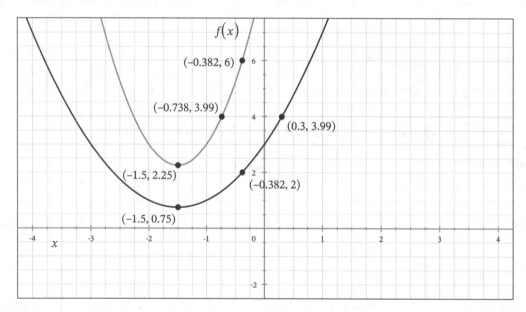

    ○ A. $f(x + 3) = (x + 3)^2 + 3(x + 3) + 3$

    ○ B. $f(x - 3) = (x - 3)^2 + 3(x - 3) + 3$

    ○ C. $3f(x) = 3(x^2 + 3x + 3)$

o. If $(1, 4)$ is a point on a function, find the corresponding point on a function that is transformed from that function by *first* being reflected across the x-axis, *then* scaled vertically by 2, *then* compressed horizontally by 2, and *then* shifted horizontally to the left by 3.

3. **Identifying Functions** – List the equation(s) that correctly describe(s) these graphs.
Each problem is worth 2 points.

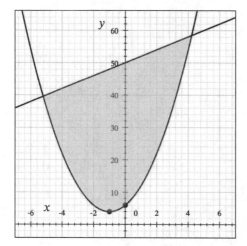

a.

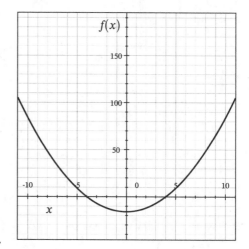

b.

○ A. $y \geq 5x^2 + 3x + 6$ and $y \leq 2x + 6$

○ B. $y \geq 2x^2 + 4x + 6$ and $y \leq 2x + 6$

○ C. $y \leq 2x^2 + 4x + 6$ and $y \leq 2x + 6$

○ D. $y \geq 5x^2 + 3x + 6$ and $y \leq 2x + 50$

○ E. $y \geq 2x^2 + 4x + 6$ and $y \leq 2x + 50$

○ F. $y \leq 2x^2 + 4x + 6$ and $y \leq 2x + 50$

○ A. $f(x) = x^2 + 4x + 6$

○ B. $f(x) = 4x^2 + 3x - 12$

○ C. $f(x) = x^2 - 16$

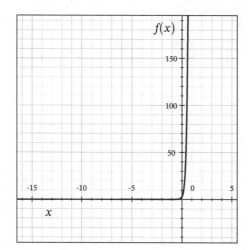

c.

○ A. $f(x) = x^2 + 5$

○ B. $f(x) = 3e^{7x}$

○ C. $f(x) = 3e^{-7x}$

Intentionally left blank

4. **Miscellaneous**

   Each problem is worth 2 points.

   a. Identify the pattern and describe this sequence algebraically: {5, 7, 9, . . . }. You may decide whether to start counting the positions at 0 or 1. Your answer should be in the form of $a_n =$ _____, where $n \geq$ _____.

   b. Find the requested sum:

   $$\sum_{k=0}^{3} 2^k + 5$$

5. **Applying Algebra**

   Each problem is worth 4 points.

   a. Suppose you have done an informal test study on college students regarding changing their method of receiving information. For the first day of the study, your test group reported spending 2 times their normal average amount of time studying using a book, $\frac{1}{2}$ the amount of their normal  average time studying on electronic devices, and 2 times the normal amount of time studying in class. Altogether, on the first day they spent 11 hours studying. The next day, they spent 3 times their normal amount of time studying using a book, and they spent just their normal time studying on an electronic device and just their normal time at class, for a total of 9 hr. The third day, they spent just their normal amount of time studying from a book, 4 times their normal amount of time studying on an electronic device, and no time at class, for a total of 9 hr. What was their normal average time spent studying using a book, on an electronic device, and in the class? *Normal average time spent studying using a book:* _____

   Normal average time spent studying using an electronic device: _____

   Normal average time spent studying at class: _____

   b. Suppose a gum ball machine has 4 red gum balls, 5 yellow gum balls, 3 black gum balls, and 10 blue gum balls. How probable is it that someone will get 2 black gum balls in a row?

c. 10 Scripture verses are placed inside of a box for people to draw from. 5 are from the New Testament, and 5 are from the Old Testament. Of the 5 from the New Testament, 2 are from the book of Philippians. Of the 5 from the Old Testament, 3 are from the book of Isaiah. How probable is it that someone will draw either a New Testament verse *or* a verse from the books of Philippians or Isaiah?

   $P(NT \cup Philippians \text{ or } Isaiah) = $ _____

d. In physics, something called the time-dilation formula[1] can be thought of as a composite function of $g(v) = \dfrac{1}{\sqrt{1 - \dfrac{v^2}{c^2}}}$ into $f(v) = t_0 v$. Find the composite function by finding $f(g(v))$.

e. Suppose that the graph describes the altitude of a missile over time (in seconds). At what point in time does the missile hit its highest point?

   $a(t) = -t^2 + 45t$

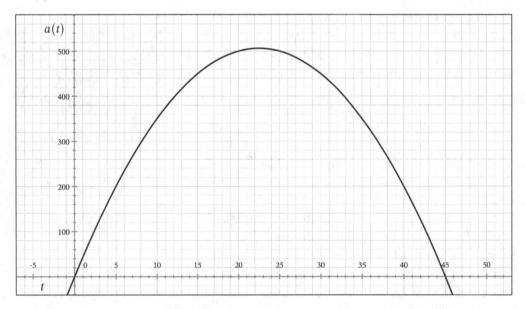

f. A man is planning for his retirement. Say he has $100,000 in the bank earning 5% annual interest compounded monthly. How much will this be worth in 20 years? Round your answer to the nearest cent.

g. How long will it take an animal population of 500 to shrink to 200 at a continuous rate of $\dfrac{-0.0035}{day}$?

h. Suppose a computer program randomly generates a quiz of 10 questions from 100 questions it has programmed into it. How many different versions of the quiz could it generate? You only care about quizzes with different problems, not the order of the problems.

1   W. Thomas Griffith and Juliet Brosing, *The Physics of Everyday Phenomena: A Conceptual Introduction to Physics*, 6th ed. (New York: McGraw-Hill, 2009), p. 442–443. *Note:* What we've written as $g(v)$ is frequently written as γ and used as its own formula too.

i. 🎯 **Challenge Problem for Extra Credit**

Problem is worth 2 points if correct and no points deducted if wrong or skipped.

Given you have already selected one quiz, what is the probability in the situation described in 5h of getting a second quiz the same as the first?

j. 📚 If a ball is thrown upward, its height as a function of time can be described like this: $h = vt - 16.1t^2$, where v is the initial velocity. If the initial velocity is $100 \frac{ft}{s}$, at approximately what times will it be at a height of 100 feet?

k. 📚 A farmer bought 100 acres of land for $4,000. If part of it cost him $34 an acre and the remainder $49 an acre, find the number of acres bought at each price.

_____ acres at $34 an acre

_____ acres at $49 an acre

l. If the voltage flowing through an outlet (V) equals the current (I) times the resistance (R), or $V = IR$, and the power (P) equals the current squared times the resistance (or $P = I^2R$), what will the power (P) be if the voltage is 1.5 volts and the resistance is 10 ohms?[2] Be sure to include the correct units of measure in your answer.

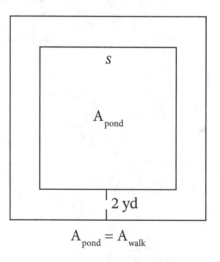

6. 🎯 **Challenge Problems for Extra Credit**

Each problem is worth 4 if correct and no points deducted if wrong or skipped.

a. 📚 A square pond is surrounded by a gravel walk with a uniform width of 2 yards. The area of the walk is equal to that of the pond. Find the approximate dimensions of the sides of the pond.

$s \approx$ _____

b. 📚 The perimeter of a triangle is 74. The sum of two sides is greater by 10 than the third side, and the difference of the same two sides is 10 less than the third side. Find the length of each side.

length of each side: _____, _____, and _____

s

A_{pond}

2 yd

$A_{pond} = A_{walk}$

---

2   Equations from W. Thomas Griffith and Juliet Brosing, *The Physics of Everyday Phenomena: A Conceptual Introduction to Physics*, 6th ed. (New York: McGraw-Hill, 2009), p. 269.